Acknowledgments

While it would be impossible to individually thank the many, many people who came together to make *Evolution's Achilles' Heels* a reality, we must mention a select few. Carl Wieland spent hours brainstorming with me in the early stages of the project and without his help it would never have gotten off the ground. Gary Bates helped formulate the initial outline and was involved at all stages of production, and without his guidance the project would never have been finished. Scott Gillis helped with coordination, checking early drafts for readability, and was a general motivator during the duration of the project. Lita Cosner and She'Na Cain spent hours proofreading. Jessica Spykerman was in charge of the layout, and never seemed to complain about the many changes we asked her to perform. Jason Fuller donated his time and talent to design the main Achilles graphic on the cover. I would also like to thank the chapter authors for their willingness to participate in this joint project. My wife, always supportive, helped get me over many bumps in the road. Lastly, but most importantly, *soli Deo gloria*!

Robert Carter
Powder Springs, GA
May 2014

Contents

Dr Carl Wieland, M.B., B.S.

Dr Wieland serves as the Managing Director of *Creation Ministries International (Australia)*, a position he has held since 1987, when it was called Creation Science Foundation. He was the founding editor of *Creation* magazine (in 1978) that now has subscribers in well over 100 countries.

Carl's formal qualifications are in medicine and surgery, and he is a past president of the Christian Medical Fellowship of South Australia. Full time with CMI since 1986, Carl is considered by many to be a pillar of the creationist community and a stalwart defender of the faith.

He is the author of several books, including *Beyond the Shadows: making sense of personal tragedy* and *One Human Family*. He has also penned many articles for *Creation* magazine, the *Journal of Creation*, and our website, creation.com.

Dr Wieland was chosen to write the introduction to this book for one simple reason: he has a tremendous experience in the field and a wide grasp of the various subjects we will cover. In essence, his position and experience allow him to write a summary and introduction to this very important work.

See **creation.com/dr-carl-wieland**

FOREWORD

Dr Carl Wieland, M.D.[1]

Nine Ph.D. scientists highlight fatal flaws in evolutionary science.

In my more than 35 years of involvement in the origins controversy, there has never been anything quite like this book. Nine Ph.D. scientists, experts in various disciplines, each take on a separate area of evolutionary theory and belief. And never has it been more sorely needed. In our age, the materialist/naturalist dogma rides high, brazenly confident in its assertion that it has the authority of science on its side.

First, an explanation. The word *evolution* in this book's title means much more than 'genetic change'; more even than 'the origin of life's diversity'. The term will be used to encompass the whole grand-scale scenario that modern culture takes as foundational in its rejection of the Creator God of the Bible: that stars, planets, and galaxies supposedly came about when nothing somehow exploded; that lifeless chemicals, by largely mysterious processes, are supposed to have somehow formed the first living thing (a biological machine so complex as to be able to make copies of itself and to harness usable energy from the environment); and that from this fortuitous first life has come the entire array of species, both past and present. Microbes have supposedly become not just microbiologists, but mosquitoes and magnolias, mushrooms and meerkats, and all of this over billions of years of trial and error—random changes filtered by the unremarkable (and ultimately unguided) process of natural selection.

---

1. My actual medical qualification is that of the British system, i.e. M.B., B.S.; the US equivalent is used here to clarify that my training is as a medical doctor.

Rather than choosing to confront areas that might be regarded as soft targets, *Evolution's Achilles' Heels* represents a well-argued frontal assault on what many would see as invincible strongholds for today's evolution-grounded, anti-theistic establishment thinkers. The eight arenas of intellectual combat, each with their own chapter and their own scientist/author, are:

1. Natural Selection
2. Genetics and DNA
3. The Origin of Life
4. The Fossil Record
5. The Geologic Record
6. Radiometric Dating
7. Cosmology and the Big Bang
8. Ethics and Morality

Why Achilles' heels?

Achilles was a heroic figure in Greco-Roman lore who was seemingly invincible in battle. In one version of the myth, this invincibility was bestowed upon him as a baby, through being dipped in the river Styx by his mother. However, the area on the back of his heel where she had gripped the infant missed out on contact with the protective fluid. The resultant point of vulnerability would eventually prove fatal to Achilles by permitting the entry of a poisoned arrow. Even today, the powerful tendon running to the back of the heel is referred to (including by doctors if in everyday conversation) as the "Achilles tendon".[2]

Achilles' heel has, therefore, become an obvious and powerful metaphor for an unsuspected but deadly flaw, especially where this is in the face of a seeming invincibility. It speaks of a vulnerability which, when discovered and exposed, proves fatal.

It is fitting, then, that these eight areas of knowledge and enquiry are more or less those which most people think display evolution's greatest strengths. It is these which supposedly provide the grounds for its illusion of seeming invincibility.

The illusion is particularly powerful, by the way, because of its inherent circularity. It is true that the way the data are interpreted and presented

---

2. Scientific name can be *tendo Achillis*, but more often *tendo calcaneus* (or calcaneal tendon), where *calcaneus* = heel. This powerful tendon connects calf muscles to the heel. When it ruptures, for example during intense running acceleration, it tends to make a sharp popping sound. Coupled with the sudden debilitation and sharp pain in the heel, it can make it seem as if one has been shot. In ancient warfare, cutting an opponent's Achilles tendon was an effective way to hobble him.

continually *seems* to reinforce this dominant paradigm of our culture. But this is largely because of an unspoken rule, one that is often unsuspected by even its staunchest adherents. This rule is that the data may only be understood and interpreted within the presuppositions of the paradigm itself. This includes the assumption of strict naturalism when it comes to origins. For example, a well-known evolutionist professor (actually an immunologist) at an American University wrote:

> Even if all the data point to an intelligent designer, such an hypothesis is excluded from science because it is not naturalistic.[3]

Here, he is admitting that explanations outside nature are automatically ruled out; only natural causes are permitted. This, therefore, excludes *a priori* as impermissible anything that might lead to a conclusion on origins other than a world that made itself, with no divine assistance either needed or apparent.[4]

Once these intellectual shackles are broken, however, it becomes unsurprising to find out that each of these eight areas of knowledge also encompasses some of the greatest *weaknesses* in evolutionary theory. Any one of these zones of weakness constitutes a fatal flaw—an Achilles' heel, as it were. Together, they constitute a formidable challenge to the evolutionary belief system.

The nature of 'facts'

This whole controversy, incidentally, has never been about unearthing 'facts for creation' vs 'facts for evolution'. When it comes to matters of history (as opposed to experimental or operational science, the science that concerns itself with how the world works[5]), the issue has never been the facts so much as their interpretation. We all have the same world—the same 'facts'. Those on both sides of the controversy observe the same stars, rocks, animals and fossils; and we see the same natural selection and mutation. And philosophers of science have long reminded us (the TV forensic/crime series *CSI* notwithstanding) that raw, uninterpreted facts *never* speak for themselves. As the late Harvard professor, Stephen Jay Gould, once wrote, "Facts do not 'speak for themselves'; they are read in the light of theory."[6]

In any case, the argument is less about the type of science that has given us so many benefits for humanity, the one that studies how the world works based on repeatable experiment and observation, than about competing beliefs about *history*. Objections like, "Genesis is not a science textbook!" miss the point. Genesis presents a majestic yet compact and rather straightforward eyewitness

---

3. Todd, S.C., correspondence to *Nature* **401**(6752):423, 30 September 1999.
4. See Wieland, C., The rules of the game, *Creation* **11**(1):47–50, 1988; creation.com/rules; and Wieland, C., A tale of two fleas, *Creation* **20**(3):45, 1998; creation.com/2fleas.
5. Batten, D., 'It's not *science*', Feb 2002; creation.com/its-not-science.
6. Gould, S. J. (1941–2002), *Ever Since Darwin*, W.W. Norton, New York, NY, pp. 161–162, 1977.

account of *one-off, unobservable, and unrepeatable events*—the history of the origins of 'life, the universe and everything'.

The evolutionary notion is ultimately an idea about history, too. It is a story that tells of a very different set of *one-off, unobserved and unrepeatable events*. This highlights that we are in the realm of *beliefs about the past* when dealing with the issue of origins. It is the responsibility of every individual to determine which interpretation of the facts makes more sense of the available data.

In a rare yet refreshing recognition of the limits of science when it comes to adjudicating on past events such as these, a prominent Australian science educator once pointed out:

> The Genesis account of creation may even be the correct one but there is no way science can prove or disprove that, and the creationists know it.[7]

One sometimes sees evolution's true believers proclaiming their scientific 'openmindedness' by stating that they would be willing to abandon Darwinism if the evidence demanded it. To bolster this, they point to the many professional disputes within evolutionism on such things as the mechanism of macro-evolution. But that is precisely the point; there is no doubt that evolutionists would in principle accept an alternative to the neo-Darwinian *mechanism*, so long as the overall 'fact' of an evolved (self-made) world is not thereby challenged. Put another way, there may be many debates and controversies within secular scientific circles over the *how* of evolution (in the sense mentioned earlier, a self-made world), but never over the *whether*. Such foundational presuppositions are sacrosanct to establishment thinkers, even if they are rarely stated outright. And it is precisely one's presuppositions (a.k.a. axioms—starting beliefs or assumptions that are taken for granted without proof) about reality that largely determine one's interpretation of it.

That's not to suggest that there is anything inappropriate about basing scientific constructs on presuppositions. There isn't. In fact it's unavoidable, and it is the way most science works. When it comes to building scientific models of origins, biblical creationists have their underlying presuppositional framework, too: the straightforward truth of the Bible, in particular the Genesis record, affirmed and taught by the Lord Jesus Christ and authenticated by His rising from the dead.

Genesis was obviously taken as real history by Jesus and all of the New Testament writers. Matthew, Mark, Luke, John, Paul, James, Peter, Jude, and the author of Hebrews all referred to the early chapters of Genesis as *history* in their writings.[8] It was also taken as trustworthy history by the overwhelming

---

7. MacInnis, P., The seven types of science; abc.net.au, 22 August 2002. MacInnis taught on evolution at the Australian Museum.
8. Cosner, L., The use of Genesis in the New Testament, *Creation* **33**(2):16–19, 2011; creation.com/nt.

majority of Christians, including intellectual giants such as Sir Isaac Newton, for nearly 20 centuries—until the neo-pagan revival of long-ageism and naturalism began during the Enlightenment period of the 17th century. This commenced well before Darwin's *Origin of Species* was published, and has gathered momentum ever since.

A big problem is that while the axioms of biblical creationism are clearly stated up front—on the table, as it were—the fact that the evolutionary edifice is constructed on similarly unprovable faith/belief[9] assumptions is much less widely appreciated. And biblical creationists' overt presuppositional basis is often misunderstood as a negative, since it shows how 'biased' they are (read: hopelessly and rigidly shackled by their commitment to the Bible).

This may help explain why many Christians instinctively shy away from this presuppositional approach, failing to appreciate its power and usefulness in Bible/science apologetics. For one thing, it faces reality about human biases. It acknowledges that they will always exist and that they need to be recognized and clearly stated in the discussion. In a sense, it also says, "OK, assume that the Bible is true; what would we expect to find?"[10]

Whereas, by acceding to antitheistic demands to "leave the Bible out of it", we firstly play to the untenable myth that there is such a thing as a philosophically 'neutral' arena (i.e. one in which facts, aimlessly floating around without reference to underlying ideas, somehow determine their own interpretation). We also end up unnecessarily hobbling ourselves by not even having a basis upon which to build any sort of model. Which means, of course, that we would have nothing to use for comparison with models based on the competing assumptions of naturalism.

Not surprisingly, then, in this book you will find repeated identification of the naturalistic assumptions behind the evolutionary story. This will demonstrate the scientific weaknesses of evolutionary thought, and also help the reader to make fair comparisons.

Directly derived from the creationist's axiom about biblical inerrancy are others about the young age of the earth and cosmos (thousands, not billions, of years old) as well as the reality of a year-long, globe-covering watery catastrophe, the Flood of Noah. It follows that, if the axioms/presuppositions are in fact valid, then it will be possible to demonstrate (repeatedly and in many subject areas) how the models based upon them conform to reality.

---

9. Biblical faith is never presented as a blind, leap-in-the-dark type of belief that ignores evidence. Rather, we are supposed to have reasons for what we believe, and be able to communicate these (1 Peter 3:15). Believers are to love the Lord our God not just with all our heart and soul, but all our *mind* as well (Matthew 22:37).

10. Or, "Let's see what the world looks like by taking off the glasses of our secularized, evolutionized culture and putting on Bible glasses."

Inevitably in a complex world, both creationists and evolutionists will find at times that their favored model does not conform directly to the evidence without a secondary or *Lakatian*[11] hypothesis to salvage the core belief. An expectation based upon a belief in the Bible's trustworthiness is, however, that constructing scientific models based on biblical inerrancy will in the long haul prove more fruitful, with less need for such 'tinkering', than competing ones.

In fact, the models that have been constructed on the basis of such biblical presuppositions have actually been extraordinarily fruitful, particularly when one contemplates the number of personnel involved. The minuscule handful of people actually thinking and researching in such areas pales into insignificance next to those similarly occupied within the taxpayer-funded juggernauts of evolutionism.

Building models or critiquing evolution?

As important as creationist model-building and model-refining is, though, *Evolution's Achilles' Heels* is not primarily about that. Its focus is unashamedly on critiquing evolution. Granted, believers are not supposed to be argumentative and objectionable. In giving reasons for what we believe, we are to do so "with gentleness and respect" (1 Peter 3:15). But we *are* supposed to "demolish arguments" that are set up in opposition to God. This is how the Apostle Paul described that aspect of the mission of the followers of Jesus in 2 Corinthians 10:5.

Besides being a false view of history, the stranglehold of evolutionism on public thought is profound, and is a huge barrier to the Gospel for millions. To ignore the need for boldly and assertively pointing out evolution's (*multiple* and readily demonstrable) Achilles' heels while only spending time on such things as the fine details of creationist biological classification, or where in the rocks the Flood/post-Flood boundary is, would be like playing the fiddle while Rome burns. Once people understand the huge scientific weaknesses of evolution (and how it undermines the Gospel), there is already plenty of material available for digging deeper.[12] And the hope is that through works such as this, God will move many more to dedicating their lives to this battle, which is ultimately for the hearts and minds—and souls—of men and women. Then, God willing,

---

11. After Hungarian science philosopher Imre Lakatos (1922–1974) who added to Thomas Kuhn's ideas about how a ruling paradigm is replaced not by the slow accumulation of conflicting data but by a scientific 'revolution' after a long period of ignoring such contradictions. Lakatos referred to secondary or auxiliary hypotheses which are erected to protect the core hypothesis. And this is not an illegitimate procedure as such. If a model has a huge number of correlations with reality in its favour, then to overthrow it before seeing if an auxiliary hypothesis can readily accommodate the new data within the overall paradigm seems only reasonable. It is the same procedure Christians sensibly apply when faced with an apparent contradiction in the Bible, namely to see if there is a way to understand the passage that presupposes the truth of the paradigm (the inerrancy of Scripture).

12. The interested reader can start with creation.com!

those in the scientific creationist community will be able to attend to even more of the model-building.

Creation or evolution: is there a third option?

A corollary to this notion (that one should not be attacking evolution but rather strengthening creation) is the complaint that undermining evolution is not necessarily demonstrating biblical creation, anyhow. However, just as the concept of evolution is far broader than just the neo-Darwinian concept of (and mechanism for) universal common descent, so too one needs to step back a little to appreciate the fundamental nature of this controversy. At the end of the day, there really are only two options. Either the world was made or it made itself. If it was not made, then hydrogen is a gas which not only has appeared from nothing, but left to itself, has turned into people (and everything else). If it was made, then we are talking about a *making entity* that, by definition, is so stupendous that the only viable candidate, really, is the infinite/personal God of the Judeo-Christian Bible.[13] By invoking the philosophical law of the excluded middle, one can truly say that the credibility of the Genesis account is greatly strengthened by identifying and exposing the Achilles' heels of (grand-scale) evolution, by definition.

Those who have been used to seeing the commonly repeated criticisms of creation may be surprised to see just how seriously deficient the case for evolution is overall. In fact, many of the assumptions underlying evolutionism within the various subject areas fly in the face of known scientific laws and principles in physics, chemistry and probability.

Where does this lead?

The opening salvo, by biologist Dr Don Batten, is on the whole issue of natural selection (something both logical and observable) as a mechanism by which the animate world has supposedly made itself. It is fitting that it should be the first in line, as it represents the central point of departure from reality for Darwin. The others follow in logical sequence, stretching back into imaginary evolutionary time. If reason has not yet departed too extensively from this post-modern culture, it is not too much to expect that this book will open the eyes of many to how the Bible, not evolution, fits the facts of the real world.

—■—

13. Notwithstanding subsequent claims to revealed truth that give all the appearances of having been at least partly derived from that work, with whatever deletions, additions or distortions that might imply. Examples are Mormonism and Islam.

Dr Donald Batten

Ph.D. Plant Physiology, University of Sydney

Dr Batten is an expert in the cultivation of tropical plants, specifically mung bean, lychee, guava, custard apple, and mango. No stranger to the world of science, Don has written extensively both in the secular and Christian world, with multiple articles in scientific journals and books. His work on environmental adaptation, environmental physiology, and mineral nutrition with these important world crop plants makes him an excellent referee for a discussion on natural selection, for he had to deal with this concept constantly in his work. He brings with him decades of experience as a scientist and creationist as he deals with the first subject in *Evolution's Achilles' Heels*.

See **creation.com/dr-don-batten**

NATURAL SELECTION

Dr Don Batten Ph.D. Plant Physiology
[University of Sydney]

Natural Selection: the cornerstone of Darwinian evolution

The full title of Charles Darwin's 1859 book expressed the concept of natural selection: *On the Origin of Species by Means of Natural Selection, or the Preservation of Favoured Races in the Struggle for Life.* 'Nature' preserved individuals that were best suited to the environment.

Natural selection is really a very straight-forward, commonsense idea. Creatures with features (traits) suited to survival in a given environment tend to survive better than those that do not have those features. For example, wolves with small ears, short legs and a thick coat of hair will tend to survive better in the Arctic than wolves with big ears, long legs and thin coat. These differences impact the ability of the animals to retain or lose heat; important traits for survival in a cold or hot environment respectively.

Although 'nature' is not a sentient being, and, therefore, cannot do any 'selecting', *natural selection* is a convenient phrase to use when discussing the survival or death of individuals, and their genes, over time in different environments. In 1868 Darwin clarified that natural selection had no direction; no ultimate purpose or goal:

> This preservation, during the battle for life, of varieties which possess any advantage in structure, constitution, or instinct, I have called Natural Selection; and Mr. Herbert Spencer has well expressed the same idea by the Survival of the Fittest. The term "natural selection" is in some respects a bad one, as it seems to imply conscious choice; but this will be disregarded after a little familiarity .... For brevity sake I sometimes speak of natural selection as an intelligent power;—in the same way as astronomers speak of the attraction of gravity as ruling the movements of the planets, or as agriculturists speak of man making domestic races by his power of selection. In the one case, as in the other, selection does nothing without variability, and this depends in some manner on the action of the surrounding circumstances on the organism. I have, also, often personified the word Nature; for I have found it difficult to avoid this ambiguity; but I mean by nature only the aggregate action and product of many natural laws,—and by laws only the ascertained sequence of events.[1]

However, creatures need to reproduce, not just survive; otherwise their traits will not be passed on to offspring. So anything that helps a creature to breed successfully (produce offspring that survive to reproduce) contributes to its 'fitness', and hence the species' ability to persist in a specific environment. How much influence the environment has on dictating fitness is a matter of debate, but this was Darwin's basic idea.

As we just read, Darwin also approved of Spencer's phrase "survival of the fittest", but many of today's evolutionists don't like the term because it leads people to think in terms of 'biggest', 'fastest', or 'strongest' and these traits do not always increase the ability to produce viable offspring. The 'fittest' are, by definition, those that produce the greatest number of *surviving offspring*. He who has the most children, wins! There is confusion on this topic, going all the way back to Darwin himself. Just before the passage quoted above, he said, "It has truly been said that all nature is at war; the strongest ultimately prevail, the weakest fail." Despite the confusion, biologists use 'natural selection' in terms of differential reproduction. This is an important distinction.

Photos from istockphoto

Natural selection was the only mechanism Darwin proposed in *Origin of Species* to explain the origin of all the diverse life forms on earth; all from a single original life form (or from a few life forms, as Darwin allowed). He had no knowledge of genetics and mutations, or their molecular basis in DNA (see Chapter 2). He proposed that small variations were always occurring and that

---

1. Darwin, C.R. *The variation of animals and plants under domestication*, 1st edition, vol. 1, issue 1, John Murray, London, UK, p. 6, 1868.

those that favoured survival would be preserved, thus propelling an organism towards an entirely different organism (given enough time).

Evidence for natural selection is commonly held up as proving evolution. Since organisms are often able to adapt to changes in their environment via natural selection, there is no shortage of stories of natural selection and so we are continually bombarded with the message that evolution is 'happening all the time'. But is this really *evolution*?

'Special' versus 'General' theories of evolution

What is evolution? Is it 'change over time' or 'the common ancestry of all species'? While trying to combine these two ideas, Darwin's theory entailed the formation of new species (speciation), although he did not really explain how new species formed (and how it happens is still somewhat controversial). I discuss the definition of the word 'species' later. For now we just have to understand that speciation simply involves the origin of, for example, a variety of rabbit that no longer breeds with its ancestor rabbits. This is quite different from seeing a new species as a step in turning microbes into mankind.

Darwin assumed that the variation seen between species was limitless, so that natural selection could change a microbe into a mongoose over eons of time. He assumed that the observed variations between dog breeds, pigeon breeds, or in the beaks of different species of finch[2] in the wild demonstrated the type of change that could be extrapolated, almost without limit, to explain not only the species of finches but the origin of finches, pigeons, dogs and everything else. He did not discuss the evolution of humans until 12 years later in *The Descent of Man, and Selection in Relation to Sex,* presumably because including human evolution in *Origin* would have reduced the likelihood of its acceptance.

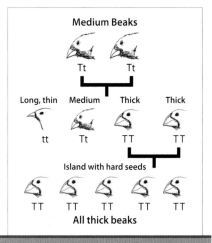

Sorting of pre-existing genes could produce variety in beak shapes. Then natural selection could remove information for thin beaks.

It is a huge leap to go from looking at variations in an existing feature (such as shorter, thinner, longer, fatter beaks) to explaining the *origin* of beaks, finches, birds, reptiles, mammals and everything else. How does looking at the

2.   Darwin observed such finches while in the Galápagos. See Wieland, C., Darwin's finches, *Creation* **14**(3):22–23, 1992; creation.com/darwins-finches.

variations in dogs explain the *origin* of dogs (wolves)? There is a fundamental logical disconnect here and this highlights a major Achilles' heel of evolution.

Indeed the evolutionist, Professor G.A. Kerkut, a well-known British authority on invertebrates, distinguished the 'special theory of evolution' (speciation) from the 'general theory of evolution' (the common ancestry of all living things). He argued that the latter, GTE, is conjectural:

> This theory can be called the 'General Theory of Evolution' and the evidence that supports it is not sufficiently strong to allow us to consider it as anything more than a working hypothesis. It is not clear whether the changes that bring about speciation are of the same nature as those that brought about the development of new phyla [major divisions of living things, of which there are about 80, including microbes]. The answer will be found in future experimental work and not by the dogmatic assertions that the General Theory of Evolution must be correct because there is nothing else that will satisfactorily take its place.[3]

Incidentally, Kerkut included the origin of life in the GTE. Why is it, then, that so many today do not want to include the origin of life in their definition of evolution? See Chapter 3.

Nowadays, we understand why simple changes in species (STE) cannot be extrapolated to the origin of the diversity of all living things (GTE). The type of observable variation evolutionists like to dub as 'evolution' is due to re-arrangement of existing genetic information (alleles), or accidental, and almost always degenerative, changes in that existing information. However, microbes-to-mankind evolution requires the formation of new, complex, information-laden suites of genes containing the instructions for making, for example, muscle cells, bone, nerves, feathers on reptiles, etc., where none existed before. Darwin had no idea what would be involved in bringing about such major changes and modern biology has revealed a sheer complexity that stands against belief in simple changes accumulating over time.

In November 1980, some of the world's leading evolutionary biologists held a conference, billed as "historic", at the Chicago Field Museum of Natural History. Reporting on the conference in the journal *Science*, Roger Lewin wrote:

> The central question of the Chicago conference was whether the mechanisms underlying microevolution can be extrapolated to explain the phenomena of macroevolution. At the risk of doing violence to the positions of some of the people at the meeting, the answer can be given as a clear, No.[4]

---

3. Kerkut, G.A., *Implications of Evolution*, Pergamon, Oxford, UK, p. 157, 1960.
4. Lewin, R., Evolutionary theory under fire, *Science* **210**(4472):883–887, 1980.

Francisco Ayala, then Associate Professor of Genetics, University of California, was quoted as saying that he now was convinced "that small changes do not accumulate."[5]

Nevertheless, many evolutionists today persist in apparent ignorance of this. That is, they continually promote the idea that 'Big Change = Small Change x Millions of Years'. This is a logical fallacy known as equivocation, or bait-and-switch. It is akin to saying "because a cow can jump over a fence, it is only a matter of time and practice for it to jump over the moon".

Some teachers also use other equivocation tricks to disarm students who might resist accepting big-picture evolution (GTE), saying things like, "Evolution means change. Here is an example of change, therefore evolution is a fact." Another lame definition is evolution is 'change in allele (gene) frequency'. Of course allele frequencies change, but this does not explain the *origin* of the genes (of which the alleles are variants), which 'goo-to-you' evolution needs to explain, not just variations in the frequency of existing alleles.

John Endler, a prominent evolutionist and an elected fellow of the US National Academy of Sciences, makes the point in this way:

> Evolution may be defined as any net directional change or any cumulative change in the characteristics of organisms or populations over many generations ... It explicitly includes the origin as well as the spread of alleles, variants, trait values or character states.[6]

Many evolutionists speak as if evolution only involves the latter, and leave the origin of the traits out of the discussion. This omission was evident in the works of Charles Darwin, and prevails in evolutionary thought today, but it is lame.

Evolution is not just 'change'. It is not merely changes in trait prevalence (allele frequency) in a population (STE). It also must entail the origin of radically new traits that are not just modifications to existing ones (GTE), and this is where Darwin, and many since that time, have continually failed.

Natural selection is not evolution

Many high-profile evolutionists speak of Darwinism/evolution and natural selection as if they are one and the same. For example, Dr Richard Dawkins speaks of experiments that demonstrated natural selection operating on the colouration of guppies (camouflage to protect against predators versus males being

Photo wikipedia.org

5. Lewin, ref. 4, p. 884.
6. Endler, J. A., *Natural Selection in the Wild*, Princeton University Press, NJ, USA, p. 5, 1986.

colourful enough to attract females) as "a spectacular example of evolution before our very eyes."[7]

Dr John Endler, quoted above, carried out this clever research on guppies. Would he agree with Dawkins that this is "a spectacular example of *evolution*"?[8] In his book *Natural Selection in the Wild*, published in 1986, Endler clearly stated why the two are not the same:

> Natural selection must not be equated with evolution, though the two are intimately related.[9]

> Natural selection is common enough in natural populations to have been detected in a wide variety of organisms, and strong selection is not as rare as has been previously assumed; natural selection is therefore likely to be important in evolution. However, natural selection does not explain the origin of new variants, only the process of changes in their frequency.[10]

> Thus natural selection may affect the patterns of the origins of combinations of traits, even though it will not explain the mechanisms of their origins. This was tangentially discussed by Fisher (1930), Simpson (1944), and Rensch (1959), but has received virtually no attention since then. It would repay further study.[11]

Note that Fisher, Simpson and Rensch were very high profile evolutionists. Fisher is recognized as one of the formulators of the modern evolutionary synthesis.

In regard to the guppy research, while natural selection might help explain the relative abundances of colourful and less-colourful guppies, depending on the balance between sexual selection[12] (females favouring colourful mates) versus the risk of being eaten by a predator (favouring dull colours), it does not explain the *origin of the colours*. Even given that some mutations in a previously-existing colour gene might affect the way the guppy looks, this does not explain the origin of the gene itself. This is a critical difference to consider, but one which Darwin, and evolutionists since him, have consistently underplayed.

Can Dawkins and company really be ignorant of the fact that natural selection is not the same as evolution when such high-profile evolutionists, even one whom Dawkins cites when it suits his argument, have clearly pointed this out?

---

7. Dawkins, R., *The Greatest Show on Earth*, Free Press, New York, p. 139, 2009. See also Sarfati, J., Dawkins playing bait and switch with guppy selection, February 2010; creation.com/dawkins-guppy.
8. See Catchpoole, D., Defining terms, January 2011; creation.com/defining-terms.
9. Endler, J.A., ref. 6, p. 8.
10. Endler, J.A., ref. 6, p. 245.
11. Endler, J.A., ref. 6, p. 246.
12. Sexual selection is a special form of natural selection where the male or female of a species shows a mating preference for a partner with certain traits (such as colour).

Following Darwin's example, evolutionists, despite claims to the contrary, still like to talk of natural selection as a creative force, but it cannot create anything. It can only eliminate the unfit, not create the fit. Natural selection is not the same as evolution. 'Survival of the fittest' (elimination of the unfit) does not explain the *arrival* of the fit.

Natural selection is not original to Darwin

Considering how obvious the concept of natural selection is, it is not surprising that the idea did not originate with Charles Darwin.

Photos from wikipedia.org

Left to right: Carolus Linnaeus, James Hutton, Patrick Matthew, Edward Blyth. All these men wrote about ideas similar to Darwin's idea of natural selection years before the *Origin of Species* was published.

Carl Linnaeus (1707–1778), the famous Swedish developer of the basics of the system of naming and classification of organisms we use today, also called the 'father of taxonomy', apparently understood the idea of natural selection and that of a struggle for survival. An article on Linnaeus on the University of California Museum of Paleontology website says:

> Linnaeus noticed the struggle for survival—he once called Nature a "butcher's block" and a "war of all against all". However, he considered struggle and competition necessary to maintain the balance of nature, part of the Divine Order.[13]

The Scottish deist, James Hutton, wrote in 1794 (in a chapter of a 2,000-page, 3-volume unpublished treatise[14]) about dogs that relied on "nothing but swiftness of foot and quickness of sight" for survival, that the slower dogs would perish and the swifter would be preserved. But if an acute sense of smell was "more necessary to the sustenance of the animal", then "the natural tendency of the race, acting upon the same principle of seminal variation, would be to change the qualities of the animal and to produce a race of well scented hounds, instead

---

13. Waggoner, B., Carl Linnaeus (1707–1778), revised and updated 2000; ucmp.berkeley.edu.
14. Reviewed by Paul Pearson in *Nature* **425**(6959):665, 2003. Pearson says that Hutton "used the selection mechanism to explain the origin of varieties in nature", although "he specifically rejected the idea of evolution between species as a 'romantic fantasy'."

of those who catch their prey by swiftness". He wrote that the same "principle of variation" must also influence "every species of plant, whether growing in a forest or a meadow".[15]

Hutton was clearly writing of natural selection, if not using the exact term (the term was not coined until 1859, when the *Origin of Species* was published).

A Scottish-American doctor, William Wells (1757–1817), in 1813 described a concept of natural selection. He said that in Africa some inhabitants:

> would be better fitted than the others to bear the diseases of the country. This race would consequently multiply, while the others would decrease.[16]

He proposed that this vigorous race would be dark-skinned and that:

> as the darkest would be the best fitted for the climate, this would at length become the most prevalent, if not the only race, in the particular country in which it had originated.[17]

A Scottish orchardist, Patrick Matthew (1790–1874), published a book in 1831 titled *On Naval Timber and Arboriculture* and mentioned natural selection in an appendix. Matthew publicly claimed that he had anticipated Charles Darwin, and even described himself on the title pages of his books as "Discoverer of the Principle of Natural Selection".[18] Darwin denied knowing about Matthew's contribution, pointing out that it appeared in an appendix of an obscure book. Yet, even if Darwin did not know about this specific example, it is proof that identical ideas were circulating within Victorian society prior to 1859.

Pearson pointed out that Wells, Matthew and Darwin had all lived in the university city of Edinburgh, "a place famous for its scientific clubs and societies", which was also Hutton's home town.[19] It would be strange indeed if Darwin was unaware of these prior ideas and it might be that Darwin's theory, either deliberately or subconsciously, developed from the melting pot of philosophical speculations running through his social circles. The point is that Darwin not only did not originate the idea of natural selection, but that it was not all that uncommon an idea among at least some people of the time.

Edward Blyth (1810–1873) probably influenced Darwin most. An English chemist and zoologist, Blyth wrote three major articles on natural selection, which he published in *The Magazine of Natural History* from 1835 to 1837, beginning when Darwin was still circumnavigating the world on the *Beagle*.

---

15. Quoted in Pearson, P., ref. 14.
16. Quoted in Gould, S.J., Natural selection as a creative force, *The Structure of Evolutionary Theory*, Belknap Press of Harvard University, Cambridge, MA, USA, p. 138, 2002.
17. Quoted in Gould, S.J., ref. 16.
18. Pearson, P., ref. 14.
19. Pearson, P., ref. 14.

This was one of the leading zoological journals of that time, in which Darwin's friends Henslow, Jenyns, and Lyell also published articles.

Loren Eiseley was Benjamin Franklin Professor of Anthropology and the History of Science at the University of Pennsylvania before his death. Eiseley spent decades tracing the origins of the ideas attributed to Darwin. In a 1979 book, he wrote that "the leading tenets of Darwin's work—the struggle for existence, variation, natural selection and sexual selection—are all fully expressed in Blyth's paper of 1835."[20] Why did Darwin not acknowledge Blyth in reference to natural selection? Russell Grigg suggests:[21]

1. Blyth was a Christian and what we would nowadays call a 'special creationist' [at least at that time]. E.g. concerning the seasonal changes in animal colouring (such as the mountain hare becoming white in winter), Blyth said that these were "striking instances of design, which so clearly and forcibly attest the existence of an omniscient great First Cause". And he said that animals "evince superhuman wisdom, because it is innate, and therefore, instilled by an all-wise Creator".[22]

2. Blyth correctly saw the concept of natural selection as a mechanism by which the sick, old and unfit were removed from a population; that is, as a preserving factor and for the maintenance of the status quo—the created kind. [Special] Creationists like Edward Blyth [at least at that time—there is evidence that after publication of *The Origin of Species* he took on board Darwin's idea of unlimited change, including common ancestry of man and apes] (and English theologian William Paley) saw natural selection as a process of culling; that is, of choosing between several traits, all of which must first be in existence before they can be selected.

These are only some of the people who wrote about natural selection before Darwin. We cannot forget Alfred Russel Wallace (1823–1913). While living in the Malay Archipelago, he independently developed a theory of evolution almost identical to that of Darwin, including a fully-formed concept of natural selection. In 1858, he sent Darwin a copy of his manuscript, *On the Tendency of Varieties to Depart Indefinitely from the Original Type*, which set out what is now known as the 'Darwinian' theory of evolution. Many consider him to have been very unfairly treated by Darwin and his friends, Charles Lyell and Joseph Hooker, who scrambled to get Darwin the priority at the Linnaean Society of London.

20. Eiseley, L., *Darwin and the Mysterious Mr X*, E.P. Dutton, New York, NY, USA, p. 55, 1979.
21. Grigg, R., Darwin's illegitimate brainchild, *Creation* **26**(2):39–41, 2004; creation.com/brainchild.
22. Blyth, E., quoted in Eiseley, L., ref. 20, p. 108.

Eramus Darwin's bookplate with three scallops on the diagonal. In 1771 he added the words '*E conchis omnia*' (everything from shells) to demonstrate his belief in evolution.

Regarding *evolution* (as distinct from natural selection), many others had proposed ideas of the evolution of all living things from some primeval ancestor(s), extending back to pre-Christian times.[23] Darwin's own anti-Christian grandfather, Erasmus Darwin, published a two-volume treatise on evolution called *Zoonomia* in 1794. The Latin motto on his family shield *E conchis omnia* translates as "all from shells". Thus, not only did Darwin's grandfather believe in evolution, but he included it on the public face of the family, the family coat of arms!

Before Darwin, continental Europe saw many writing of evolutionary ideas to try to explain the origin of everything without the need for divine creation.[24] The desire to get rid of the Creator-God is a deep-seated human trait that did not originate with Darwin.

Darwin's predecessors, including Hutton and Matthew, saw natural selection as conservative, or maintaining fitness, and having limited ability to effect change. However, Darwin invoked natural selection as a creative force to try to explain an evolutionary view of the origin of all living things. This is where he differed from his predecessors, but this is also where he failed, for natural selection is not creative.

Natural selection is not a refutation of creation

The article on Linnaeus on the University of California Museum of Paleontology website says,

> In his early years, Linnaeus believed that the species was not only real, but unchangeable—as he wrote, *Unitas in omni specie ordinem ducit* (The invariability of species is the condition for order [in nature]). But Linnaeus observed how different species of plant might hybridize, to create forms which looked like new species. He abandoned the concept that species were fixed and invariable, and suggested that some—perhaps most—species in a genus might have arisen after the creation of the world, through hybridization. In his attempts to grow foreign plants in Sweden, Linnaeus

23. Bergman, J., Evolutionary naturalism: an ancient idea, *J. Creation* **15**(2):77–80, 2001; creation.com/naturalism-old.
24. Bergman, J., Did Darwin plagiarize his evolution theory? *J. Creation* **16**(3):58–63, 2002; creation.com/darwin-plagiarize-evolution.

also theorized that plant species might be altered through the process of acclimatization. Towards the end of his life, Linnaeus investigated what he thought were cases of crosses between genera, and suggested that, perhaps, new genera might also arise through hybridization.

Was Linnaeus an evolutionist? It is true that he abandoned his earlier belief in the fixity of species, and it is true that hybridization has produced new species of plants, and in some cases of animals. Yet to Linnaeus, the process of generating new species was not open-ended and unlimited. Whatever new species might have arisen from the *primae speciei*, the original species in the Garden of Eden, were still part of God's plan for creation, for they had always potentially been present. ... The concept of open-ended evolution, not necessarily governed by a Divine Plan and with no predetermined goal, never occurred to Linnaeus; the idea would have shocked him.[25]

In other words, it seems that Linnaeus initially thought that *species* were the created kinds, but he later came to realize that the created kinds could include similar species and even genera. The idea of 'fixity of species' (that is, no new species are possible) derived from ancient authorities like Aristotle; appeals to ancient authority were very important prior to this time. The *Latin* (Vulgate) translation of the Bible, where the Hebrew word for 'kind' (*min*) was translated as 'species' (*speciem/species*), also lent support to the idea, although the word was also translated as *genus*. So, in spite of Linnaeus' findings in the 1700s, a common view in the mid-1800s was that 'species' were fixed; that one species could only produce the same species and could never give rise to another species. Deism was rife in the intelligentsia (e.g. Lyell), which entailed belief in some sort of impersonal supernatural 'first cause', but not the Creator-Redeemer revealed in the history and teachings of the Bible. In this view, the 'great architect of the universe' created the different species more-or-less where they were found. Furthermore, the established church of Darwin's day

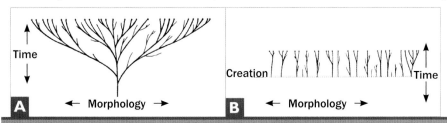

A. Original evolutionary tree, which postulates that all today's species are descended from one common ancestor. **B.** The Creationist orchard. Diversity has occurred with time within the original Genesis 'kinds' (*baramins*).

25. Waggoner, B., ref. 13.

Darwin's famous "I think" sketch from his first notebook on the transmutation of species (1837).

had already capitulated to long ages and its corollary, no global flood of Noah's day.[26] Thus, accepting what might be considered a non-biblical idea on the nature of species might not be surprising.

This 'fixity of species' provided a nice straw-man target for Darwin. It was rather obvious that the finches on the Galápagos Islands were derived from some finches from the mainland and that they had subsequently diversified into apparently different 'species' on the islands (although Darwin did not recognize them as finches at the time and only later realized their significance when John Gould identified them as such). Presto! Fixity of species overturned. However, experiments were never performed to see if the species of finches were able to interbreed. Studies in recent times have shown hybridizing occurring naturally,[27] so Darwin's finches were probably not even biological species anyway! And Linnaeus would have recognized them as belonging to the same created kind.

In these views, Linnaeus presaged the views of today's creationist biologists: organisms can adapt, new 'species' form, but the scope is limited and the sort of changes seen do not explain the origin of fundamentally different types of organisms. What we see is the outworking of the created ability to adapt/diversify within the limits of the created kinds, such that Earth's ecological niches could be filled with life. Natural selection is part of this process, as the creationists Linnaeus and Blyth recognized long ago. So if natural selection is part of the creationist model, how can it be a refutation of the concept of creation, or evidence for evolution as opposed to creation? If both evolution and creation claim the same territory, then the argument must lie elsewhere. Thus the argument shifts from STE (relatively trivial changes in species), which is obvious, straightforward and observed, to GTE (origin of the diversity of all living things), which, due to our modern understanding of the biochemical complexity of life, is much, much more difficult to believe today than it was in Darwin's day.

What is a "species"?

According to the Oxford Dictionary, biologists define a species as "a group of living organisms consisting of similar individuals capable of exchanging

26. For example, the churchmen who mentored the young Darwin at Cambridge University: see Grigg, R., Darwin's mentors, *Creation* **32**(1):50–52, 2009; creation.com/clergy-mentor-darwin.
27. Wieland, C., Book review: *The Beak of the Finch; Evolution in Real Time*, *J. Creation* **9**(1):21–24, 1995; creation.com/beak_finch.

genes or interbreeding." This is well accepted amongst biologists, including creationist ones. In other words, if two organisms can breed together, they strictly belong to the same (biological) species. However, because of the difficulty of performing hybridization experiments, species names are often given based on appearance (morphology) and so they are often not consistent with breeding barriers (there are many more species names than there are biological species).

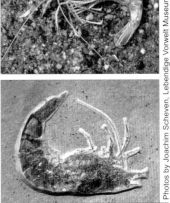

Top: Genus *Penaeus*, bottom: genus *Antrimpos* (supposedly 150 million years old).

When it comes to fossilized remains, interbreeding cannot be tested. The millions-of-years, deep-time thinking that so governs how geologists and palaeontologists think also affects their naming of fossil species. When they find a fossil that they 'date' at millions of years old but which looks very similar to a living species, their belief in the grand scheme of evolution leads them to discount the possibility that the fossil might be that of the very same species. There are thousands of examples of 'living fossils' that look identical to modern species and yet they are almost always given a different *genus* name, not just a different *species*.[28] This misnaming gives the false impression of organisms changing whereas the evidence is often that they have changed very little or not at all. It aptly demonstrates how one's starting paradigm governs the interpretation of 'facts'.

Fossils found on different continents also tend to get different names, adding to the confusion.

Imagine that the different breeds of dogs did not exist in the world today. If palaeontologists found fossils of Great Dane and Chihuahua dogs, it would be

28. For a catalogue of many from Mesozoic rocks ('dinosaur era'), see: Werner, C., *Evolution: the Grand Experiment Vol. 2—Living Fossils*, New Leaf Press, Green Forest, AR, USA, 2009.

interesting what names they would give them. They would almost certainly give them different species names and probably put them in different genera. Would they even put them in the same family? This illustrates another point, that it is not the *amount* of change/difference that is important to evolution, but the *type* of difference. While Great Danes and Chihuahuas look very different, we know that the differences are ones of degree: modifications of existing features, rather than anything radically new. One does not have feathers or a beak or any such 'non-wolf' feature. Can such things arise, given enough time? The more we learn about the complex genetics and biochemistry behind these features, the harder it becomes to believe the evolutionary notion.

In Genesis 1:11, the Bible speaks of God creating plants: "God said, 'Let the land produce vegetation: plants yielding seeds according to their kinds, and trees bearing fruit with seed in it according to their kinds.' It was so."

The formula, "according to their kinds" or "after their kinds" is used repeatedly (10 times) in reference to the creation of different types of living things in Genesis chapter 1. This aligns with a fundamental biological principle that everyone sees repeatedly and understands from childhood: organisms reproduce true to their kind: dogs produce dogs, cats produce cats, mango trees produce mango trees, etc. No one has ever *observed* otherwise (fossil evidence for and against change over time will be dealt with in Chapter 4), but evolution entails the belief that, time and time again, one basic type of organism has changed into something radically different (such as worms changed over time into humans, as one prominent evolutionist characterized it in *New Scientist*[29]). Speciation (changes within the created kinds) is assumed to be proof of the larger idea of GTE, and yet, as pointed out above, speciation is a well-accepted part of the creationist model.

Hybridization events give us a clue as to how organisms today derived from the original created kind. Based on the biblical criterion for kinds, creationists deduce that if two creatures can hybridize with true fertilization, the two creatures are (descended from) the same kind.[30] Also, by extension, if either of these creatures can hybridize with a third creature, they are all members of the same kind.[31] However, if two creatures cannot breed together it does not necessarily follow that they are not from the same kind, because degenerative changes due to mutations, such as chromosomal rearrangements, can cause breeding barriers between individuals that are otherwise identical.

29. British paleontologist Simon Conway Morris stated that "Once we were worms" in *New Scientist* **179**(2406):34, 2003.
30. Marsh, F.L., *Variation and Fixity in Nature,* Pacific Press, Mountain View, CA, USA, p. 37, 1976.
31. Scherer, S., Basic Types of Life, in Scherer, S. (ed.), *Typen des Lebens,* Pascal-Verlag, Berlin, p. 197, 1993; Dembski, W.A., *Mere Creation,* InterVarsity Press, Downers Grove, IL, USA, ch. 8, 1998.

In 1985, Hawaii's Sea Life Park reported the birth of a calf from the mating of a male false killer whale (*Pseudorca crassidens*) and a female bottlenose dolphin (*Tursiops truncatus*).[32] The birth surprised the park staff, as the parents are rather different in appearance. Here we have a hybrid between different genera in the same family, Delphinidae (dolphins, false killer whales and killer whales). Since the offspring in this case is fertile (the hybrid female has since given birth to a calf), these two genera are really, by definition, a single 'polytypic' biological species. Other genera in the group look much more alike than the two that produced the offspring in Hawaii, which strongly suggests that the 12 living genera might have all descended from one original created kind. Such events help remind us that modern taxonomical classifications are indeed artificial constructs, originally begun by Linnaeus, but now based on attempting to determine the GTE events of the past. It is really not the exact science it is often made out to be.

Mark Interrante CC-BY-SA via wikipedia

Kekaimalu the wholphin, a 19-year-old offspring of a false killer whale and an Atlantic bottlenose dolphin, mated with another dolphin to produce a girl dolphin-whale-dolphin, Kawili Kai (shown here).

The creationist biologist Dr Frank Marsh wrote of these concepts in the 1940s. As zoologist Wayne Frair said:[33]

> He [Marsh] argued, very convincingly, that scientific evidence favored the concept of separate kinds which had diversified to produce all the varieties existing among fossil and living forms. Material in that book was a very important reason why I accepted the 'kinds' concept as my own working view.

Marsh coined the term 'baramin' for a created kind (from the Hebrew *bara*, 'create' and *min*, 'kind') and defined criteria for discerning the descendants of the created kinds. 'Baraminology' is the systematic study of the created kinds. For example, veterinarian Dr Jean Lightner investigated if sheep and goats both belong to the same baramin. Lightner summarized her findings:

> … sheep (*Ovis aries*) and goats (*Capra hircus*) belong to a monobaramin (a group belonging to the same kind). Further hybrid data indicate that other species in the genera *Ovis, Capra, Ammotragus, Hemitragus* and probably *Rupicapra* fall within this monobaramin as well. An alleged hybrid between

32. Batten, D., Ligers and wholphins? What next? *Creation* **22**(3):28–33, 2000; creation.com/liger.
33. Frair, W., My experiences as a creationist student in zoology departments of several universities, March 2011; creation.com/frair.

sheep and European roe deer suggests that this monobaramin may actually include several ruminant families; however, a better documented example is desirable before reaching strong conclusions. The variation seen within this monobaramin, at least some of which are adaptive changes, indicate that mutation and chromosomal rearrangement have contributed to the development of currently existing species.[34]

The rise of new 'species' is not a problem for creation

Clearly the origin of new species is part of the creation model. New biological species have been seen to arise. For example, 'new species' have arisen in *Drosophila*, the fruit fly so popular in undergraduate genetics laboratories. A common mechanism seems to be the occurrence of an inversion, a chance re-arrangement of a chromosome (a type of mutation) where a piece of the chromosome is reversed in direction. This suppresses 'gene flow' between the flies with the inversion and the flies without the inversion, thus genetically separating them into two groups. This allows them to drift apart, even when they are still able to hybridize.[35] Such an occurrence is touted as 'evolution', but there are no new genetic specifications created, such as would be needed to change a fly into something else—all we have is the physical rearrangement of the order of the genes on one chromosome. So, once again this has nothing to do with the metaphysical belief in molecules-to-man evolution, the general theory of evolution (GTE), whereby natural processes produced all of the diversity of life from a universal common ancestor.

The biblical creation model includes the destruction of air-breathing, land-based life in Noah's Flood, with only a pair of each kind of animals, or with some animals in seven pairs, surviving on the Ark. The animals that fill today's various ecological niches derive from those animals saved on the Ark. We conclude, therefore, that considerable diversification of species has occurred in the 4,500 years since the Flood, and that adaptation and speciation have been quite rapid at times. Indeed, there is plenty of evidence for rapid

Wikimedia commons: L Church

The length of the legs of anole lizards have been observed to change rapidly under the right conditions ... observable evidence in favor of Biblical natural history.

---

34. Lightner, J.K., Identification of species within the sheep-goat kind (Tsoan monobaramin), *J. Creation* **20**(3):61–65, 2006; creation.com/tsoan.

35. Stevison, L.S., Hoehn, K.B., and Noor, M.A.F., Effects of inversions on within-and between-species recombination and divergence, *Genome Biol. Evol.* **3**:830–841, 2011.

speciation, which seems to always surprise evolutionists because of their 'deep time' mindset.[36]

For example, researchers in Trinidad relocated guppies (*Poecilia reticulata*) from a waterfall pool teeming with predators to previously guppy-free pools above the waterfalls where there was only one predator, and it preyed on small guppies only, so large guppies would be safe. The descendants of the transplanted guppies adjusted to their new circumstances by growing bigger, maturing later, and having fewer and bigger offspring.[37]

The speed of these changes surprised the evolutionists, because their standard millions-of-years view is that the guppies would require long periods of time to adapt. One evolutionist said:

> The guppies adapted to their new environment in a mere four years—a rate of change some 10,000 to 10 million times faster than the average rates determined from the fossil record.[38]

And there are many other examples.

The process of speciation does not support evolution

No observed speciation event lends any support to the idea that speciation leads to brand new organisms—new kinds. For example, referring to the guppy data above, an evolutionary geneticist commented, "As far as I know, these are still guppies."[39]

Biologists have extensively studied cichlids, a type of fish found on three continents and popular in aquariums. They vary greatly in their appearance and are often held up as an example of 'evolution in action'. However, creationist zoologist Dr Arthur Jones did his doctoral studies on cichlid variation and his studies confirmed his belief in biblical creation. Dr Jones wrote,

> Those years of research were fascinating. For all the diversity of species, I found the cichlids to be an unmistakably natural group, a created kind. The more I worked with these fish the clearer my recognition of 'cichlidness' became and the more distinct they seemed from all the 'similar' fishes I studied. Conversations at conferences and literature searches confirmed that this was the common experience of experts in every area of systematic biology. Distinct kinds really are there and the experts know it to be so. Developmental studies then showed that the enormous cichlid diversity (over 1,000 'species') was actually produced by the endless permutation

---

36. Catchpoole, D. and Wieland, C., Speedy species surprise, *Creation* **23**(2):13–15, 2001; creation.com/speedy-species-surprise.
37. Reznick, D.N. *et al.*, Evaluation of the rate of evolution in natural populations of guppies (*Poecilia reticulata*), *Science* **275**(5308):1934–1937, 1997.
38. Morell, V., Predator-free guppies take an evolutionary leap forward, *Science* **275**(5308):1880, 1997.
39. Morell, V., ref. 38.

of a relatively small number of character states: four colors, ten or so basic pigment patterns and so on. The same characters (or character patterns) appeared 'randomly' all over the cichlid distribution. The patterns of variation were 'modular' or 'mosaic'; evolutionary lines of descent were nowhere to be found. This kind of adaptive variation can occur quite rapidly (since it involves only what was already there) and some instances of cichlid 'radiation' (in geologically 'recent' lakes) were indeed dateable (by evolutionists) to within timespans of no more than a few thousand years. On a wider canvas, fossils provided no comfort to evolutionists. All fish, living and fossil, belong to distinct kinds; 'links' are decidedly missing.[40]

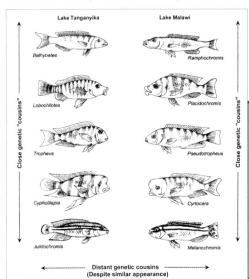

Falk cites parallel but independent development of cichlid fish in lakes Tanganyika and Malawi as proof of evolution. However, all it shows is similar assortment in varied combinations of the same characters from the same ancestral gene pool.*

Kocher *et al.*, Similar morphologies of cichlid fish in Lakes Tanganyika and Malawi are due to convergence, *Molecular Phylogenetics and Evolution* 2(2):158–165, 1993.

The genetic processes behind speciation involve the sorting and recombination of existing genetic information, as Arthur Jones points out above. Genetic aberrations (such as chromosomal inversions) can create breeding barriers and aid in speciation.

Furthermore, speciation involving adaptation to a particular environmental niche requires the elimination of individuals not suited to that niche. In our example earlier, wolves with short hair will be selected against in Arctic climes, resulting in the loss of the genes for short hair from the population. Therefore, the process of adaptation via speciation actually removes genetic information from the population. Once the genes for short hair are lost from the population, the wolves can no longer adapt to hot conditions; they are specialized for cold conditions.

40. Arthur Jones Biology, in Ashton, J. (ed.), *In Six Days—Why 50 Scientists Choose to Believe in Creation,* Master Books, Green Forest, AR, USA, 2001, pp. 241–248; creation.com/jones. There is a nice illustration of the variety of cichlids in lakes in Africa in: Kocher, T.D. *et al.*, Similar morphologies of cichlid fish in Lakes Tanganyika and Malawi are due to convergence, *Molecular Phylogenetics and Evolution* 2(2):158–165, 1993. This can also be seen at: Williams, A., Taking firm hold of an illusion, *J. Creation* 20(3):45–49, 2006; creation.com/Falk.

This highlights a problem for evolutionary ideas of speciation. If adaptation through natural selection constantly removes genetic information (variation), species will continue to become more and more specialized as they are 'fine tuned' to that environment. This fine tuning will prevent them from going backwards if the environment changes. In some sense, it would benefit a species to remain as a generalist, but selection pushes them to specialization. Thus, species are pigeonholed over time into niches from which there might not be an easy escape. We can see this with polar bears, which came from 'normal' bear ancestors,[41] but which would not fare very well now if the Arctic warmed and the ice melted. A rapid change in many species through adaptation, controlled in part by natural selection, fits nicely in the creation model.

No one has ever observed speciation that involves the addition of a new biochemical pathway. Nor has anyone developed a workable model for such changes. Speciation entails the rearrangement and/or *loss* of existing genetic information from populations. Speciation gives no support to the GTE.

Natural Selection does not produce new information

Natural selection can only operate on the genetic information that specifies the traits already present in a population. It cannot create that information. Most evolutionists understand this, but they do a poor job of communicating this to the public.

The modern concept of evolution (the 'neo-Darwinian synthesis') invokes mutations to create the new information (genetic instructions/specifications for proteins, etc.). There are many different types of mutations, but all of them involve accidental changes to the nucleotide ('letter') sequence on the DNA. In short, mutations are the only game in town for creating the stupendous quantities of information in all living things; the specifications for how to make such things as feathers, bone, muscle, nerves, hair, skin, blood cells, hemoglobin and even to orchestrate the largely unknown sequence of events that human embryo development requires. Such specifications were missing from the presumed first microbe, the universal common ancestor (UCA), but mutations supposedly added them all, one tiny change at a time, each sufficiently advantageous that natural selection could 'see' it and select it so that it was established (the technical term is 'fixed') in the population.

These sequential mutations must account for novel biochemical pathways involving multiple enzymes (which are proteins), and stupendously

---

41. Edwards, C.J. *et al.*, Ancient hybridization and an Irish origin for the modern polar bear matriline, *Current Biology* **21**:1251–1258, 2011.

sophisticated nano-machines comprised of multiple protein components (such as ATP synthase,[42] RNA polymerase, helicase, and gyrase).

The problem is that not even one of the components of these pathways or nanomachines could ever arise by chance (mutations), let alone all the components, and all are needed at the same time for many of these things to have *any* use. Indeed many biochemical pathways can create toxins if incomplete (this is a mechanism for the toxicity of some pathogenic bacteria, where a mutated gene results in an enzyme being 'knocked out' from a pathway, leading to the accumulation of the chemical that was normally the substrate for the missing enzyme).

To transform a prokaryote (such as a bacterium) into a eukaryote (such as a yeast, plant or animal), mutations must invent the kinesin intracellular transport system that eukaryotes possess, involving multiple integrated components, all of which are necessary for it to be of any use.[43]

These are insurmountable obstacles for accidental changes (mutations) to create/modify existing genetic instructions.

Mutations are necessary for evolution

How much information do mutations have to add to change a minimal microbe into a human? The essential microbe's genome is about 500,000 nucleotides ('letters').[44] A human has some three billion. So to change the former into the latter, mutations have to invent nearly three billion nucleotides ('letters') of information/specifications. In terms of proteins alone, a basic microbe has several hundred, but a human over 100,000. Furthermore, humans have all the instructions for the sequence of events during embryo development (which reside in the 98% of DNA that many biologists mistakenly labelled 'junk' because of their evolutionary assumptions, see Chapter 2).

When mutations were discovered, evolutionists adopted them as the mechanism for creating all the new information for evolution to proceed from pond-scum to

---

42. Sarfati, J., Design in living organisms (motors: ATP synthase), *J. Creation* **12**(1):3–5, 1998; creation. com/motor and Thomas, B., ATP synthase, *Creation* **31**(4):21–23, 2009; creation.com/atp-synthase.
43. See description and animation in Smith, C., Fantastic voyage, *Creation* **30**(1): 20–23, 2007; creation. com/fantastic-voyage.
44. Christen, B. *et al.*, The essential genome of a bacterium, *Molecular Systems Biology* **7**:528, 2011. The necessary parts of the genome of *Caulobacter crescentus*, at 8 bp resolution, amounted to 480 ORFs (protein coding genes), 402 regulatory sequences and 130 non-coding elements, including 90 intergenic segments of unknown function; 492,941 base pairs in total. Interestingly, of the 320 essential *Caulobacter* proteins that are shared by *E. coli*, more than one third are non-essential in *E. coli*. However, *E. coli* has its own essential proteins that are not shared with *Caulobacter* or not essential for *Caulobacter*. The authors concluded that the essential genome for a bacterium depends on the interaction of all the components of the particular bacterium. For example, ATP synthase is essential for *Caulobacter* but not for *E. coli* because the latter can make ATP from fermentation.

scientist. This was a major component of the 'new' Darwinism, or 'the modern synthesis', that was to emerge in the 1930s and 40s.

Ionizing radiation and certain chemicals could induce mutations, so plant breeders embarked on a frenzy of 'mutation breeding', very hopeful of creating fantastic new plant varieties and species that would be helpful to mankind. They saw it as an opportunity for 'fast-forward evolution'. Large sums of money were spent on these programs, but the results were so disappointing that few such programs continue in advanced-economy countries.

Some useful mutations have been found, such as ones that cause dwarfing (helping crop plants not fall over when laden with grain), non-shattering pods (allowing the seeds to be harvested rather than spill onto the ground), low-phytate corn (which cows can eat), or variations in flower colours in ornamentals such as chrysanthemums.[45] However, when studied at a molecular level, we always find that something was broken to produce these new traits, rather than created. This should be self-evident for dwarfing and non-shattering pods. With the low-phytate corn, mutations damaged the metabolic pathway that makes phytate. For flower colour it might not be so obvious, but it is caused by flower colour being due to a combination of different pigments. A mutation that knocks out one pigment results in a different flower colour, which of course can be commercially valuable.[46]

Fruit flies (*Drosophila* spp.) are a favourite subject for laboratory studies of genetics, especially for student projects. Countless experiments on *Drosophila* with chemical-and radiation-caused mutations have produced all manner of defective flies, but nothing to support the belief that mutations could create new genetic specifications to transform these flies into anything other than fruit flies.

Evolution should be seen in microbes, if anywhere

If evolution were to be observed anywhere it should be in microbes. Many species of bacteria were first identified and named in the late 1800s, and yet they still have the same identifying characteristics today.

One tendency in bacteria that seems to fly in the face of 'upward' evolution, which would involve gain of new genes is the tendency towards *deletion* of

---

45. The IAEA and FAO jointly publish *Plant Mutation Reports* twice yearly.
46. For example: Catchpoole, D., Morning glory's designer label clothing, *Creation* **29**(1):49–51, 2006; creation.com/morning-glorys-designer-label-clothing.

genes.[47] This is particularly so in obligate parasites and microbes in culture, where many genes in the original form are no longer necessary for survival and these tend to be lost by deletion.

In 1988, Dr Richard Lenski, at Michigan State University, founded 12 cultures of *E. coli* and grew them in his laboratory, generation after generation, for twenty years (he deserves marks for persistence). The culture medium contained some glucose but lots more citrate, so once the microbes consumed the glucose, they would continue to grow only if they could evolve some way of using citrate. Lenski expected to quickly see evolution in action. This was an appropriate expectation for one who believes in evolution, because bacteria reproduce quickly and can have huge populations, as in this case. They can also sustain higher mutation rates than organisms with much larger genomes, such as vertebrates like us. All of this adds up, according to neo-Darwinism, to the almost certainty of seeing lots of evolution happen in real time (instead of imagining it all happening in the unobservable past). With the short generation times, in 20 years this had amounted to some 44,000 generations, equivalent to some million years of generations of a human population. However, the evolutionary opportunities for humans would be far, far less, due to the small population numbers limiting the number of mutational possibilities; and the much larger and much more complex genome, which cannot sustain a similar mutation rate without error catastrophe (i.e., extinction); also, sexual reproduction means that there is a significant chance of failing to pass on a beneficial mutation.

After many years of no result, Lenski seemed to have given up on 'evolution in the lab' and resorted to computer modelling of evolution with a computer program called Avida. Indeed, Lenski had good reason to abandon hope. He had calculated that all possible simple mutations must have occurred several times over but without any addition of even a simple adaptive trait. But then, with great fanfare they announced that one of their 12 strains had acquired the ability to use citrate by the 31,500[th] generation.

Now *E. coli* can already digest citrate under anaerobic conditions and all that has to happen for it to utilize it under aerobic conditions is to break the mechanism that suppresses citrate uptake in the presence of oxygen; I speculated this in 2008.[48] It is much easier to *break* something than to *make* something, and evolution has a poor track record of making anything, as we have seen. Lenski's lab subsequently found the mutations responsible for this novel ability, published in 2012.[49] Citrate is taken into the cell by a transporter

47. Mira A., Ochman H., and Moran N.A., Deletional bias and the evolution of bacterial genomes, *Trends in Genetics* **17**(10):589–596, 2001.

48. Batten, D., Bacteria 'evolving in the lab'? June 2008; creation.com/lenski.

49. Blount, Z.D. *et al.*, Genomic analysis of a key innovation in an experimental *Escherichia coli* population, *Nature* **489**:513–518, 2012.

protein. This protein is specified by the citrate transporter gene, *citT*, which is normally *turned off* in the presence of oxygen. Very close to the *citT* gene are genes that have a promoter that *turns on* those genes in the presence of oxygen. A single mutation resulted in the duplication of the promoter to a position that turned on the *citT* gene so that the citrate transporter protein was now produced in the presence of oxygen. Further mutations duplicated *citT*, resulting in more of the citrate transporter being manufactured, so that more citrate was taken up.

As I suspected as a creationist biologist, something was *broken*; the mechanism that suppressed *citT* in the presence of oxygen. Mutations did not create a new gene or even a new promoter; they just copied-and-pasted what was already there in the bacterium's genome, in the process producing a bacterium that can no longer turn off the *citT* gene in the presence of oxygen (note that away from the artificial environment of the lab, these bacteria would be maladapted because production of a transporter protein when it is not needed would be wasteful).

This is consistent with the analysis of molecular biologist Dr Michael Behe, looking at another microbe with vast populations of organisms, the malaria parasite, *Plasmodium*.[50] It has developed resistance to multiple anti-malarial drugs and humans have developed some measure of resistance to it (e.g. sickle cell anemia and thalassemia). Behe shows that all the cases of adaptation, in both *Plasmodium* and humans, are due to *breaking* things, not creating new complex features. For example, chloroquine resistance in *Plasmodium* is due to a fault in a transport protein that moves the poison into the organism's vacuole. Behe likens the struggle to trench warfare, where the defending forces will destroy their own bridge, or blow up a road, to impede the enemy's advance. It is not really an arms race, because in an arms race the opposing forces invent new weapons; the natural processes ('evolution') operating in *Plasmodium* and humans have not invented *new* weapons.

Behe also looked at pyrimethamine resistance in *Plasmodium*, DDT resistance in mosquitoes and warfarin resistance in rats. In every case things are *broken* by mutations to create resistance.

The existence of databases of mutations that cause human disease underlines the wrecking that mutations do. For example, as of October 2011, Online Mendelian Inheritance in Man[51] listed 2,665 genes with one or more mutations that are known to cause disease. Public health authorities are concerned about exposure of people to mutagens and ionizing radiation because the mutations

---

50. See review Batten, D., Clarity and confusion—A review of *The Edge of Evolution*, *J. Creation* **22**(1): 28–33, 2008; creation.com/edge-evolution. Behe also provides a commentary on the mutant citrate-digesting *E. coli*: Behe, M., Rose-colored glasses: Lenski, citrate, and BioLogos, 13 Nov 2012; www.evolutionnews.org/2012/11/rose-colored_gl066361.html.

51. omim.org

they cause will cause disease, not X-men (science fiction supermen whose new powers or features supposedly came about due to mutations).

The results of mutation breeding and mutations in microbes underline once again that random changes (mutations) do not create the needed genetic specifications to transform simpler organisms into more complex ones with new traits that require additional DNA specifications (brand new genes and their control systems).

Nevertheless, mutations of one form or another are the only mechanism for evolutionists to explain the almost incomprehensible quantities of genetic information in the biosphere. Change over time? Yes. Changes that caused microbes to become microbiologists? No! It just does not add up.

Natural Selection is a conserving process

Darwin thought that natural selection could detect even the smallest variation. However, this was naïve. In reality, natural selection can only select for strong effects, i.e. extreme variants, such as something that causes death or prevents death. Kimura recognized that most mutations were of too small an effect for natural selection to act upon; there existed a range of mutations that were invisible to natural selection. Such mutations are said to be within 'Kimura's Box'.

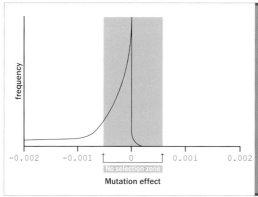

Kimura's Box: Most mutations are deleterious (to the left of the vertical line), but only slightly so (therefore piled up against the line). Beneficial mutations are thought to be very rare (they make up the little hump to the right of the line). But any mutation with a small effect (close to the line) cannot be seen by natural selection and will persist. They are effectively hidden from selection.

Another evolutionist, J.B.S. Haldane, had determined in the 1950s that traits needed a selective advantage of at least 10% for natural selection to have a reasonable chance of establishing them in the population (a 10% selective advantage means that individuals with the trait produce 10% more surviving offspring than those without the trait).[52]

52. Haldane, J.B.S., The cost of natural selection, *J. Genetics* 55:511–524, 1957; Maynard Smith, J., *The Theory of Evolution*, Penguin Books, Harmondsworth, UK, p. 239, 1958.

Evolutionists had assumed, on the basis of population genetics and their assumptions about the timeframe and process of evolution, that the mutation rate in organisms is quite low, on the order of 1 per individual per generation, or less. Recognizing that most mutations were deleterious, they had to assume that there were not many of them, or natural selection could not get rid of the preponderance of bad ones; there would be mutational meltdown, especially over their millions of years' timeframe.

However, in recent years the mutation rate has been measured and it is at least 50-fold higher than had been assumed based on evolutionary ideology. This creates a *huge* problem for the whole idea. Dr John Sanford, retired Cornell University geneticist (currently Courtesy Associate Professor) and inventor of the gene gun,[53] has shown that this high rate of mutation, combined with the fact that most of the mutations are *slightly* deleterious (falling within Kimura's Box), means that these slightly deleterious mutations are invisible to natural selection and are accumulating in humans and other organisms. This process is relentless and it is destroying us, not creating us. We are heading for extinction, along with every other complex organism.[54]

Sanford asks that if most information-bearing nucleotides (DNA 'letters') individually make an infinitesimally small contribution to the genome, how did they get there, and how do they stay there through 'deep time'? Natural selection cannot see them individually; it can only 'see' overall fitness (ability to survive and reproduce) and the contribution of any one nucleotide is generally so tiny as to be invisible; it is buried in the 'noise' of all the other nucleotides. Dr Sanford summarized the problems for evolution:[53]

1. mutations arise faster than selection can eliminate them;

2. mutations are overwhelmingly too subtle to be 'selectable';

3. biological noise and 'survival of the luckiest' overwhelm selection;

4. bad mutations are often physically linked to good mutations, so that they cannot be separated in inheritance (to get rid of the bad and keep the good). The result is that all higher genomes must clearly degenerate.

Informed evolutionists are aware of these problems and have offered 'synergistic epistasis' (where the effects of multiple mutations occurring together are supposedly greater than their sum)[55] as a solution. However, Sanford has

---

53. Sanford, J. interviewed by Batten, D., Plant geneticist: "Darwinian evolution is impossible", *Creation* **30**(4):45–47, 2008; creation.com/sanford.

54. Sanford has presented this analysis in the book *Genetic Entropy and the Mystery of the Genome*, FMS Publications; 3rd edition, March 2008 (available through creation.com). For a review of the first edition, see: Truman, R., From ape to man via genetic meltdown: a theory in crisis—A review of *Genetic Entropy & The Mystery of the Genome* by John C. Sanford, *J. Creation* **21**(1):43–47, 2007; creation.com/sanford-review.

55. See Sanford, J., Critic ignores reality of Genetic Entropy, March 2013; creation.com/genetic-entropy.

shown that this would make the problem worse. Dr Tomoko Ohta, evolutionist and a key student of Kimura who published extensively with him, came to be known as the 'Queen of Population Genetics'. She is an honorary member of the American Academy of Science. One of Sanford's co-workers asked her about synergistic epistasis and she agreed that it would make the problem worse.[55] Sanford and co-workers have also done numerical simulations using a sophisticated population genetics model called 'Mendel's Accountant'[56] to show this.

A process that steadily degrades a genome (increases 'genetic entropy') cannot produce a better organism in the long run. Sanford's analysis is devastating to the evolutionary paradigm. It is hard to see how it could be defended in the light of his critical analysis. And coming from such a high-profile geneticist, it cannot be lightly dismissed.

Nevertheless, evolutionists are continually holding up examples of 'evolution' via adaptive mutations to try to convince us that it really does work. However, the sorts of examples they provide include *loss* of sight in cave fish[57] and cave salamanders,[58] *loss* of functional wings in beetles on a windy island,[59] *loss* of control of enzyme production or a *defective* uptake channel causing antibiotic resistance,[60] and a *defective* gene in tomcod fish that helps them survive in waters polluted with PCBs.[61] That is, we are being given 'broken' organisms as examples of adaptive mutations and natural selection.

Sticklebacks

A modern 'icon of evolution', the stickleback fish (*Gasterosteus* spp.), provides yet another example of natural selection, and perhaps even an adaptive (helpful) mutation, but again shows how the processes involved give no support to fish-to-fisherman evolution (GTE).

Sticklebacks come in two forms, a saltwater (marine) and freshwater (lake) form. The saltwater type has prominent body spines and numerous armour plates. These help protect the fish from predators. The freshwater form exhibits great variety in morphology, but they generally have shorter dorsal and pelvic spines and substantially fewer armour plates; some having *no* pelvic spines or armour plates.[62]

56. Mendel's Accountant; mendelsaccountant.info; Sanford, J. *et al.*, Mendel's Accountant, *SCPE* **8**(2): 147–165, 2007; www.scpe.org/index.php/scpe/article/view/407/77.
57. Wieland, C., Blind fish, island immigrants and hairy babies, *Creation* **23**(1):46–49, 2000; creation.com/blind-island.
58. Sarfati, J., Christopher Hitchens—blind to salamander reality, July 2008; creation.com/hitchens.
59. Wieland, C., Beetle bloopers, *Creation* **19**(3):30, 2003; creation.com/beetle-bloopers.
60. Wieland, C., Superbugs not super after all, *Creation* **20**(1):10–13, 1997; creation.com/superbugs.
61. Wieland, C., Rapid tomcod 'evolution by pollution'? February 2011; creation.com/tomcod.
62. Catchpoole, D., The Stickleback: Evidence of evolution? September 2009; creation.com/stickleback.

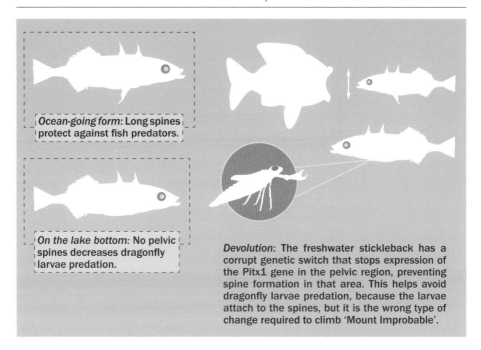

Ocean-going form: Long spines protect against fish predators.

On the lake bottom: No pelvic spines decreases dragonfly larvae predation.

Devolution: The freshwater stickleback has a corrupt genetic switch that stops expression of the Pitx1 gene in the pelvic region, preventing spine formation in that area. This helps avoid dragonfly larvae predation, because the larvae attach to the spines, but it is the wrong type of change required to climb 'Mount Improbable'.

The story goes that the freshwater form has 'evolved' from the saltwater form. And the idea of the freshwater form deriving from the saltwater one is not unreasonable and would fit neatly within a creation model of post-Flood colonization and diversification.

The saltwater fish migrate up streams to freshwater lakes to spawn and the different forms can interbreed, which suggests that they belong to the same created kind (baramin).

Biologists have observed that when saltwater stickleback fish are introduced to freshwater lakes, over a number of years the amount of body armour and size of spines reduces. A number of factors make armour and spines 'unfit' in lakes: the lack of larger predators, the cost of making the armour in the calcium-depleted lake water and the presence on the lake bottom of predatory dragonfly larvae, which use the pelvic spines to grab sticklebacks that swim over them. Sticklebacks with reduced armour and lacking pelvic spines are clearly more 'fit to survive' in the lake environment and natural selection operates to increase the number of fish with less armour and spines.

What is behind these changes? Has some new feature been invented by 'evolution'? Geneticists have located a mutated genetic switch that affects the expression of a gene called *Pitx*. In the pelvic region, the corrupted genetic switch prevents spines forming in that area. Elsewhere, it affects "a whole suite of bony characters"[63] not just the external bony plates but also jaw shape and bones associated with protecting the gills. In other words, the freshwater forms of the sticklebacks have come about by the *corruption* of a genetic switch, such that certain traits are *turned off*.

Even leading promoter of all things evolutionary, Dr Jerry Coyne (University of Chicago), candidly admitted, regarding these mutations in the genetic switches of sticklebacks, "But these examples represent the loss of traits, rather than the origin of evolutionary novelties."[64] And yet these differences are still paraded as 'evidence for evolution'. In the anniversary 'Year of Darwin', 2009, *Nature* journal honoured the stickleback as one of "15 Evolutionary Gems". One high-profile evolutionist, Sean Carroll, called it, "One of the most compelling case studies of evolution."[62]

Here we have another nice example of natural selection, adaptive mutation, even speciation, but nothing that provides evidence that spines and armour could have arisen anew, by mutations and natural selection.

Even the mutated genetic switch is already present in the saltwater fish, although in low numbers.

The reverse of the above has also been seen: where the pollution in Lake Washington (near Seattle) was cleaned up and visibility increased so much that low-armour sticklebacks were more vulnerable to predation by cutthroat trout, the number of full-armour sticklebacks increased from 6% to 49% in five decades. This was touted as "rapid, reverse evolution". However, again, nothing new has been invented by 'evolution'. The full-armour genes were already in the population (initially 6%); natural selection has merely increased the frequency of these genes.[62] This is nothing more than the usual equivocation trick; 'evolution is just change in gene frequency'.

There is nothing happening here that supports the General Theory of Evolution (GTE), which needs the invention of *suites of new genes*, not the damaging of an existing genetic switch (and the mutated switch already existed anyway) or the changing of the frequencies of *existing* genes.

Genetic switches created to facilitate adaptation?

Creationist veterinary researcher Dr Jean Lightner has suggested that genetic switches like the one operating in sticklebacks could have been created to facilitate adaptation, being deliberately made with a propensity to mutate but without negatively affecting other traits. She found that a particular protein acts

63. Pennisi, E., Evolutionary biology: Changing a fish's bony armor in the wink of a gene, *Science* **304**(5678):1736–1739, 2004.
64. Coyne, J.A., Switching on evolution—how does evo-devo explain the huge diversity of life on Earth? *Nature* **435**(7046):1029–1030, 2005.

like a multi-function switch to generate a wide range of coat colours in animals. This protein only affects coat colour, so mutations are well tolerated. When functioning normally, this protein can switch on the production of the dark pigment called eumelanin. A lighter yellow to red pigment is also produced. Mutations can break the switch so that it fails to stimulate the production of the dark pigment. This results in the tan/blond colour of a retriever dog, for example. Alternatively, a 'switch stuck in the **on** position' over-stimulates the production of eumelanin and this results in a dark black colour.

Dr Lightner remarked:

> The creator might well have designed this special switch gene with the ability to vary in this way to create a variety of colour patterns.[65]

Many such genetic switches could exist to enable variation and adaptation. However, evolutionists have no mechanism to explain their existence. All their 'proofs of evolution' are nothing more than examples of modifications to existing switches.

The category called 'gain of function mutations' sounds like it includes mutations that add new functions/traits/genes to organisms rather than just breaking something. However, evolutionists have defined a 'gain-of-function mutation' as "a mutation that confers new or enhanced activity on a protein". Dr Lightner gives examples.[66] One involves control of the production of thyroid hormone. Here, a receptor that controls the production of the hormone can be mutated so that it is 'stuck on' and unresponsive to thyroid stimulating hormone, causing the thyroid to produce excessive amounts of thyroid hormone. "Enhanced activity of a protein"? Yes, but the excess thyroid hormone causes disease. Lightner writes:

> Despite the deceptive wording found in the gain-of-function definition, there is no increase of information or improvement of biochemical pathways. Without a mechanism for developing such pathways, evolution is nothing more than a myth.

Epigenetics interferes with natural selection

The discovery of epigenetics in recent times has added another problem for natural selection.

Epigenetics refers to the modification of gene activity, mainly via the attachment of methyl (-CH_3) groups to specific nucleotides (cytosine) in the DNA. The process is called methylation. The bulky methyl group blocks the transcription

---

65. Lightner, J., interviewed by Batten, D., Getting it right, *Creation* **32**(3):40–43, 2010; creation.com/creationist-veterinarian.
66. Lightner, J., Gain-of-function mutations, *J. Creation* **19**(3):7–8, 2005; creation.com/gain-of-function.

machinery (RNA polymerase), so a methylated gene does not produce any protein product (it is 'silenced').

The environment drives methylation. Evidence is building that methylated genes can be transmitted from one generation to the next.[67] And methylation can be reversed. Examples of epigenetic inheritance include petal number in plants and coat colour in mice. In the mice, in certain circumstances the diet of the mother affects the coat colour of her progeny. The coat colour is also able to pass to the grand-mice, but the effect wears off over the generations if the diet is changed. The removal of the environmental trigger allows the methylation patterns to change back to the original state.[68]

Such epigenetic effects make it even harder for natural selection to work because it presents a moving target. As Dr Robert Carter explains:

> For example, say that the diet of mice generates epigenetic changes in the offspring that result in a coat color that gives good camouflage. Mice without that coat color could be at a disadvantage. However, there is no difference in the underlying genes that determine coat color. The mice have different colors because of something they ate. Some individuals would be eliminated that had no genetic disability and, when the effect wears off, all that selection would have been wasted.[69]

Epigenetics adds more 'noise' to what natural selection 'hears'. This, added to the invisibility of lots of slightly deleterious mutations and the invisibility of nearly all the rare beneficial mutations, and it is a wonder that there are any examples of natural selection operating.

Natural Selection is too slow

The famous evolutionary geneticist J.B.S. Haldane (1892–1964) was one of the three founders of the field of study known as population genetics. Haldane recognized a serious problem for evolutionary theory and described it in a key paper published in 1957—the 'cost of substitution'.[70] When a beneficial mutation occurs in a population, it has to increase in frequency for the population to evolve (if the mutation remained in one individual, then evolution cannot proceed; this is fairly obvious). In other words, it has to substitute for (replace) the non-mutated genes in the population. But the rate at which this can happen

67. See, for example, Whitelaw, E., Sins of the fathers, and their fathers, *European J. Human Genetics* **14**:131–132, 2006; Pembrey, M.E. *et al.,* Sex-specific, male-line transgenerational responses in humans, *European J. Human Genetics* **14**:159–166, 2006; Jimenez-Chillaron, J.C. *et al.,* Intergenerational transmission of glucose intolerance and obesity by in utero undernutrition in mice, *Diabetes* **58**:460–468, 2009.
68. Morgan, H. *et al.,* Epigenetic inheritance at the agouti locus in the mouse, *Nature Genetics* **23**:314–318, 1999.
69. Carter, R., Darwin's Lamarckism vindicated? March 2011; creation.com/epigenetics-and-darwin.
70. Haldane, J.B.S., The cost of natural selection, *J. Genetics* **55**:511–524, 1957.

is limited. A major factor limiting the rate of substitution is the reproduction rate of the species. For a human-like creature with a generation time of about 20 years and low reproduction rate per individual, the rate of growth in numbers of a mutation in a population will be exceedingly slow.

Imagine a population of 100,000 apes, the supposed progenitors of humans. Suppose that a male and a female both received a mutation so beneficial that they out-survived everyone else; all the rest of the population died out—all 99,998 of them. And then the surviving pair had enough offspring to replenish the population in one generation! And this repeated every generation (every 20 years) for 10 million years, more than the supposed time since the last common ancestor of humans and chimps. That would mean that 500,000 (10 million/20) beneficial mutations could be added to the population. Even with this completely unrealistic scenario, which maximizes evolutionary progress, only about 0.02% of the human genome could be generated. Considering that the difference between the DNA of a human and a chimp, our supposed closest living relative, is *at least* 5%, or 150 million bases[71] ('letters'), evolution has an obvious problem in explaining the origin of the genetic information in a creature such as a human. This is where the idea of 'junk DNA' originated; with evolutionists' realization that natural selection could not create enough DNA, so the vast majority must be non-functional (see the next chapter for more on junk DNA).

©Eric Isselée/ 123rf.com

However, with more realistic rates of fitness/selection and reproduction rate, the number of beneficial mutations that can be accommodated plummets. Haldane calculated that no more than 1,667 beneficial substitutions could have occurred in the supposed 10 million years since the last common ancestor of apes and humans. This is a mere one substitution per 300 generations, on average. The origin of all that makes us uniquely human has to be explained within this limit.

In the sense in which Haldane used the word (in population genetics) a substitution is a single mutational event that spreads through the entire population (becomes 'fixed'). It can be a gene duplication or a chromosomal inversion, or a single nucleotide substitution, insertion or deletion. Biologists have found that the vast

---

71. See Tomkins, J. and Bergman, J., Genomic monkey business—estimates of nearly identical human-chimp DNA similarity re-evaluated using omitted data, *J. Creation* **26**(1):94–100, 2012; creation.com/chimp. The difference may even be as high as 30%, as geneticist Richard Buggs showed: Chimpanzee? October 2008; www.refdag.nl/chimpanzee_1_282611.

majority of substitutions are indeed single nucleotides, so Haldane's limit puts a severe constraint on what is possible with evolution, because 1,667 single nucleotide substitutions amounts to less than one average-sized gene.

It should also be noted that Haldane made a number of simplifying assumptions that actually optimized the number of substitutions that would be possible. So in reality, the number of substitutions possible is much less than Haldane calculated.

Haldane's analysis shows that natural selection of mutations cannot account for the genomes of organisms such as humans; it is far too slow. Evolutionists have done their best to try and ignore this problem, but Walter ReMine recently attempted to force open the issue with a fresh analysis of the problem, also clarifying some confusion that Haldane had on the matter.[72]

Natural Selection, if it works at all, is a creationist position

Does natural selection work at all? Well, it seems to in some situations, as we have seen in some examples. But it is overplayed. Some of the classic examples of natural selection, such as the peacock's tail, which Darwin supposed was created by the preference of females for males with showy tails ('sexual selection'), have turned out to be baseless just-so stories.[73] And once again,

Photos from istockphoto

72. Batten, D., Haldane's dilemma has not been solved, *J. Creation* **19**(1):20–21, 2005; creation.com/haldane. See also ReMine, W., Cost theory and the cost of substitution—a clarification, *J. Creation* **19**(1):113–125, 2005; creation.com/cost.
73. Catchpoole, D., Peacock tail tale failure, June 2008; creation.com/peacock-tail-tale-failure.

even if the story of selection had held up with experimental testing, the story did not explain the *origin* of the tail,[74] only possibly its maintenance, natural selection being a conservative force, as originally envisaged by the 19th century special creationist, Blyth.

Where does this lead?

Mutations and natural selection are clearly inadequate as a mechanism for the GTE. The modern explosion in molecular biology has only added to the case against evolution as a viable explanation for the diversity of life on earth. The next chapter will explore what lies behind evolutionary theory, the field of genetics, and how modern discoveries in genetics render the idea of evolution (GTE) quite untenable.

74. Burgess, S., The beauty of the peacock tail and the problems with the theory of sexual selection, *J. Creation* **15**(2):94–102, 2001; creation.com/peacock.

Dr Robert Carter

Ph.D. Marine Biology, University of Miami, USA

Dr Carter, an expert on coral reefs, spent the better part of his Ph.D. studying the genetics of one particular protein family found in jellyfish and corals—the green fluorescent protein (GFP) and cognates. Since then, he has focused his effort on studying *human* genetics. His first attempt led to the publication of a consensus sequence for the earliest human mitochondrial genome, literally Eve. He is now pursuing additional aspects of human genetics, including studying patterns of diversity and mutation, and how they relate to the biblical model of genetics given to us in Genesis.

After toying with different ways to meld Genesis and evolution while growing up, he accepted evolution as a 'fact' in his freshman year at university. Challenged later on to rethink his position, he jettisoned evolution in favor of biblical creation, but it was not until his first year of graduate school that he became fully convinced of the merits of the young-earth position.

As a creationist with a depth of knowledge of genetics, and as a former evolutionist, even if only briefly, he is a natural choice to head up a chapter describing the second Achilles' heel of Darwinian evolution, genetics.

See **creation.com/dr-robert-carter**

GENETICS AND DNA

Dr Robert W. Carter Ph.D. Marine Biology
[University of Miami] | **2**

In Chapter 1, we saw that natural selection was not Darwin's brainchild. We also saw that it is insufficient to explain Darwin's grand idea that all species are related through common descent. In this chapter, we will explore something Darwin knew nothing about—genetics. Despite his ignorance on this topic, one cannot discuss evolution via natural selection without discussing potential changes in the inheritable material of life. The answers to questions like, "How are genes passed from one generation to the next?" and, "What mutation rate is sustainable in a population over time?" are key to understanding this Achilles' heel of evolution.

A short history of genetics

For thousands of years, philosophers argued about the means by which organisms pass traits to their offspring. For most of human history, we did not know what caused variation within species nor how variation was passed from one generation to the next. Up to the end of the 19th century, most people probably held to *blending inheritance*. That is, offspring were a combination or average of the two parents. This made sense in some ways, as it is easy to spot traits of both parents in many children, but wouldn't this also mean that all traits should average out over time? People knew this problem, but they did not have many better ideas.

Because of the time in which he lived, Charles Darwin knew nothing of genetics. Thus, his ideas of evolution were developed in a vacuum where speculative ideas abounded. Not satisfied with the prevailing ideas of inheritance, Darwin invented his own theory called *Pangenesis*.[1] He envisioned 'corpuscles' being produced by the various organs in the body in response to environmental stimuli. These corpuscles would then travel to the gonads and be stored until they could be passed on to the next generation. There was no physical or experimental basis for this view, however. Also, it appealed directly to an older theory called *Lamarckism* or *Lamarckian inheritance*. Jean-Baptiste Lamarck (1744–1829) taught that the individual responded to the environment by growing stronger, taller, more far-sighted, or able to withstand excessive heat, for example. The individual then passed on the newly acquired traits to his or her offspring, who would then start off life a little stronger, taller, etc., than the parents did. The phrase associated with this belief is "the inheritance of acquired characteristics".

Darwin certainly ascribed to it,[2] but he was wrong.

The strangest thing about Darwin's Pangenesis theory, though, is that it was published (1868) immediately after the father of modern genetics, Gregor Mendel, discovered the laws of genetic inheritance (first published in 1866[3]). Working alone in his monastery garden, Mendel figured out that many traits

Photo from wikipedia.org

Gregor Mendel

come in discrete units (white *or* purple flowers, yellow *or* green seeds, etc.), with each variant called an *allele*. He also determined that each individual carries two alleles for each trait (e.g. white + white, purple + white, or purple + purple), and that each parent gives only one copy of each to their offspring. The offspring, therefore, are not an average (blend) of the parents, but a combination of discrete traits that are passed from parent to child. Mendel may have been a monk, but he was not unfamiliar with science, having been trained in physics and philosophy at the university level. In his day, the 'Church' was a place where much science was traditionally performed, as

1. Darwin, C.R., The variation of animals and plants under domestication, London, John Murray, 1868; darwin-online.org.uk.
2. Carter, R., Darwin's Lamarckism vindicated? March 2011; creation.com/epigenetics-and-darwin.
3. For an English translation, see Druery, C.T. and Bateson W., Experiments in plant hybridization, *Journal of the Royal Horticultural Society* **26**:1–32, 1901.

attested by Darwin's theological and scientific training at Cambridge[4] in his (permanently stalled) path to become a country vicar.

Darwin had all the same tools as Mendel, more time at his disposal, and could probably muster better finances for his scientific work, yet he did not develop anything like modern genetic theory. Darwin wrote painstaking descriptions on genetic variation and inheritance patterns in multiple species of plants and animals, even noting Mendel's famous 3:1 ratio[5] of wild type to recessive in a dual hybrid cross on one occasion.[6] Darwin wrote multiple essays and papers on these topics.[7] Why, then did he not discover genetics? We can never be certain, but Darwin wanted species to be infinitely mutable because he had a commitment to a continuous distribution of species, with innumerable links among them, stretching back to infinity. This necessitated or lent itself to a search for a continuous distribution of traits, hence Pangenesis theory and his appeals to Lamarckism. But genes do not code for distributions. They code for discrete traits. While it is true that many traits are caused by the additive effects of many different genes (giving the appearance of a continuum), this just makes the relationship between the environment and genetics that much more complicated. Darwin was looking in the wrong direction. Mendel was an experimentalist and came up with the correct answer. Darwin was a theoretician, and he may have missed it due to philosophical considerations alone.[8]

This was not a unique fault of Darwin's however, as most people of the day failed to see it. It would be several decades before Mendel's ideas gained popularity. Yet throughout his entire life, Darwin was ignorant of the fundamental processes upon which evolutionary theory needed to operate. It turns out that the laws of genetics are not friendly to evolutionary theory.

Modern genetics

Starting after the turn of the (20th) century, the study of genetics began to pick up steam. It was discovered that brand new traits, called mutations, can appear suddenly in an individual, and Mendel's work was revived. It took some doing,

---

4. His father sent him to study at Cambridge after he dropped (or failed) out of medical school in Edinburgh. After graduating from Cambridge, he went on his famous five-year round-the-world voyage on the *Beagle*, and never did go on to become a parson.
5. Mendel showed that, when crossbreeding two individuals that both carry a dominant and recessive version of a gene (e.g. dominant purple petals and recessive white petals), one obtains a 3:1 ratio of wild type (purple) to recessive (white). This occurs because the only plants that will have white flowers are the ones that receive two copies of the recessive gene. Thus, ¾ of the plants will have purple flowers and ¼ will have white flowers: a 3:1 ratio of purple to white.
6. Howard, J.C., Why didn't Darwin discover Mendel's laws? *Journal of Biology* **8**:15, 2009.
7. Including: *The Variation of Animals and Plants under Domestication*, 1868; *The Effects of Cross and Self-Fertilisation in the Vegetable Kingdom*, 1876; and *The Different Forms of Flowers on Plants of the Same Species*, 1877.
8. Howard, J.C., ref. 6.

but by the 1920s, mutation, natural selection, and genetics were combined into what is called the *Modern Synthesis*. Blending inheritance, Pangenesis, and Lamarckism were all discarded in favor of the new understanding, which, some 150 years later, is pretty much indistinguishable from what is believed by most evolutionists today.

The field of genetics slowly grew for the first half of the century, and then exploded in the 1950s. In 1952, the famous Hershey–Chase experiment proved that DNA was the carrier of heredity (there was evidence for this prior to that time, but many people still thought proteins did the job). In 1953, Watson and Crick discovered that DNA was in the form of a double helix. The Meselson–Stahl experiment in 1958 showed that the two DNA strands are separated and copied independently. Soon after that, the *protein code* was worked out and we learned that three DNA letters code for one amino acid in a protein.

The groundwork for modern genetics had been laid. Gene sequencing was developed in the following decades. This was then automated. The turn of the millennium soon ushered us into a new world, for, in 2003, the *Human Genome Project* published a transcript of about 93% of the linear strings of DNA found in a human nucleus. Audacious in scope, scale, and financing, it cost US taxpayers more than three billion dollars to sequence about three billion letters of DNA. That monumental (and expensive!) feat changed everything. Today, with the rapid amplification of technology, there are companies that can easily sequence the equivalent of several human genomes every day, they can do it for just a few thousand dollars each, and even that will be passé in a few short years. Technological advances are allowing new discoveries at a rapid rate and many of our traditional ideas are being challenged.

Data are piling up quickly. We can now answer questions that we could only dream about a decade or two ago. Perhaps for the first time in history, we have a significant field of science with more data than theory! Welcome to the world of modern genetics.

DNA as an information storage medium

All life depends on specific information (an instruction set, as it were) to survive and reproduce. Much of that information is coded in DNA, a molecule which is unsurpassed as an information storage medium. One can put an amazing number of instructions in just a tiny bit of DNA. Think of a printed page. Each letter on the page may be three or four millimeters high and there are several thousand letters on a standard page of text. If we printed out the human genome as text and bound it into Bible-sized books (depending on the translation, there are approximately 3.5 million letters in the average English Bible), it would take 850 Bibles to hold it. And, since you inherit one copy from your mother and the other from your father, you hold two copies of the genome in each cell in your body (with the exception of red blood cells, which don't have a nucleus). The letters of DNA, however, are only a few *billionths* of a meter tall. At that size, all three billion letters could easily fit inside something much smaller than the period at the end of this sentence. In the cell, they are strung together in chains (chromosomes) that, if lined up from end to end, would be about 2 m (6 feet) long. Those long, fragile, sticky strings are packed into a nucleus only 6-10 μm (millionths of a meter) in diameter. The entire instruction set for building and maintaining a person is stored in something so small you cannot see it without a microscope!

Yet those chains are not very stable. Single-stranded DNA is liable to break. In the nucleus, each strand is paired with a complimentary strand and the two twist around each other to form the classic double helix shape. A piece of DNA is actually two separate, but complimentary, molecules glued together by electrostatic interactions. The three billion DNA letters in the human genome are found in 23 separate chromosomes, ranging from about 50 million to about 250 million letters in length. Even in this configuration, however, DNA is not very stable. It is still super-sensitive to degradation and it is estimated that there are up to one million DNA 'lesions' (e.g. breaks in the string, damage caused by radiation, or destruction of individual bases when reacting with oxygen) in a normal cell every day[9] (and you have about 100 trillion cells in your body!). Imagine the effort a single cell must go through daily to maintain its complement of DNA. Now multiply that effort. What's 1,000,000 x 100,000,000,000,000? That's what it takes to keep your genome working in your body, on a daily basis.

DNA fragility is one of many Achilles' heels of evolutionary genetics, but it is an important one. In order for DNA to be useful, it needs a huge complement of repair enzymes to maintain it. There are many different ways DNA can be damaged and there are specific enzyme complexes that deal with each type of damage, but what is even more challenging to the evolutionary model is that those enzymes are also coded in the DNA, yet DNA cannot be sustained in the cell without them. This is a chicken-and-egg problem *par excellence*! These enzymes are also sensitive to changes. Mutations in the DNA repair and copying enzymes are often catastrophic. How, then, did they originate through the process of mutation and natural selection over time? Without them, life cannot exist, yet life had to originate without them and had to start using DNA to store information before the DNA toolkit evolved. Since this will be dealt with in more depth in the next chapter on the origin of life, let it suffice to say that DNA is the last thing one would ever expect early life to start using for information storage.

9.   Lodish, H. *et al.*, Molecular Biology of the Cell, 5th ed., W.H. Freeman and Company, New York, 2004.

DNA and information theory

The order of the nucleotides on the DNA molecule has all the characteristics of a message, laden with information.[10,11] A message may be passed on, but in the real world, there can be no message without a message sender. The ultimate puzzle of life is not the complexity of the molecules upon which life depends (although this is a huge puzzle). It is not the complex arrangement of the parts living organisms use (although this is another huge puzzle). No, the ultimate puzzle of life is the origin of the information upon which life is based. As in the last section, this is broaching the subject of the origin of life, which is not the focus of this chapter. What we are most concerned about here is the maintenance of the information in the genome over the lifetime of the organism and from one generation to the next.

Information maintenance is another Achilles' heel of evolutionary genetics, for it does not work without a near-perfect information maintenance system. And yet, even with the amazing DNA repair systems in the human body, we still pick up about 100 new mutations, per person, per generation.[12] It is estimated there are between one and three mutations per cell division.[13] That's not a bad error rate for the little molecular machines in charge of rapidly copying the DNA immediately before a cell divides, but put this in context of the number of cell divisions required to form a person; you currently carry every possible mutation, multiple times over, and the number only increases over time. Because of this accumulation of errors over time, it is estimated that a 60-year-old person has 40,000 mutations *in each cell* lining the intestinal tract.[14] In fact, barring accidents and disease, this inexorable accumulation of errors will lead to the death of all of us.

Happily, a creator (God) engineered a brilliant mechanism to protect humanity from the effects of these mutations. When an egg is fertilized, the zygote goes through a limited number of cell divisions before the cells for the next generation are formed. In a female baby, there are but 23 cell divisions before the ovaries are complete. The eggs within the ovary will be nurtured and protected until

10. Batten, D., Book review: *The Biotic Message: Evolution versus Message Theory, J. Creation* **11**(3):292–298; creation.com/biotic.
11. Gitt, W., Scientific laws of information and their implications—part 1, *J. Creation* **23**(2):96–102; creation.com/laws-of-information-1. See also other parts in this series.
12. Lynch, M., Rate, molecular spectrum, and consequences of human mutation, *Proc. Nat. Acad. Sci. USA* **107**(3):961–968, 2010. Similar numbers have come from many other studies, including Neel, J.V. *et al.*, The rate with which spontaneous mutation alters the electrophoretic mobility of polypeptides, *Proc. Nat. Acad. Sci. USA* **83**:389–393, 1986; Nachman, M.W. and Crowell, S.L., Estimate of the mutation rate per nucleotide in humans, *Genetics* **156**:297–304, 2000; Kondrashov, S., Direct estimates of human per nucleotide mutation rates at 20 loci causing Mendelian disease, *Human Mutation* **21**:12–27, 2002.
13. Eyre-Walker, A. and Keightley, P.D., High genomic deleterious mutation rates in hominids, *Nature* **397**:344–347, 1999.
14. Lynch, M., ref 12.

ovulation, sometimes 40 or more years later, without dividing any further. Most don't know it, but, when a woman is carrying a girl baby, three generations are present simultaneously: mom, baby girl, and the eggs in the recently formed baby's ovaries. Things are a little different in men, however. A male goes through about thirty cell divisions in the womb before his reproductive cells are ready, but they start to divide rapidly at the onset of puberty, and they will keep dividing until he dies. This means that a father should pass more mutations to a child he has in his old age than to a child he has in his youth.[15]

Limited studies of mutations passed from parents to children have turned up some surprising results, however. It turns out that the number of mutations picked up from each parent can be quite variable, sometimes with more coming from the father and sometimes more from the mother.[16] This is a challenge to standard models of human genetic history, which assume a *molecular clock* of equal mutation rates through time and across the geographic range of humanity. We will discuss the implications of this in more detail below.

While most of these mutations are not catastrophic (or we would all be dead already), they are still bad. Geneticists like to call them *slightly deleterious* mutations, and their accumulation in the human genome is a real challenge to evolutionary theory.[17] These are bad mutations, and are being added at a rate faster than natural selection can theoretically remove them. Indeed, only the worst mutations can even be 'seen' by natural selection (Chapter 1). Thus, evolution is running backward, unable to prevent the slow degradation of the information necessary for life. If this is true, how could that information have risen in the first place? And how could species have survived all these millions of years without going extinct?

'Junk' DNA is (mostly) functional!

We have heard the old canard for decades. It goes something like, "Only 2 to 3 percent of the human genome is functional. The rest is worthless, junk DNA—garbage left over from our evolutionary heritage." Although this is still a commonly-held belief, recent discoveries have shown it to be wrong. Why, then, have we heard about it so often and for so long? It is because biological evolution needs junk DNA to solve a great mathematical problem.

In the late 1950s, the famous population geneticist J.B.S. Haldane showed that natural selection cannot possibly select for millions of beneficial

---

15. Crow, J.F., The origins, patterns, and implications of human spontaneous mutation, *Nature Reviews: Genetics* **1**:40–47.

16. Conrad, D.F. *et al.*, Variation in genome-wide mutation rates within and between human families, *Nature Genetics* **43**:712–714, 2011.

17. Kondrashov, A.S., Contamination of the genome by very slightly deleterious mutations: why have we not died 100 times over, *J. Theor. Biol.* **175**:583–594.

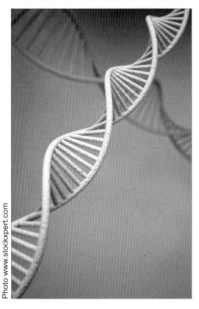

mutations, even over the course of human evolutionary history. Instead, and despite several simplifying assumptions *in favor of evolutionary theory*,[18] only a few hundred beneficial mutations could have been selected since our common ancestor with chimps.[19] This has become known as *Haldane's Dilemma* and, despite many claims to the contrary, Haldane's Dilemma was never solved.[20] What happened instead was a figment of evolutionary imagination. In the late 1960s, Kimura developed the idea of *neutral evolution*.[21] He reasoned that, if most of the DNA in a cell were non-functional, it would be free to mutate over time. Thus, there would be no *cost* to the organism to maintain the non-functional portions ('cost' is measured in terms of how many extra babies must be born in the population for natural selection to kill in order to eliminate the bad mutations and maintain fitness over time,[22] given the assumption that natural selection can see the bad mutations it needs to eliminate, of course).

Ohno is credited with inventing the term *junk DNA* about four years later.[23] The idea of junk DNA is extremely important to evolutionary mathematics. What would happen if it turned out that there was no such thing? What would happen if, instead of being 97% junk, the genome were 97% functional?

Modern technology has now killed the concept of junk DNA. This occurred after the completion of the Human Genome Project. However, even before this, it was clearly wrong, but there seemed to be stubborn refusal to reject junk DNA theory. There are many reasons why people today believe the majority of DNA in the cell is functional. For example, functions have been found for many retrotransposons,[24] which were once thought to be pieces of viruses that had inserted themselves into our genomes over the course of millions of years.

18. ReMine, W.J., Cost theory and the cost of substitution—a clarification, *J. Creation* **19**(1):113–125, 2005; creation.com/cost.

19. Haldane, J.B.S., The cost of natural selection, *Journal of Genetics* **55**:511–524, 1957.

20. Batten, D., Haldane's dilemma has not been solved, *J. Creation* **19**(1):20–21, 2005; creation.com/haldane. See also saintpaulscience.com/Haldane.htm.

21. Kimura, M., Evolution rate at the molecular level, *Nature* **217**:624–626, 1968.

22. ReMine, W.J., ref. 18.

23. Ohno, S., So much "junk" DNA in our genome, Evolution of genetic systems, Brookhaven Symposia in Biology, no. 23 (Smith, H.H., ed.), pp. 366–370, 1972.

24. Carter, R.W., The slow, painful death of junk DNA, *J. Creation* **23**(3):12–13, 2009; creation.com/junkdnadeath.

Also, functions have been found for much of the vast stretches of non-protein-coding DNA that sits between genes. It turns out that most of the genome is active. The ENCODE project was a multi-university, multimillion dollar, multi-year study designed to determine how much of the human genome was transcribed (turned into RNA, a measure of function). They only analyzed 1% of the genome, but they included both protein-coding and 'junk' DNA regions in the analysis. This project demonstrated that, on average, any given letter of the genome is used in six different RNA transcripts.[25] This does not mean everything is turned into protein, far from it. It also does not mean that everything has a mandatory function or even that the letters are used often. What it means is that most every letter does *something*. Since *form follows function* is a general rule of biology, the fact that these regions are active strongly suggests they have a function. Why else would the cell allow so much transcription? A significant portion of cellular resources are dedicated to making non-protein-coding RNA. Thus, the cell would be greatly benefitted by turning off this waste of energy. Natural selection over millions of years would have killed off the parasitic RNA processing. It has not done so because it is necessary for cellular function. In fact, the genome can now be seen as an RNA computer (see below).

The general lack of junk DNA is yet another Achilles' heel of evolutionary genetics, for, without it, evolutionary mathematics does not work, and more functions are still being found for the non-protein coding DNA. In fact, the 'junk' looks like it is more active than the 'genes', turning the old idea that we are protein-based organisms on its head. In the words of an evolutionary biologist, J.S. Mattick:

> The failure to recognize the full implications of this—particularly the possibility that the intervening noncoding sequences may be transmitting parallel information in the form of RNA molecules—may well go down as one of the biggest mistakes in the history of molecular biology.[26]

Ultra-complex gene processing

Biology students of the past were always taught the *one gene, one enzyme hypothesis*. Based on the amazing discoveries over the course of the 20th century, it seemed a straightforward conclusion that a 'gene' was a piece of DNA that coded for a specific protein. A 'gene' had specific starting and ending points, sections that coded for protein (*exons*), perhaps a few intervening sequences (*introns*) that needed to be cut out of the primary RNA transcript before translating the 'gene' into a protein, and upstream and downstream

25. Birney, E. *et. al.*, Identification and analysis of functional elements in 1% of the human genome by the ENCODE pilot project, *Nature* **447**:799–816, 2007.
26. J.S. Mattick, as quoted in Gibbs, W.W., The Unseen genome: gems amid the junk, *Scientific American*, pp. 47–53, Nov 2003.

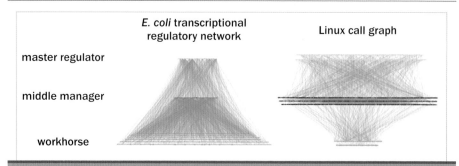

A comparison of the programming architecture of the *E. coli* bacterium to the call graph of the Linux operating system reveals interesting comparisons and stunning differences between the two systems.

regulatory areas where things could bind to the DNA and control the expression of the 'gene'. It was easy to walk through a 'gene' and see these places. One could even translate the DNA into protein on-the-fly from the sequence of the messenger RNA strand, if one knew the three-letter codes for each amino acid (which is not that hard to do). There is a grave problem with the one gene, one enzyme hypothesis, however, for like Darwin's idea of Pangenesis and the existence of junk DNA, it is also wrong.

From the results of the ENCODE project specifically, the world has been given a glimpse inside the most sophisticated computer operating system in the known universe—the human genome. But it is not a protein computer. Actually, the genome is more like an RNA supercomputer that *outputs* protein. In a similar way to your computer, which has a hard drive, re-writable memory (RAM), and a screen for output, the genomic computer has DNA for information storage, RNA for information comparison and calculation, and protein for output.

Efforts have been made to compare genome control processes to human-designed computer systems.[27] The parallels are interesting, but the differences are striking. For example, when compared to the computer operating system, Linux, the *E. coli* bacterial genome has fewer high-level regulators, which in turn control fewer middle-level managers, which in turn control many more low-level outputs. It is as if its genome is optimized to do what it does as efficiently as possible. Instead of Linux, a better comparison might be to military computers, which typically have very short programs with minimal instructions. This is true because they are designed to do a limited set of things as efficiently as possible instead of many different things at once (like the simultaneous use of graphics, games, music, and word processing that Linux allows). Yet, here

27. Yan, K.-K. *et al.*, Comparing genomes to computer operating systems in terms of the topology and evolution of their regulatory control networks, *Proc. Natl. Acad. Sci. USA* **107**(20):9186–9191, 2010.

is another puzzle: it took us many man-hours to design the computers that fly B-52 bombers, yet a single error in any program of any subsystem can cause catastrophic failure of the system it is controlling. The human genome is far more complex and can withstand thousands of errors without crashing. It controls more things simultaneously and is better designed!

When the human genome was completed, researchers were shocked to find only about 23,000 'genes' in the genome.[28] We already knew that the number of proteins the human body produces is many more times than this. How could this be? A few years later, The ENCODE project gave us strong hints that the human genome has a huge amount of *alternate splicing*.[29] Each part of a 'gene', we have learned, can be used in multiple different proteins.[30] Somehow, the body knows how to create different combinations of what were thought to be distinct protein-coding genes and splice them together to create several hundred thousand unique proteins. Not only that, but different cell types can create different proteins from that complicated process. Not only *that*, but different proteins are produced at different times and, somehow, the cells know what to produce, when to produce it, and under which conditions.[31] There is something controlling this process, and it is not necessarily in the protein-coding portion of the genome.[32]

Imbedded within each 'gene' is a series of small codes. Each is only a few letters long, but there are multiple codes at the beginning and end of each exon and intron. They make up what has been called the *spliceosome*, that is, the part of the genome that controls the complicated process of exon recombination, or *gene splicing*. The complexity of the spliceosome, indeed the complexity of the entire genome of all eukaryotes, is yet another Achilles' heel of evolutionary genetics. The genome is too complicated and the 'target' for mutation is much too large for known species to survive for millions of years,[33] let alone for them to have evolved in the first place.

You may be wondering why I have put the word 'gene' in quote marks throughout this chapter? It is because we no longer have a definition of the word.[34] At least, the definition has changed to mean something entirely new for all organisms more complex than bacteria. Genetics has taken a turn toward complexity and the simple, old idea has become outmoded. From here on out, when the word

---

28. Stein, L.D., Human genome: end of the beginning, *Nature* **431**:915–916, 2004.
29. Birney, E. *et al.*, ref. 25; see also Williams, A., Astonishing DNA complexity update, July 2007, creation.com/dnaupdate.
30. Barash, Y. *et al.*, Deciphering the splicing code, *Nature* **465**:53–59, 2010.
31. See Anon., Human genes sing different tunes in different tissues, PhysOrg.com, 2 Nov 2008.
32. Carter, R.W., Splicing and dicing the human genome, July 2010; creation.com/splicing.
33. Lynch, M., ref. 12.
34. Gerstein, M.B. *et al.*, What is a gene, post-ENCODE? History and updated definition, *Genome Research* **17**:669–681.

'gene' appears, take it in the classical sense: a gene is a piece of DNA that codes for protein. The only problem with this definition is that any particular piece of DNA might be used in multiple proteins, depending on context.

Hyper-complexity of a four-dimensional genome

Let's kick it up a few notches and look at another level of complexity. When we sequenced the human genome, we thought we would then understand how the genome works. This was a naïve error. What we had done was sequence the linear string of nucleotides only. This was only the first dimension of a genome that operates in at least four dimensions. What does this mean? Think about DNA. It is a string, a line, which, by definition, is one-dimensional. When the human genome was completed, the junk DNA theory seemed to be supported by the fact that genes were found scattered throughout the genome and there seemed to be no clustering of related functions. "Aha," they said, "gene order is random, a product of random changes over time." However, this was a bit shortsighted, for they were only looking at the first dimension.

We just learned about alternate splicing. Here, one part of the genome affects another part, either directly or through RNA and/or protein proxies. This is part of the second dimension of the genome. In order to draw these interactions, one would need to write out the genome and draw lots and lots of arrow from one place to another. To do this, you would need many sheets of paper, which have two dimensions (height and width).

The second dimension of the genome is extremely complex and includes specificity factors, enhancers, repressors, activators, transcription factors, histone acetylization signals, DNA methylation signals, post-transcriptional regulation of RNA, alternate splicing, and many other things. It plays a major role in the tight coordination and regulation of the vast network of events that occur both in the nucleus and throughout the cell. In this dimension, the order is not significantly important, for gene regulators have to float around in order to find their targets anyway. Having the target immediately next to the regulator is not necessary. It is at the next level that things get very interesting.

The third dimension of the genome is the 3-D structure of the DNA in the nucleus. At this level, genes are not randomly distributed in the nucleus, but are ordered and clustered according to need. Genes that are used together in series may not be found next to each other on the chromosomes, but when the chromosomes fold, they are often found next to each other in 3-D space, and are also often clustered near a nuclear pore or close to a center of transcription.[35]

---

35. Schoenfelder, S. *et al.*, Preferential associations between co-regulated genes reveal a transcriptional interactome in erythroid cells, *Nature Genetics* **42**:53–61, 2009; See also Scientists' 3-D view of genes-at-work is paradigm shift in genetics, sciencedaily.com, 16 Dec 2009.

```
CTAACCCTAACCCTAACCCTAACCCTAACCCTAACCCTCTGAAAGTGGACCTATCAGCAGGATGTGGGTGGGAGC
AGATTAGAGAATAAAAGCAGACTGCCTGAGCCAGCAGTGGCAACCCAATGGGGTCCCTTTCCATACTGTGGAAGC
TTCGTTCTTTCACTCTTTGCAATAAATCTTGCTATTGCTCACTCTTTGGGTCCACACTGCCTTTATGAGCTGTGA
CACTCACCGCAAAGGTCTGCAGCTTCACTCCTGAGCCAGTGAGACCACAACCCCACCAGAAAGAAGAAACTCAGA
ACACATCTGAACATCAGAAGAAACAAACTCCGGACGCGCCCCTTTAAGAACTGTAACACTCACCGCGAGGTTCCG
CGTCTTCATTCTTGAAGTCAGTGAGACCAAGAACCCACCAATTCCAGACACACTAGGACCCTGAGCAACCCCTA
GAAGAGCACCTGGTTGATAACCCAGTTCCCATCTGGGATTTAGGGGACCTGGACAGCCCGGAAAATGAGCTCCTC
ATCTCTAACCCAGTTCCCCTGTGGGGATTTAGGGGACCAGGGACAGCCCGTTGCATGAGCCCCTGGACTCTAACC
CAGTTCCCTTCTGGAATTTAGGGGCCCTGGGACAGCCCTGTACATGAGCTCCTGGTCTGTAACACAGTTCCCCTG
TGGGGATTTAGGGACTTGGGCCTTCTGTCTTTGGGATCTACTCTCTATGGGCCACACAGATATGTCTTCCAACTT
CCCTACACAGGGGGGGACTTCAAAGAGTGCCTTGAGCTGATCTGGTGATTGCTTTTTTGTACTGTTATTTATCTTA
TTCTTTTCATTGTGAGGTACTGATGCAAACACTTTGTACGAAAAGGTCTTTCTCATCTCGGGAGTCCCCGTCTAT
TTGTCCCGGTCCCTGTTAACCCAGTCCCCGACAGGAGCCCCTTCTGCACCTTGAGCTCTCACCACTCACCGTCCA
TCCAGCCCCAGCTCTGCCTGCAACCCACCCATCCCTGGGACTCGGGCCTCCCCTCTCTAGTGGTCTGGTCATCAG
GCCAGGGGCACGTGGAAGAAGCTATCGTGGCAAAGGGAGCAGTCATATCCCAAAATCTGTGGTTGGTTTACCAC
CACCATGGAAACCCCAGGGTGGGACTCTAGTTTCAGGTTGGAGCTGAGCCCTGTCGGGAATGAGCTTTCCCCAGC
TATGGCTTCTTGGGGCCCCTGTGCCCTGAGCTGTGTCTCCCAGCATCGGGTCCCCACCATGCATATGGCCCACTC
AGGCACAGTGCCGCGATGGCTGCATGCGTGAGGGGGGGCCTGGGCCCAGGGCTGGGAGTCCTTTGTGTCTCATGGC
CATGATTGTCCTTCCGAGTATGATATGGTGGCCAATTTCTTTTATTCTGTCGTTCAGAGTGAGTAAATGATGTAG
AGTTCATGCAGAAAAAAATACAACAAAAACCAAGGGAACATAGAATTGGAAAACGCGTCACAGCAATGAGTTAAA
TAGGTAACAAATTTCATCATTTGAAGAAAGACTTAGAGTGCCAAAAGTGCCTCTTAAGTCTCCTTTAAAAAGTAG
CAAAATTCATCCCTGAAGAAGCATCTTGGCCTTTTTCATGTACTCAGAGTGCTGGTGAAGAACAAAGATTGCTGA
AACATTATGTACCTAACAGCGTTACAGGGTGTAGATAACACACTGGAAAACCTGGTCGTTACAGTGGACATATTC
CAGGAAGTCCTTGCCTGAGGTTTTCCAAGTTATGGAATTGCTTGAGATTGGAAGAGGCGATGGAGGGTACAACTG
TAATGCCCAACCTCATTTTTGCTAACCCTGTTTTTAGACTCTCCCTTTCCTTCAATCACCTAGCCTTCTTTCCAC
CTGAAAGGACTCTCCCTTAACTGAGAGAACCGGACAGACTCCATCTTGGCTCTTTCACTGGCAGCCCCTTCCTCA
AAGACTTAACTCGTCAAGCTGACTCCCAGGACATCCGAGAATGCAATTAACTGACAACCTACTGTGGCGAGCTA
CATCCGCAGTCCCCAGGAATTCGTCCGATTGATAACGCCCAATTACCCGCGTCTATCACCTTGTAATAGTCTTAA
AGCACCTGCACCTGGAACTGTTTACTTTCCTGTAACCATTTATCCTTTTAACATTTTGCCTGATTTACTTATGTA
AAATTCTTTTAACTAGACCGCCACTCCCCTTTCTAAACAAAAGTATAAAAGAAAATCTAGCCCCTTCTTTGGGAC
TGAGACAATTTTGAGGTTAACGCAGGGTGCCTGTAATCCTAAGGGAGGAGACCGCCACTTCTGCTGCCCTTCCCT
TCCCCACACCCCCTTCTCTAGTTTATGAAACAGGGAAAAAGGGAGAAAGCAAAAAGATAAAAAAAACAGAAGTAA
GATAAATAGCTAGACGACCTTGGCAGCACCACCCGGCACTGGTGGTTAAATAATAATAATAATAATATTAACCCC
TGACCTAAACTACTTGTGTTATCTGTAAATTCCAGACACTGTATGAGGAAGCCCTGCAAAACTTTCTGTTCTGTT
ATCTGATGCGTGTAGCCCCCAGTCACGTTCCGATGCTTGCTCGATCTATCACGACCCTTTCAAGTGAACCCCTTA
GAGTCGTAAACCCTTAAAAGGGCCAGGAATTTCGTTTTCGGGGAGCTCGGCTCTTCAGGCCCAAGTAAACCTGCC
GTATCTCACCTGAGACCAACCCCCAACTACAAAACTCAACCTGGAATTTTCCCAGGACCAAACCCATCTATATTC
TGTAACCCGAAACCTCAAAGCCTAACCCTAACCCTAACCCCTACAGTTGAGGTCCCCCCGCCCCTGTGGTTCCAG
CTCAAGACAACCTGCCCCCTCGTGGGTTTGCAGGCCCTCTGGTGGGGGTGGGAGCTGGGGGCCCACATACAGCTCT
CTGAGCTTAAGCCATTTTCTTCCTTCATTCCTTCCTTCCTCCCTCCCTTCCCTTCCTTCCTCCCTCCCTCC
TTCCCTCCCTCCCTTTTTTTTTTCAGGGTCTTGCTCTGTCACCCAGGCTGGAGTGCAGTGGCATGATCACAGCTG
ACTGCAGCCTCGGACTCCCAGGCTCAAGTTATCTTCCCTCCTCAGCCTCCAGAGTAGGTGGGACTACAGGAGTGT
GCCATCGCACCCAGCGAATTTCTTAATTTTTATTTTGTAGAGATGAGGCCTCTCGATATTGTCCAGGCTTGGAAG
TAGTTCTTGAAATTCAAGAGGATCTTGAAGTTCTGACCTCCTGTCAATATCCCTTCCCCTCACCTTGACCCTCCC
ATTCTGCCCCACCTGTCAGGATCACAAGGACCCCCAGATCAGCAGATGGGAACCGGACCAAAAAGAGAAATAGTG
CTGTCCCGCCCATAAGTACCACCCCCAGACTCCCTGCTCCACCCTCTGGACCACAGGGAGGCCCCATGCTCCATC
CCTGAAAACCACCCCCAGACCCCCTGCTCCTCCCCACGGGACCGCCCCCAGATCCACTGTTCCTGTCCTCCGGAC
CACACCGGACAGCTCCTTCCCTCGGCGCCCATCCCCAGACCCCAGCTCCTCCCCTCAGGATCATCCCCAGACCCCC
GCTCCTCCCATCAGGACCGCCCCCAGAACCCCCTGCTCCTCCCCACAGGACCACCCCCAGACCCCCGCTCCTCCC
CTAAGGACCACCCACAGACCCCCACGCTTCCCC
```

Thus, something is holding them in place. Since the DNA is equivalent to a huge bundle of string, the parts of that bundle that are buried are difficult to access while other parts are exposed on the outside or in internal pockets.[36,37]

36. Eitan, Y. and Tanay, A., Probabilistic modeling of Hi-C contact maps eliminates systematic biases to characterize global chromosomal architecture, *Nature Genetics* **43**(11):1059–1067, 2011.
37. Is the shape of a genome as important as its content? PhysOrg.com, 29 Oct 2010.

Part of the code imbedded within the first dimension affects the 3-D folding of the DNA, which, in turn, affects gene expression patterns. This third dimension is extremely important.[38]

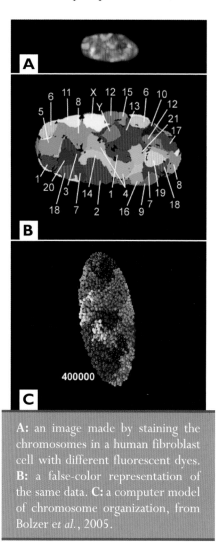

A: an image made by staining the chromosomes in a human fibroblast cell with different fluorescent dyes. B: a false-color representation of the same data. C: a computer model of chromosome organization, from Bolzer et al., 2005.

The fourth dimension of the genome involves changes to the first, second, and third dimensions over time. The chromosomes are in a particular shape in the nucleus, but that shape changes during development because different cell types need different complements of genes and other genetic instructions. The shape can change in the short term as cells respond to stimuli and unwrap portions of DNA in order to get at buried genes, only to re-wrap that section when the gene is no longer needed.[39] There are also changes in the 'junk' DNA. For example, a great deal of *retrotransposon* (a.k.a. jumping genes or mobile elements) activity happens as the brain develops, with pieces of DNA from several different classes (L1, Alu, and SVA) copying themselves and jumping around in the genome of individual brain cells. This helps the various brain cells to differentiate.[40] Also, liver cells tend to have many chromosomal duplications. The final genome of the various cells in the body is not necessarily the one the fertilized egg cell had when it started dividing, and the shape of the genome varies from cell to cell and through time. These examples are not accidental, but a carefully controlled symphony of genomic changes over four dimensions. I hope you are impressed, for the genome was designed by a master Architect.

38. Bolzer, A. *et al.*, Three-dimensional maps of all chromosomes in human male fibroblast nuclei and prometaphase rosettes, *PLoS Biol* **3**(5):e157, 2005.
39. See: A new look at how genes unfold to enable their expression, PhysOrg.com, 14 July 2008.
40. Baillie, J.K. *et al.*, Somatic retrotransposition alters the genetic landscape of the human brain, *Nature* **479**(7374):534–537.

This is all extremely complicated, but it underscores the next Achilles' heel of evolutionary genetics. Darwinism needs life to be simple. Natural selection needs the ability to take the little tweaks caused by mutation and select the best from a herd or group of animals. Once a species is in existence, perhaps natural selection could work in limited ways (see previous chapter), but can this process explain how the species came into existence in the first place? Hardly, for a simple process of error accumulation and selection could not create a complex, interleaved, four-dimensional system with an amazing amount of data compression and flexibility. And, once that system is in place, it will be seriously threatened by future random changes through mutation. That is the situation we are in today. It is fine to imagine small changes to an already-existing, complex system. To use those small changes as an explanation for the origin of that system itself, however, is tantamount to saying there was no intelligence involved in the production of the latest computer operating systems. Yet the genome far surpasses in complexity and efficiency any operating system in the world today.

Codon Degeneracy

To date, human-designed computers operate in base-2, because transistors only give us two letters with which to work (0 and 1, off and on), but the resulting math is pretty simple and we have been able to build sophisticated computer chips that operate on this principle. The genome, on the other hand, is base-4. Instead of just 0 and 1, there are four letters in the genome (A, C, G, and T). This is not necessary, for the same information could be spelled out in a system using any number of letters. Why base-4?

Strangely, it takes three letters to code for a single amino acid in a protein. In the genome, these three-letter *codons* are strung together in groups (exons), with each group producing a functional part of one or more proteins. There are 20 amino acids used in human proteins, but there are 64 possible codons (three positions with four possible letters allows 4 x 4 x 4 = 64 codons). This means that some amino acids, like alanine, are assigned to multiple codons (GCA, GCC, GCG, and GCT). Others, like tryptophan have but one (TGG). You will notice that the four codons for alanine all start with the letters 'GC'. This means that any mutation that changes the final letter will produce the same amino acid even though the codon is different. This is referred to as *codon degeneracy* and it adds a bit of robustness to the genome, for at least some mutations in protein-coding regions have little net effect. I said "little" because the transfer RNAs for the various codons are not found in the cell at the same frequency. There have been cases where a single letter change, even though the amino acid was not changed, created a bad mutation. As the protein was being translated, a pause occurred while the rare tRNA was found. This caused the protein to fold incorrectly, resulting in a malformed enzyme. More recent data indicates that protein translation in general may be affected by codon usage, at least in bacteria, where the rate of translation depends on the exact codons used. Bacterial cells avoid gene promoters *inside* their genes. When they occur, translation is often slowed temporarily because the bacterial ribosome tends to stick to promoter sequences.[41] Thus, having alternate codons available allowed the Designer to intelligently engineer genes with fewer internal contradictions with other gene features.

Besides all this, there is a very good reason for codon degeneracy and a base-4 genome. Not only is this the most optimal way to code for 20 amino acids,[42] but it also allows for *multiple overlapping codes.*

Multiple overlapping codes

There is a considerable amount of data compression in the genomes of all higher organisms. Any given section of each of these genomes might be doing several things simultaneously. A single letter of DNA might be part of an exon that is in turn used in twenty different proteins. At the same time, that letter might be part of the splicing code that tells the cell when to produce each of those proteins. That letter also might be part of the *histone code* that the cell uses to know where to wrap the DNA around certain protective proteins called histones. That letter also might affect the 3-D structure of the DNA. It might be part of the pervasive epigenetic code (Chapter 1), and it might be part of a three-letter codon that is translated into a specific amino acid. Because the genome is base-4, and because of codon degeneracy, the Designer was able to select from alternate codons when faced with fulfilling multiple simultaneous requirements. Degeneracy allowed Him to overlap multiple genomic commands without having to compromise the design requirements of the proteins.

Multiple, overlapping DNA and RNA codes defy naturalistic explanation and make it impossible for natural selection to operate as an agent of long-term evolutionary change. Selection runs into a 'wall of insurmountable difficulty' when faced with mutations that affect more than one trait simultaneously. Polyfunctionality (also called *pleitropy*) means that a given mutation can affect completely unrelated traits (say, color vision, the ability to tolerate garlic, and mitochondrial efficiency, although this would be an extreme example). This is still yet another Achilles' heel of evolutionary genetics. How could a simple process of trial and error, always seeking the simplest answer to an environmental problem, create an interleaved and multilayered system of

41. Li, G.-W., Oh, E., and Weissman, J.S., The anti-Shine-Dalgarno sequence drives translational pausing and codon choice in bacteria, *Nature* **484**(7395):538–541, 2012.
42. For example, in a base-2 system, it would take at least 5 letters to code for 20 amino acids, with less degeneracy ($2^5 = 32$ possibilities).

regulation? In fact, this system is one of the wonders of the universe. Without this level of multitasking, the genome would have to be much larger and it might not be possible for DNA-based, multicellular organisms to exist at all without it.

Evidence for Genesis in our genes

Modern genetics has revealed an amazing world of complexity to us, but this is not all it can do, for genetics also gives us the ability to test theories of history. With the many different ancient creation myths in existence, would it surprise you to learn that one in particular is an excellent match for what we have learned through genetics? Would it surprise you to learn about the abundant testimony to Creation, the Flood, and the Tower of Babel in our genes?

Because Genesis claims to be a history book, and because it claims an all-encompassing history of humanity, it makes certain and specific predictions about human genetics. These predictions deal with the creation of two original people (Adam and Eve), a *population bottleneck* that occurred about 1,600 years later in the time of Noah when the world population was reduced to eight souls, and the predicted single dispersal of humanity from a central point in the Middle East a few hundred years later. We must use caution when approaching this subject, for human science has had a pretty bad track record of getting things right throughout the centuries. There is much we could be wrong about today.

However, upon careful and critical analysis of the available data, one can easily see the biblical narrative in our genes. While people like Francis Collins, the head of the Human Genome Project and a proclaimed evangelical Christian, claim there is no evidence of Adam and Eve,[43] there is little to no evidence that most of these people have thought about what the biblical predictions actually are.

The Bible states that all of humanity came from a single couple. This is a profound statement about genetics, for it severely limits the amount of human genetic diversity we should find today. But let's not get stuck thinking like evolutionists and only consider models that involve a progression back to infinity. Everyone after Adam and Eve has to connect back to them through the normal process of sexual recombination and reproduction, but this is not necessarily true of the founding couple. God could have engineered multiple cell lines into Adam's testes. Likewise, he could have frontloaded Eve's ovaries with multiple human genomes, all very different from one another. The early population could have had a remarkable range of diversity. Alternatively, there

---

43. Carter, R.W., The non-mythical Adam and Eve: refuting errors by Francis Collins and BioLogos, August 2011; creation.com/biologos-adam.

may have been but one original genome and Eve was a near-clone (without the Y chromosome), perhaps even a haploid clone, of Adam. Thus, biblical models of human genetic history have many options. Which one should we choose?

For theological reasons, I favor Eve being a clone of Adam. Thus, she fell under the *curse* God applied to Adam and his descendants, and she is related to Christ, the kinsman redeemer.[44] Also, since she was formed from a rib taken from Adam's side, one might assume the cells, muscles, nerves, blood vessels, and DNA (!) of Adam were used to form her. This is not mandated by the Bible, and I am open to alternate possibilities, but I lean in that direction.

It may come as a surprise to hear it, especially if you have heard or read Francis Collins, but the amount of genetic diversity we observe today could fit neatly into Adam and Eve. In fact, the bulk of it could fit into Adam alone! There are about 10,000,000 places that carry common variations in the human genome. The average person carries somewhere around two or three million of these. That is, there are about three million places where sister chromosomes (chromosomes come in pairs; you have two copies of chromosome 1, for example) have different readings in corresponding locations. It is not a stretch to think that Adam carried nearly all of these common variants in his genome. Why do people only carry a subset of the total? This is probably due to recursion in their family trees. That is, they have inherited identical copies of different sections of the genome from the same distant ancestor through different lines. Add to this the processes of population growth, contraction, subdivision and mixing over biblical time[45] and we do not need millions of people living in the ancient past to explain current human genetic diversity.

Additionally, most common genomic variants come in two versions. When we find more versions than this, they can be explained by an early mutation (e.g. the most common version of blood type O is clearly a mutation [a broken copy] of the gene that codes for the blood type A allele,[46] and it is found worldwide) or a mutation that occurred post-Babel (e.g. the sickle cell gene common to certain parts of Africa, or the blue-eyed allele common in Northern Europe, or the many variations found in certain immune system genes, which are designed to change rapidly). Thus, since most variation could fit into a single person, it may not be necessary to call for strange models of early biblical genetics.

In the Out of Africa model, evolutionists say that humanity went through a near-extinction bottleneck before our population expanded and eventually left Africa. Why is a bottleneck part of their model? Because they are trying to explain

44. Sarfati, J., The Incarnation: Why did God become Man? December 2010; creation.com/incarnation.
45. Carter, R.W., ref. 43.
46. Sarfati, J., Blood types and their origin, *J. Creation* **11**(1):31–32, 1997; creation.com/blood-groups.

the *lack* of diversity among people spread across the world.[47] This diversity is much less than they at first assumed, based on ideas of a large population living in Africa for a million years or so. The bottleneck is an *ad hoc* addition to evolutionary theory, but low diversity is part of the creation model from the start.

Interestingly, and as an aside, animals are different. Humans are exceptionally uniform when compared to most all animal species. Chimpanzees are five to six times more diverse. The common house mouse carries huge variations in their population, including multiple chromosomal rearrangements. Examples of this nature abound in the animal world. Some of this is due to degradation of animal genomes over time. Some of this is also due to the different starting point of animals compared to people. The Bible does not say that God created two of every kind of animal. In fact, one might assume He created a functioning worldwide ecology that included high diversity (as also evidenced from the fossil record) within each kind. It is true that only two of most kinds of animal were on Noah's Ark, but they were selected from a potentially much larger genetic pool than were people. Since most of the genomic data available today is human (for obvious reasons), we are far from being able to build a model of genetic history for most animal species, but these are interesting points to consider.

Besides the number of common variations found in the human genome, there are an untold number of rare variations as well. These tend to occur only in isolated populations and are an indication of mutations that have occurred since Adam, indeed, since Babel. These include blue eyes in the European population, sickle cell anemia in the African population, and many super rare variations that only occur in a single tribe, family or individual. We share a huge amount of genetic variation. This is an indication that we came from a small population in the recent past. What we don't share uniformly (population-level variation) is an indication that our genomes are in rapid decline, with a rapid rate of mutation occurring in all people groups worldwide. More on that below.

When one considers the female-specific and male-specific sections of DNA, we can see even more confirmation of Adam and Eve. According to a lot of theory and a lot of experimental evidence, mitochondria (those little subcellular power plants that convert sugar to energy) are only passed on through the female line. Since mitochondria also have their own little genome of approximately 16,569 letters, and since this little genome is also subject to mutation over time, we can use it to build a family tree of worldwide female ancestry. This led to the announcement of an African *Mitochondrial Eve* in the evolutionary literature

---

47. Carter, R.W., The Neutral Model of evolution and recent African origins, *J. Creation* **23**(1):70–77; creation.com/african-origins.

back in 1987.[48] If there were any other females alive millions of years ago, only one managed to pass her genome to all people living today.

The date of Mitochondrial Eve is assumed to be in the hundreds of thousands of years before present, but only if one assumes a certain slow mutation rate and common ancestry with chimps. Using real-world mutation rates gives an age for Eve about 6,000 years ago.[49] A more recent study demonstrated that mutations in the mitochondrial control region (these account for approximately 2/3 of all mitochondrial mutations) occur at a rate of one every other generation.[50] Since Eve's mitochondrial sequence has been reconstructed and published, in the evolutionary literature,[51] and since most mitochondrial lines are less than 30 mutations removed from the 'Eve' consensus sequence, and since the most divergent are only 100 mutations removed, the diversity of mitochondrial DNA within the modern human population can easily fit into a 6,000-year/200-generation time frame.

The African Eve hypothesis and the evolutionary assumptions behind it have been dealt with previously,[52] so the details will not be reproduced here. We know the sequence of more than 99% of the mitochondrial genome of the original human female. There is no evidence for any other. Why do people believe Eve was just one of many females living in a large population a very long time ago? Because this is part of a *model* of evolutionary history. It is not grounded in reality, but it gives them a convenient excuse for discounting the biblical prediction that there should be but one female lineage in the world.

Like the mitochondrial genome, the male Y chromosome gives us a way to build a family tree of all the men in the world. Y Chromosome Adam supposedly existed a very long time ago as well, but at a different time than mitochondrial Eve. However, and as above, these conclusions are based on *models* that assume a lot about human history, population size and mutation rates. With the publication of the revised chimp Y chromosome,[53] and the discovery that it is only 70% identical to the human Y chromosome (even this number is generous since half of the chimp Y is missing), evolutionists are forced to conclude that the Y chromosome has mutated extremely rapidly in human history. Yet, the

48. Cann, R.L., Stoneking, M., and Wilson, A.C., Mitochondrial DNA and human evolution, *Nature* **325**:31–36, 1987.
49. Wieland, C., A shrinking date for eve, *J. Creation* **12**(1):1–3, 1998; creation.com/eve.
50. Madrigal, L. *et al.,* High mitochondrial mutation rates estimated from deep-rooting Costa Rican pedigrees, *American Journal of Physical Anthropology* **148**:327–333, 2012. See also Carter, R.W., Is 'mitochondrial Eve' consistent with the biblical Eve? Jan 2013; creation.com/mteve-biblical-eve.
51. Carter, R.W., Mitochondrial diversity within modern human populations, *Nucl. Acids Res.* **35**(9):3039–3045, 2007.
52. Carter, R.W., ref. 43; Carter, R.W., ref. 47.
53. Hughes, J.F. *et al.,* Chimpanzee and human Y chromosomes are remarkably divergent in structure and gene content, *Nature* **463**:536–539.

current human Y chromosomes found in the world are all very similar to one another. The only way to maintain similarity under a high mutation load is to have a very recent common ancestor. Viva Adam!

Another measure we can use to test the veracity of Adam and Eve is in *linkage* data. During sexual reproduction, the cells in both parents go through meiosis, where the chromosomes they inherited from their parents are mixed together. Thus, when parents pass on their genes, they are actually passing on scrambled versions of the grandparents' chromosomes. This scrambling, called *crossing over* causes DNA to be inherited in large blocks. There are sections of the genome that have not crossed over in all of human history (indicating a youthful genome). When two variants are inherited together (because they are close together on the same DNA strand), they are said to be *linked*. Linkage has been studied in detail and we have learned some very interesting things from it. First, between two and four common blocks explain most of the blocks in all human populations.[54] In other words, there are only a few original chromosomes and pieces of those chromosomes are still intact. There are only ten thousand or so blocks in the genome, which is easily explained if the human population is only about 200 generations old and there are 1–2 crossing over events per long chromosome arm per generation.

Besides the molecular clock assumption behind most evolutionary studies, the majority also assume that recombination is the same through time and across all geography. This is not necessarily so, however, as we know that crossing over is affected by genetic factors (the PRDM9 gene, specifically) and that variations exist within these factors that affect the rate of crossing over in different individuals.[55] This is a challenge to many prior evolutionary studies, including much of what has been claimed about the evidence for our African origins.

Out of Africa or Out of Babel?

We discussed the Out of Africa theory in relation to Mitochondrial Eve above. In this section, let us simply list the corresponding factors between 'Out of Africa' and Genesis. According to the most commonly told evolutionary story, we came from a small population that broke up into smaller bands during a single dispersal event that carried humanity across the globe. This dispersion occurred with three main female lineages and one main male lineage in the recent past. Oh, and it went through the Middle East before it got to Europe,

---

54. The International HapMap 3 Consortium, Integrating common and rare genetic variation in diverse human populations, *Nature* **467**:52–58, 2010.

55. Parvanov, E.D. *et al.*, PRDM9 controls activation of mammalian recombination hotspots, *Science* **327**:835, 2010; Berg, I.L. *et al.*, PRDM9 variation strongly influences recombination hot-spot activity and meiotic instability in humans, *Nature Genetics* **42**(10):859–864, 2010; See also, Carter, R.W., Does genetics point to a single primal couple? Apr 2011; creation.com/genetics-primal-couple.

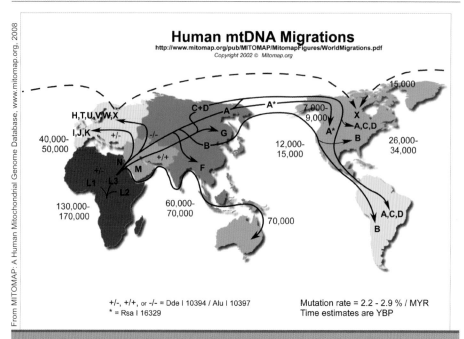

From MITOMAP: A Human Mitochondrial Genome Database, www.mitomap.org, 2008

Human mtDNA Migrations
http://www.mitomap.org/pub/MITOMAP/MitomapFigures/WorldMigrations.pdf
Copyright 2002 © Mitomap.org

+/-, +/+, or -/- = Dde I 10394 / Alu I 10397
* = Rsa I 16329

Mutation rate = 2.2 - 2.9 % / MYR
Time estimates are YBP

World mtDNA Migration According to the Out of Africa proponents has many parallels with the Genesis account.

Asia, Australia, Oceania, or the Americas. Every single one of those points is predicted by the Genesis accounts of the Flood (Genesis 6–8), Tower of Babel (Genesis 11) and the Table of Nations (Genesis 9–11). The difference is in the timing (6,000, 4,500, and ~4,000 years ago, respectively, vs. tens of thousands of years ago) and the origin (Middle East vs. NE Africa near the Red Sea[56]). Yet, the conclusions of the Out of Africa *model* are driven by the evolutionary starting assumptions.[57] In way of summary, they assume that a molecular clock is in operation, causing mutations to accumulate in all populations at the same rate throughout all time. We have already seen that this is not true. They assume all populations have roughly the same demographics (same birth and death rates, average age of marriage, average number of children, etc.). They also assume there are no differences in the DNA repair machinery between populations, because this would throw off the molecular clock. Thus, when they find more diversity in Africa, they automatically conclude this is the older population and the source for the rest of humanity. However, what if some African tribes have a different genetic history than the rest? There are many Africans who fit into the average world-type mitochondrial sequence pool. There are others who are

56. Tishkoff, S.A. *et al.*, The genetic structure and history of Africans and African Americans, *Science* **324**:1035–1044, 2009.
57. Carter, R.W., ref. 47.

much more different. Does this mean these are older sequences, or does it mean these people simply picked up more mutations in their mitochondrial lineage for any number of reasons? Interestingly, a recent study claimed that early African tribes remained small and isolated from one another for thousands of years.[58] This is a recipe for rapid mutation accumulation and genetic drift.

There are some additional correspondences between 'Out of Africa' and Genesis. Generally, humans are believed to have existed in Africa for some millions of years as *Homo erectus*. Then, without explanation, this pre-modern-human population crashed and nearly went extinct. The ten thousand *or fewer* survivors managed to hold on, rapidly evolving into modern man. The population rebounded, diversified, and then some of the genetic lineages managed to escape Africa and conquer the world. The biblical account starts with two people, Adam and Eve. The population then grows to some unknown number and crashes, being reduced to eight souls, with three reproducing couples, at the Flood, 1,600 years after Creation. The population then rebounds, but they continue to defy God as they did before the Flood, so He intervenes and scrambles their languages at a place called Babel, causing them to go separate ways by clans. Thus, several generations after the Flood, they spread out and conquer the world after the Tower of Babel incident. There is a nice general concordance between the Out of Africa scenario and Genesis after the evolutionary story is modified to fit the data. Specifically, Out of Africa has had to deal with the lack of diversity among people worldwide (hence, the population crash), and the *single* dispersal of humanity that is evident in our genes.

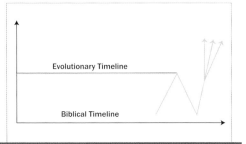

Stylized Out of Africa scenario compared to a stylized biblical account. Evolutionists believe man existed as *Homo erectus* for a million years or so in Africa. Then, for some unexplained reason, the species crashed and nearly went extinct. Modern man somehow managed to evolve in this genetically catastrophic event (catastrophic because inbreeding is very, very bad). Then, *some* of the new genetic lineages that were evolving (through mutation) left Africa to spread out and cover the globe. These lineages happened to all be closely related and nobody knows why the others stayed in Africa. In the biblical model, the population starts with Adam and Eve, grows to an unknown number, is reduced to eight people 1600 years later, then rebounds. The *entire* population then spreads out across the globe.

58. Behar, D.M. *et al.*, and The Genographic Consortium, The dawn of human matrilineal diversity, *Am. J. Human Gen.* **82**:1130–1140, 2008.

The surprising Neanderthal

What do we do, then, with claims for non-human caveman ancestors? New discoveries in archaeology and genetics have caused evolutionary views on Neanderthals, for example, to shift radically in the past decade. Neanderthals are now believed to have painted in caves, made musical instruments, had the controlled use of fire, buried their dead in a ceremonial manner with the head pointed toward the rising sun, and hunted the landscape for odd minerals in order to grind them up and use them for makeup (cosmetics).[59] The details of this list are still debated among various evolutionists, but to even bring up one of these ideas, let alone several at the same time, would have been tantamount to evolutionary heresy just a few years ago.

Thanks to rapid advances in technology, we now have the ability to pull DNA from some of the best preserved Neanderthal bones. The field of *ancient DNA*

	1	11	21	31	41	51	61	71	81	91
Human	MMQESATETI	SNSSMNQNGM	STLSSQLDAG	SRDGRSSGDT	SSEVSTVELL	HLQQQQALQA	ARQLLLQQQT	SGLKSPKSSD	KQRPLQVPVS	VAMMTPQVIT
Chimp	....	....	....	....	....	....	....	....	....	....
Gorilla	....	....	....	....	....	....	....	....	....	....
Orangutan	.....V....	....	....	....	....	....	....	....	....	....
Rhesus	....	....	....	....	....	....	....	....	....	....
Mouse	....	....	....	....	....	....	....	......E	....	....

	101	111	121	131	141	151	161	171	181	191
Human	PQQMQQILQQ	QVLSPQQLQA	LLQQQQAVML	QQQQLQEFYK	KQQEQLHLQL	LQQQQQQQQQ	QQQQQQQQQQ	QQQQ-QQQQQ	QQQQQQQQQQ	QQHPGKQAKE
Chimp	....	....	....	....	....	....	....	....Q.....	....	....
Gorilla	....	....	....	....	....	...-.....	....	....--	....	....
Orangutan	....	....	....	....	....	...-.....	....	....--	....	....
Rhesus	....	....	....	....	....	...-.....	....	....-.....	....	....
Mouse	....	....	....	....	....	...-.....	....	....Q.....	....	....

	201	211	221	231	241	251	261	271	281	291
Human	QQQQQQQQQQ	LAAQQLVFQQ	QLLQMQQLQQ	QQHLLSLQRQ	GLISIPPGQA	ALPVQSLPQA	GLSPAAIQQL	WKEVTGVHSM	EDNGIKHGGL	DLTTNNSSST
Chimp	....	....	....	....	....	....	....	....	....	....
Gorilla	....	....	....	....	....	....	....	....	....	....
Orangutan	......-...	....	....	....	....	....	....	....	....	....
Rhesus	....	....	....	....	....	....	....	....	....	....
Mouse	......-...	....	....	....	....	....	....	....	....	....

	301	311	321
Human	TSSNTSKASP	PITHHSIVNG	QSSVLSARRD
Chimp	...T......	....	.....N....
Gorilla	...T......	....	.....N....
Orangutan	...T......	....	.....N....
Rhesus	...T......	....	.....N....
Mouse	...T......	....	.....N....

The letters indicate the leading 330 amino acids of FOXP2 protein of human, chimpanzee, gorilla, orangutan, rhesus monkey and mouse. The amino acid sequences show two poly-glutamine stretches (indicated in red) and the two specific mutations (bottom row) which set the human sequence apart from the rest of the presented mammals (the N on position 304 and the S on position 326). The terminal 386 amino acids of FOXP2 are identical in all species and are not shown here. Sequences are as reported in Enard *et al.**

Enard W. *et al.*, Molecular evolution of FOXP2, a gene involved in speech and language, **418**:869–872, 2002.

59. Carter, R.W., The Painted Neanderthal, May 2010; creation.com/the-painted-neandertal.

genetics is problematic, for DNA is a fragile molecule that breaks down rapidly upon the death of an individual. Also, some of the damages are similar to those that occur over the course of time in living individuals. Thus, it is sometimes difficult to tell *post mortem* DNA decay apart from mutations that occurred in the ancestry of that individual. Another problem is contamination. Since the DNA in the ancient sample is necessarily degraded, any contamination from modern DNA will overwhelm the evidence for ancient DNA. Researchers are well aware of these problems and have gone to great lengths to overcome them, including treating any new find as a crime scene, with *clean room* techniques designed to reduce contamination from the people handling the bones.[60]

What have we learned? Would you be surprised if genetics has thrown evolutionists another curveball? After careful consideration of the issues listed above, modern studies on Neanderthal genetics have come to some surprising conclusions. Early work discovered that they had the same gene (FoxP2) that gives modern humans the ability to speak.[61] Then, they discovered that some Neanderthals carried similar versions of skin pigment genes that cause light skin and red hair, then green eyes and freckles, when they occur in people of European descent.[62] Everything was pointing to them being much more human than once thought, but then, based on mitochondrial DNA retrieved from Neanderthal specimens, the conclusion was made that they probably did not interbreed with the ancestors of modern man because Neanderthal mitochondrial sequences are not found in people living today.[63]

These conclusions were short-lived, however, for the full-length Neanderthal genome (well, 60% of it) was published a short time later.[64] If the sequences are accurate, Neanderthal is not what anyone expected. There is now evidence that they interbred with the direct ancestors of modern people, meaning, according to the biological species concept, that we are the same species. It appears that people living outside Africa carry 3–4% Neanderthal DNA. Interestingly, Neanderthal remains have not been found in Africa, but traces of their genome still persist in the places they did live (and beyond). The new evolutionary explanation is a modified Out of Africa scenario, where there was limited interbreeding between modern humans and Neanderthals as they left Africa and displaced Neanderthals on their way to world domination. But this

60. Carter, R.W., Neandertal genome like ours, June 2010; creation.com/neandergenes.
61. Borger, P. and Truman, R., The FOXP2 gene supports Neandertals being fully human, *J. Creation* **22**(2):13–14; creation.com/foxp2.
62. Lalueza-Fox, C. *et al.*, A Melanocortin 1 Receptor allele suggests varying pigmentation among Neanderthals, *Science* **318**:1453–1455, 2007.
63. Green, R.E. *et al.*, A complete Neandertal mitochondrial genome sequence determined by high-throughput sequencing, *Cell* **134**:416–426, 2008; Carter, R.W., The Neandertal mitochondrial genome does not support evolution, *J. Creation* **23**(1):40–43, 2009; creation.com/neandertal-mito.
64. Green, R.E. *et al.*, A draft sequence of the Neandertal genome, *Science* **328**:710–722, 2010.

is a departure from the status quo of only a short time ago. Do you recall how confident the evolutionists were when hitting biblical creationists over the head with the African Origins hypothesis? Much of what they believed is now not supported by their own scientific data.[65]

There is an alternate scenario that also fits the data. Instead of two large populations that barely mixed, if the Neanderthal population was much smaller than the main wave of migration, there could have been complete mixing with the same result. If the modern non-African population is 3–4% Neanderthal, then perhaps their population was but 3–4% the size, or somewhere in between with a different degree of mixing. If they were people, especially if they were a post-Flood population, mixing would be natural, for people do what people do, after all. More recent data showed that Neanderthals *across their range* were more similar to one another than are individuals within any modern people group.[66] From Spain to the middle of Russia, Neanderthals look more like one extended family—a human family—that lived on the earth in Europe and Asia after the Flood and were overwhelmed by a later migration of people.

Human vs. chimp

For several decades, we have been hearing, "Humans and chimpanzees are 99% identical." This is not true.[67] The figure was based on some early experimental evidence that compared sections of known genes to each other, so at least *some* of our DNA is very similar. But our genomes are less than 2% protein-coding, and many genes are not comparable between the two species. Humans have several hundred protein-coding genes (all tightly integrated into the spliceosome) that are absent in chimps. There are entire gene families found in humans that are not in chimps.[68] This throws a monkey wrench into evolutionary models, for there have only been a few hundred thousand generations since we were supposedly the same species.[69] How could these brand-new genes arise and be integrated into our complex genomes in such a short amount of time? Time is not the deciding factor for evolution. Evolution is measured in generations, and there have not been that many since the assumed common ancestor.

65. Carter, R.W., Neandertal genome like ours (There may be Neandertals at your next family reunion!), June 2010; creation.com/neandergenes.
66. Reich, D. *et al.*, Genetic history of an archaic hominin group from Denisova Cave in Siberia, *Nature* **468**:1053–1060, 2010. See also Wieland, C. and Carter, R.W., Not the Flintstones—it's the Denisovans, Jan 2011; creation.com/denisovan.
67. Tomkins, J. and Bergman, J., Genomic monkey business—estimates of nearly identical human-chimp DNA similarity re-evaluated using omitted data, *J. Creation* **26**:94–100, 2012; creation.com/human-chimp-dna-similarity-re-evaluated.
68. Demuth J.P. *et al.*, The evolution of mammalian gene families, *PLoS ONE* **1**(1): e85, 2006.
69. 6 million years / ~20 years per generation = only 300,000 generations.

Reference	Total genomic bases analyzed	Aligned bases	Reported DNA identity	Actual DNA identity*
Britten, 2002	846,016	779,132	95.2%	~ 87%
Ebersberger et al., 2002	3,000,286	1,944,162	98.8%	< 65%
Liu et al., 2003	10,600,000 (total for human, chimp, baboon, and marmoset)	4,968,069 (human–chimp)	98.9% no indels	?
Wildman et al., 2003	~90,000 (exons from 97 genes)	?	98.4–99.4%	?
Chimp. Chrom. 22 Consort.	32,799,845	?	98.5% excluding indels	80–85% including indels
Nielson et al., 2005	?	?	99.4% selected gene regions	?
Chimp. Seq. Consort. 2005	Whole genome (5X redundant coverage)	2.4 Gb	95.8%	81%**

* Based on the amount of omitted DNA sequence in the alignments
** Compared to data from The International Human Genome Sequencing Consortium (2004)—((.9577 x 2.4 Gb) / 2.85 Gb) x 100
? Cannot calculate actual percent identity because data was not provided.

Summary of human-chimpanzee genome comparison papers. Where possible, omitted data from the reported alignments is used to produce an actual percent DNA identity (from Tomkins and Bergman, 2012).

In fact, there are about 35,000,000 single-letter differences[70] that had to arise (half in each species), spread through the respective populations, and become *fixed* (the original letter in that location was lost completely) in those few generations. Likewise, tens of thousands of chromosomal rearrangements had to occur, spread, and fix, as well as tens of millions of basepairs of insertions and deletions. The rate at which fixations occur is slow, and most new variants are expected to be lost (because they are, by definition, rare). The rate of mutation and selection necessary for this amount of change in a mere 6 million years is staggering, yet it necessarily occurred for evolution to be true.

The lack of similarity between human and chimp Y chromosomes was discussed above. With only a 70% similarity between the one-half of the chimp

70. Varki, A. and Altheide, T.K., Comparing the human and chimpanzee genomes: searching for needles in a haystack, *Genome Research* **15**:1746–1758, 2005.

Y chromosome that exists, the mutation rate must be extraordinarily high. One wonders why human males have such similar Y chromosomes? Perhaps it is because the chromosome is only 6,000 years old!

Humans and chimpanzees are *expected* to be somewhat similar. They look like us, they act like us, they eat similar foods to us, and they have similar environmental requirements to us (except that we were smart enough to invent warm houses and warm clothes). Why would anyone expect them to not be similar to us on the gene level? In fact, think about what the evolutionist would be saying if there were no similarities. They would be claiming there is no evidence for an intelligent Creator since everyone would expect that Creator to use a common design template for similar organisms. Heads they win, tails we lose![71]

How similar are we? In the words of a famous geneticist, Svante Pääbo:

> I don't think there is any way to calculate the number ... in the end, it's a political and social and cultural thing about how we see our differences.[72]

Mutation rates are too high

Chapter 1 discussed the effects of high mutation rates and the fact that natural selection cannot 'see' most mutations. The conclusion was that most mutations, although bad, slip through the selective sieve. This means that deleterious mutations are accumulating in our species, which is the opposite of what long-term evolution requires. Apply this thought to our modern knowledge of the complexity of the genome and you will start to see the magnitude of the problem. Eukaryotic (everything but bacteria) genomes are far too complicated and the mutation target for eukaryotic genes is far too large for evolution to work. The average letter is copied into six different RNA transcripts and is used in multiple overlapping codes (histone, splicing, protein, etc.). Mutations are occurring at a staggering rate, for evolutionists, putting a limit on the longevity of the entire human race. One thing is clear, however, for Jesus has promised to return and He promised that people would still be here when He does. Thus, we will not go extinct before the *second coming*. When will that be? Based on the predicted harmful long-term results to the genome caused by mutations, certainly not millions of years hence.

The Challenge

The genome is a multi-dimensional operating system with built-in error correcting and self-modification codes. There are multiple overlapping DNA codes, RNA codes, and structural codes. There are DNA genes and RNA genes.

---

71. Statham, D., Heads I win, tails you lose: the power of the paradigm, Nov 2010; creation.com/fused.
72. Cohen, J., Relative differences: the myth of 1%, *Science* **316**:1836, 2007.

The genome was designed with a large amount of redundancy, on purpose. Despite the redundancy, it displays an amazing degree of compactness, as ~20,000 'genes' combinatorially create >>100,000 distinct proteins. The genome has also been slowly disintegrating over time, yet it has remained viable to date due to beautifully-designed error-correcting codes and inbuilt, intelligently-designed redundancy.

Darwin is famously quoted as saying:

> If it could be demonstrated that any complex organ existed, which could not possibly have been formed by numerous, successive, slight modifications, my theory would absolutely break down.[73]

I know this quote has been misused (by both sides) over the years, but still I claim the human genome is such a thing. I do not believe it could possibly have originated through naturalistic processes. I challenge the evolutionist to give us a workable scenario of genomic history, including the source of informational changes, an account of the amount of mutation necessary, and description of the selective forces necessary, all within the proper time frame. Indeed, I challenge them to come up with a way that the genome, any genome, first appeared, arising from scratch in a world otherwise devoid of instructional information.

Where does this lead?

It should be plain by now that genetics is no friend of Darwin. His ignorance of the complexity of life, the means by which species reproduce, and the fragility of complicated systems, allowed him to theorize his way around insurmountable obstacles. Darwinism should be appraised in the light of modern knowledge. Modern genetics supports the biblical account quite well. There is abundant evidence in the genes of modern man for the creation of two original people (Adam and Eve), a population bottleneck a few thousand years later (during Noah's Flood), and a subdivision of the population a few generations after that (at Babel), with the subsequent single dispersal of humanity across the globe. Not only that, but the rate of mutation, the distribution of mutations, and the fragility of the ultra-complex computer operating system called the human genome all testify to the youth of that system. One wonders if Darwin would have been able to come to the same conclusions if he were alive today (and if he openly and honestly dealt with the relevant data). But it is not just the existence of genetics that is a threat to evolution, for the *origin* of life is no friend of evolutionary theory either. In the next chapter, we will look into this, for all evolutionary origin of life scenarios defy known laws of chemistry, physics and probability.

---

73. Darwin, C., *Origin of Species*, 6th ed., 1872.

Dr Jonathan Sarfati

Ph.D. Physical Chemistry,
Victoria University of Wellington, New Zealand

Dr Sarfati is renowned in creationist circles, having published a tremendous number of articles and four solo books, as well as being a co-author of several more books. One of his books, *Refuting Evolution*, is the number one best-selling creationist book, ever! His penetrating logic shines through his works, perhaps stemming from his chess expertise (he was awarded the title of F.I.D.E. Master (FM) in 1988). Jonathan was chosen to write on the third Achilles' heel of Darwinian evolution, the origin of life. Here, he brings his considerable wit to bear on the insurmountable problem of the rise of the first living things from non-living precursors.

See **creation.com/dr-jonathan-sarfati**

THE ORIGIN OF LIFE

Dr Jonathan Sarfati Ph.D. Physical Chemistry
[Victoria University of Wellington, New Zealand]

3

Introduction

The previous chapter discussed the problems that genetics poses for evolution. But even those arguments were most generous to evolution, because they *presuppose* a self-reproducing cell with a functioning genetic system. The chapter before that, on natural selection, was likewise generous, since those arguments can work only with the pre-existence of *entities that can pass on any information selected*. The present chapter will up the ante considerably. We will see what would be required for that initial reproducing system to come into being on its own.

You are about to discover that the origin of first life is a glaring Achilles' heel for materialists. Even the simplest living single-celled organism is extremely complex, including numerous, complex machines and the instructions to build them, all stored in a way that can be both decoded for use by the organism and passed on to offspring. The simplest theorized reproducing organism would require numerous proteins and molecular machines and a way to code and store the information needed to manufacture them.[1] Is it possible for such a cell to evolve from chemical precursors?

In every known self-reproducing organism on earth today, DNA stores biological information, but that information can't be read without decoding machinery. The instructions to build this decoding machinery are themselves stored on the DNA. Is it possible to solve this vicious chicken-and-egg problem? Furthermore, most of these processes use energy, supplied by ATP, produced by the nano-motor ATP synthase. But the ATP synthase motor can't be produced without instructions in the DNA, read by decoding machinery using ATP – a three-way circle, or perhaps an egg-nymph-grasshopper problem (i.e. it is even worse than a chicken-and-egg problem). Is there a solution to this perplexing conundrum, or does it signal to us that the origin of life as we know it is impossible?

Some propose to solve these problems by having one type of molecule function as both the information storage/retrieval system and the decoding machinery. But how does the most common candidate, RNA, measure up to the requirements of first life?

Furthermore, undirected chemistry in a hypothetical primordial soup would have no chance of achieving even this minimal complexity. The alleged building blocks (amino acids) would not build the necessary long molecules needed for life; rather, the long molecules would break down. Many of the building blocks would not form at all, or would be too dilute and contaminated to be useful, and would be a mixture of left- and right-handed forms instead of the exclusively one-handed forms used by living organisms. Do these facts spell the end of all origin-of-life scenarios?

Finally, chemical evolution studies, both in the test tube and through computer simulations, involve unacceptable levels of interference from an intelligent investigator (something not available in the alleged primordial soup). Can these be submitted as evidence for the origin of life?

To top it all off, leading researchers admit that chemical evolution is accepted, not due to facts and evidence, but because of a materialistic faith. How can this, then, stand as evidence against the Bible's claim that an intelligent Being created life through an act of divine fiat?

Darwinian processes can't explain *first* life

There has always been a tension between the idea that life arose from chemical processes and Darwinian evolution, but most people are unaware of the controversy. Darwin himself seems to have struggled with the origin

---

1. Anonymous, Last universal common ancestor more complex than previously thought, *ScienceDaily*, 3 October 2012; sciencedaily.com.

of life and how to fit it into his theory. He made several cautious statements in print, and made several more comments in personal letters, but most of his writing shows a general attempt to avoid conclusions. He knew that the old ideas of spontaneous generation (of things like mice and flies) had been disproved by Francesco Redi in 1668, but he then had to come to grips with the powerful arguments of his contemporary, the creationist scientist Louis Pasteur, who had utterly debunked spontaneous generation—even of microbes—by 1861,[2] just two years after the *Origin of Species* was published.

Louis Pasteur

Photo from wikipedia.org

In the final chapter of the first edition of *Origin* (1859), Darwin wrote:

> I should infer from analogy that probably all the organic beings which have ever lived on this earth have descended from some one primordial form into which life was first breathed.[3]

That is hardly an endorsement of the spontaneous origin of life. Later, writing to a friend in 1863, he repented of his use of language while still steering clear of the subject:

> But I have long regretted that I truckled to public opinion, and used the Pentateuchal term of creation, by which I really meant 'appeared' by some wholly unknown process … It is mere rubbish thinking at present of the origin of life; one might as well think of the origin of matter.[4]

Yet, strangely, he inserted this final sentence into every subsequent edition of *Origin*:

> There is grandeur in this view of life, with its several powers, having been originally breathed by the Creator into a few forms or into one; and that, whilst this planet has gone cycling on according to the fixed law of gravity, from so simple a beginning endless forms most beautiful and most wonderful have been, and are being, evolved.

It is clear that Darwin believed in unguided evolution, but it is not clear that he believed in chemical evolution. Then, in 1871 (the year he published *The Descent of Man*, in which he clearly spells out man's evolutionary relation to lower life forms for the first time), he dived headlong into the controversy:

2. See Lamont, A., Louis Pasteur (1822–1895), *Creation* **14**(1):16–19, 1991; creation.com/louis-pasteur.
3. Darwin, C., *On the Origin of Species*, 1st ed., John Murray, London, 1859.
4. Letter to Joseph Hooker, 1863, in Darwin, F. (ed), *The Life and Letters of Charles Darwin*, vol. 3, p. 18, John Murray, London, 1887; accessed via darwin-online.org.uk.

... if (and Oh! what a big if!) we could conceive in some warm little pond, with all sorts of ammonia and phosphoric salts, light, heat, electricity, etc., present, that a proteine [sic] compound was chemically formed ready to undergo still more complex changes ...[5]

Thus, even Darwin, father of modern evolutionary theory, halted between two opinions on the most important topic of all—how did life begin?

The famous philosopher Antony Flew (1923–2010) pointed out the problem, directly addressing the claims of the leading atheistic evolutionist Richard Dawkins[6] (1941–):

It seems to me that Richard Dawkins constantly overlooks the fact that Darwin himself, in the fourteenth chapter of *The Origin of Species*, pointed out that his whole argument began with a being which already possessed reproductive powers. This is the creature the evolution of which a truly comprehensive theory of evolution must give some account.

Darwin himself was well aware that he had not produced such an account. It now seems to me that the findings of more than fifty years of DNA research have provided materials for a new and enormously powerful argument to design.[7]

This is especially notable, because Dr Flew was, until recently, known as a leading proponent of atheism, but he abandoned this belief prior to his death, to the consternation of the atheistic community.[8] One major factor in his decision was the enormous complexity of even the simplest self-reproducing cell.

Theodosius Dobzhansky (1900–1975), one of the leading evolutionists of the 20th century and an ardent materialist (despite a Russian Orthodox upbringing[9]) realized the same thing. In commenting on the origin of life, he firmly rejected theorists who invoked natural selection as an explanation, because *this requires pre-existing life*:

In reading some other literature on the origin of life, I am afraid that not all authors have used the term [natural selection] carefully. Natural selection is differential reproduction, organism perpetuation. In order to have natural selection, you have to have self-reproduction or self-replication and at least

5. Darwin, F. (ed.), *The Life and Letters of Charles Darwin*, Vol. II, D. Appleton & Co., New York, pp. 202–203, 1911.
6. For a detailed refutation of many of Dawkins' most popular arguments, see Sarfati, J., *The Greatest Hoax on Earth?*, Creation Book Publishers, Powder Springs, GA, USA, 2010, available through creation.com.
7. Flew, A. interviewed by Habermas, G., My pilgrimage from atheism to theism, *Philosophia Christi*, Winter 2004; biola.edu.
8. Flew, A., with Varghese, R., *There is a God*, Harper Collins, New York, 2007. See also review by Cosner, L., *J. Creation* **22**(3):21–24, 2008; creation.com/flew.
9. Johnson, P.E., Response to Gould, *Origins Research* **15**(1):10–11, 1993; www.arn.org. See additional documentation by O'Leary, D., Darwinist Theodosius Dobzhansky was not an orthodox Christian believer! post-darwinist.blogspot.com, 8 September 2006.

two distinct self-replicating units or entities. ... I would like to plead with you, simply, please realize you cannot use the words 'natural selection' loosely. Prebiological natural selection is a contradiction of terms.[10]

It would be good to keep this distinction in mind as we proceed.

Chemical evolution

Many evolutionists will try to dismiss the strong evidence in this chapter by claiming that origin of life from non-living chemicals has nothing to do with evolution, and claim that *abiogenesis* is the correct term for the former. But their fellow evolutionist Gordy Slack rebukes them for that:

> I think it is disingenuous to argue that the origin of life is irrelevant to evolution. It is no less relevant than the Big Bang is to physics or cosmology. Evolution should be able to explain, in theory at least, all the way back to the very first organism that could replicate itself through biological or chemical processes. And to understand that organism fully, we would simply have to know what came before it. And right now we are nowhere close.[11]

Zoologist and physiologist (and evolutionist) Gerald Kerkut (1927–2004) defined the *General Theory of Evolution* (also discussed in chapter 1) as "the theory that all the living forms in the world have arisen from a single source which itself came from an inorganic form."[12] Certainly, this part of evolution can't be *Darwinian*, as stated. It is often called *chemical evolution*. For example, the September 1978 issue of *Scientific American* was specially devoted to evolution, and one major article was 'Chemical Evolution and the Origin of Life'. This stated:

> J.B.S. Haldane, the British biochemist,[13] seems to have been the first to appreciate that a reducing atmosphere, one with no free oxygen, was a requirement for the evolution of life from non-living organic matter.[14]

An old stalwart of origin-of-life theories, Cyril Ponnamperuma, co-authored a paper with the same title, and his affiliation was with the Laboratory of Chemical Evolution, Chemistry Department, University of Maryland.[15] Similarly, in 2011,

10. Dobzhansky, T.G., quoted in Schramm, G., Discussion of Synthesis of Nucleosides and Polynucleotides with Metaphoric Esters, in: Fox, S.W. (ed)., *The Origins of Prebiological Systems and of Their Molecular Matrices*, pp. 309–310, 1963, Academic Press, New York, 1965.
11. Slack, G., What neo-creationists get right, *The Scientist*, 20 June 2008; the-scientist.com.
12. Kerkut, G.A., *Implications of Evolution*, Pergamon, Oxford, p. 157, 1960.
13. John Burdon Sanderson Haldane FRS (1892–1964) is best known as a mathematical population geneticist, but he also worked on enzymes at Cambridge, formulating the Briggs–Haldane Law of enzyme kinetics in 1925. Also a staunch atheist and communist, he proposed a naturalistic origin of life in *The Origin of Life*, see *Rationalist Annual*, p.148, 1928.
14. Dickerson, R.E., Chemical evolution and the origin of life, *Scientific American* **239**(3):62–102, September 1978.
15. Pleasant, L.G. and Ponnamperuma, C., Chemical evolution and the origin of life, *Origins of Life and Evolution of Biospheres* **10**(1):69–85, 1980.

Discover magazine produced a special issue, "Evolution: Rethinking the Story of Life", and one article was, sure enough, on the origin of life.

The simple cell?

In Darwin's day, many people swallowed the theory of spontaneous generation—that life arose from non-living matter. It was somewhat easier to believe then because the cell's structure was almost unknown. Ernst Haeckel, Darwin's German "bulldog on the continent", claimed that a cell was a "simple lump of albuminous combination of carbon."[16] There was no excuse for this, though, because light microscopy had advanced enormously, even before Haeckel's day, to a level that could resolve many subcellular components.[17]

However, the molecular biological revolution of the last half century has shown how the cell requires both high *information content* and a means to pass this information on to the next generation (*reproduction*).

Information versus chemistry

The previous chapter showed that DNA stores an enormous amount of coded information. Atheist Richard Dawkins himself has pointed out:

> [T]here is enough information capacity in a single human cell to store the *Encyclopaedia Britannica*, all 30 volumes of it, three or four times over.[18]

> The difference between life and non-life is a matter not of substance but information. Living things contain prodigious quantities of information. Most of the information is coded in DNA .... [19]

Dawkins explains much of this by natural selection, but as shown, this will not work for the first living cell. Thus the explanations are restricted to chemistry. However, there is nothing in the chemistry of DNA's building blocks themselves that would make them join up in predetermined ways, any more than forces between ink molecules make them join up into letters and words. Michael Polanyi (1891–1976), a former chairman of physical chemistry at the University of Manchester (UK) who turned to philosophy, confirmed this:

> As the arrangement of a printed page is extraneous to the chemistry of the printed page, so is the base sequence in a DNA molecule extraneous to the chemical forces at work in the DNA molecule. It is this physical indeterminacy of the sequence that produces the improbability of any

16. Haeckel, E., *The History of Creation*, translated by Prof. E. Ray Lankester, M.A., F.R.S, 3rd ed., Vol. 1, p. 184, Kegan Paul, Trench & Co., London, 1883. See also Grigg, R., Ernst Haeckel: Evangelist for evolution and apostle of deceit, *Creation* **18**(2):33–36, 1996; creation.com/Haeckel.
17. Bradbury, S., *The Microscope Past and Present*, Pergamon Press, 1968; van Niekerk, E., Countering Revisionism, *J. Creation* **27**(1): 78–84, 2013; creation.com/haeckel-fraud-proven-part-2.
18. Dawkins, R., *The Blind Watchmaker*, W.W. Norton, New York, p. 115, 1986.
19. Dawkins, R., *The Greatest Show on Earth*, Free Press, New York, p. 405, 2009.

particular sequence and thereby enables it to have a meaning—a meaning that has a mathematically determinate information content.[20]

To explain: the information in this book is *not* based on the properties of the ink molecules on the paper (or pixels on the screen, if you are reading it in electronic format), but on the way they are *arranged* into letters, words, phrases, sentences, and paragraphs. An ink spill will not generate the plays of Shakespeare! Also note the letters are meaningless unless one understands the *language* they are in. For example, 'gift' in English means 'present', but in German it means 'poison'. The wrong convention can mean the wrong message. One German friend told me that the first time he came to an English-speaking country, he thought we were stark raving mad for having 'poison shops' everywhere.

Information, not chance, is the key to life. Information is not random (goo), neither is it regularly predictable like crystals, which contain little *information*. The leading evolutionary origin-of-life researcher in the 20th century, Leslie Orgel (1927–2007), confirmed this:

> Living things are distinguished by their specified complexity. Crystals such as granite fail to qualify as living because they lack complexity; mixtures of random polymers fail to qualify because they lack specificity.[21]

Rather, information is a non-repeating, non-predictable arrangement of signals that can be read and understood by some pre-engineered system with a predetermined set of rules for storing, retrieving, and interpreting instructions. In all modern forms, information is created by an intelligent agent in order to convey a message. And life is based on information. As physicist and evolutionist Paul Davies (1946–) says:

> We now know that the secret of life lies not with the chemical ingredients as such, but with the logical structure and organisational arrangement of the molecules. ... Like a supercomputer, life is an information processing system. ... It is the software of the living cell that is the real mystery, not the hardware.[22]

But he does nothing to solve this mystery. Instead he continues, "How did stupid atoms spontaneously write their own software?" He answers, "Nobody knows ..." and admits, "There is no known law of physics able to create information from nothing."

The origin of information is a tremendous Achilles' heel for evolutionary theory. There is simply no natural analogy for its appearance. Randomness is the antithesis of information. So is precise regularity (as in crystals). For information,

---

20. Polanyi, M., Life's irreducible structure, *Science* **160**:1308, 1968.
21. Orgel, L., *The Origins of Life*, John Wiley, New York, p. 189, 1973.
22. Davies, P., Life force, *New Scientist* **163**(2204):27–30, 1999.

which is neither random nor infinitely repeating, to arise naturalistically, in the absence of mind or programmed machinery, would require overcoming such huge probabilistic barriers as to be rightly called 'impossible'.

Alex Williams explained this further in applying this to the cell machinery:

> Polanyi pointed to the machine-like structures that exist in living organisms ... Just as the structure and function of these common machine components cannot be explained in terms of the metal they are made of, so the structure and function of the parallel components in life cannot be reduced to the properties of the carbon, hydrogen, oxygen, nitrogen, phosphorus, sulphur and trace elements that they are made of. There are endless examples of such irreducible structures in living systems, but they all work under a unifying principle called 'autopoiesis' ["self-making"].[23]

From that same article by Williams:

> Autopoiesis is a unique and amazing property of life—there is nothing else like it in the known universe. It is made up of a hierarchy of irreducibly structured levels. These include: (i) components with perfectly pure composition, (ii) components with highly specific structure, (iii) components that are functionally integrated, (iv) comprehensively regulated information-driven processes, and (v) inversely-causal meta-informational strategies for individual and species survival ... Each level is built upon, but cannot be explained in terms of, the level below it. And between the base level (perfectly pure composition) and the natural environment, there is an unbridgeable abyss.

Thus, the specific shape of biomolecules cannot be predicted from the properties of hydrogen, oxygen, and carbon. Likewise, the order of the DNA letters cannot be predicted from the chemical characteristics of the individual letters. At each level, there is an unbridgeable gap. Williams refers to each gap as a *Polanyi impossibility*, and he detailed many such gaps between living and non-living systems. These gaps constitute another Achilles' heel for evolutionary thought. Thinking that the natural world somehow found a way around them is akin to believing that all hydrogen atoms could suddenly form a straight line from one end of the universe to the other, at random. Clearly, this will never occur even if it is conceptually possible. This is the root of the idea behind the Polanyi impossibility.

The 'chicken and egg' problem won't go away

Remarkably, this decoding machinery, which *translates* the DNA 'language', is itself encoded in the DNA, which is a real 'chicken and egg' problem. The noted philosopher of science Sir Karl Popper (1902–1994) pointed out:

---

23. Williams, A., Life's irreducible structure, *J. Creation* **21**(1):109–115, 2007; creation.com/autopoiesis.

What makes the origin of life and of the genetic code a disturbing riddle is this: the genetic code is without any biological function unless it is translated; that is, unless it leads to the synthesis of the proteins whose structure is laid down by the code. But ... the machinery by which the cell ... translates the code consists of at least fifty macromolecular components which are themselves coded in the DNA. Thus the code cannot be translated except by using certain products of its translation.

This constitutes a baffling circle; a really vicious circle, it seems, for any attempt to form a model or theory of the genesis of the genetic code.

Thus we may be faced with the possibility that the origin of life (like the origin of physics) becomes an impenetrable barrier to science, and a residue to all attempts to reduce biology to chemistry and physics.[24]

Although Popper wrote this four decades ago, the origin of the genetic code remains as much an enigma now as it was then. Dawkins admitted as recently as 2009:

The 'Catch-22' of the origin of life is this: DNA can replicate, but it needs enzymes in order to catalyse the process. Proteins can catalyse DNA formation, but they need DNA to specify the correct sequence of amino acids.[25]

Indeed, the origin of the genetic code is a vicious circle: protein machines are needed to read the DNA, but instructions to build these protein machines are themselves encoded on the DNA. Furthermore, they use energy, which requires ATP, made by the nano-motor ATP synthase. Yet this is encoded on the DNA as well, decoded by machines needing ATP! The proteins are the machinery, and the DNA is the reproductive material, yet both are needed at the same time for the cell to function at all. And of course, this would be useless without any *information* to reproduce.

Amazing machines involved in DNA decoding

Transcription and the scrunching machine

Even the initial copying of the correct, protein-coding section of the DNA to mRNA requires intricate machinery. This involves an enzyme called *RNA polymerase*, comprising four protein chains. And another protein is required to tell the RNA polymerase where to start reading the DNA template. The enzyme complex then moves along the DNA strand, adding the matching RNA letters one at a time, before stopping in exactly the right place.

---

24. Popper, K.R., Scientific Reduction and the Essential Incompleteness of all Science, in Ayala, F. and Dobzhansky, T. (eds.), *Studies in the Philosophy of Biology*, University of California Press, Berkeley, CA, USA, p. 270, 1974.
25. Dawkins, R., ref. 19, p. 420.

Richard Ebright and his team from Rutgers University have discovered more intricacies in this process of *transcription*.[26] Indeed, it is this transcribed mRNA that is translated into proteins in the complex machines known as ribosomes.

DNA is double stranded and only one strand is copied, so it must be unwound for copying. The copying machine, called RNA polymerase (RNAP), first locks on to the start of the gene (i.e. protein-coding sequence). The anchored RNAP then reels in the DNA—*scrunching*.[27] This unwinds the double strand so the mRNA copy can be formed off one of them. Also, the unwinding stores energy; like winding the rubber band of a rubber-powered airplane. And just like the toy plane, this energy is eventually released, with the machine then breaking free of its starting point and shooting forward. This also rewinds the unwound DNA ('unscrunching') which then escapes from the back of the machine.

Translation and the Ribosome

The ribosome is the vital machine in the cell that reads the information on the mRNA and turns it into protein. Even in a 'simple' bacterium such as *E. coli*, which lives in your intestines, ribosomes comprise 50 different proteins and three different ribosomal RNAs (rRNAs). In more complex organisms with cell nuclei (eukaryotes), there are 73 different proteins involved and 4 rRNAs. One expert said:

> The ribosome, together with its accessories, is probably the most sophisticated machine ever made. All of its components are active and moving, and it is environmentally friendly, producing only GDP and phosphate.[28]

The ribosome also makes sure that a protein grows *linearly*. Outside a machine, a growing peptide chain would easily form undesirable *side branches*, where side groups react with each other (e.g. the amino acids aspartic acid and glutamic acid have a –COOH branch that could react with the–NH_2 branch on lysine or arginine). In industrial peptide synthesis, the side groups must be blocked by *protecting groups*, then unblocked when synthesis is finished by removing those groups. But in the alleged primordial soup, there were no organic chemists to do this at the right times. Thus, the naturalistic origin of life is made that much more problematic by this additional consideration of *real* chemistry. Life is based on molecules (DNA, RNA and protein) that are not produced outside specially ordered chemical systems (chemical factories including living cells).

26. Revyakin, A. *et al.*, Abortive initiation and productive initiation by RNA Polymerase involve DNA scrunching, *Science* **314**(5802):1139–1143, 2006; Kapanidis, A.N. *et al.*, Initial transcription by RNA polymerase proceeds through a DNA-scrunching mechanism, *Science* **314**(5802):1144–1147, 2006; see also Nanotech tools yield DNA transcription breakthrough; physorg.com, 16 November 2006.
27. Roberts, J.W., RNA Polymerase, a scrunching machine, *Science* **314**(5802):1139–1143, 2006.
28. Garrett, R., Mechanics of the ribosome, *Nature* **400**(6747):811–812, 1999.

There is no life without ribosomes. Indeed, life is not even conceivably possible without them, as basic chemistry prevents the repeatable formation of proteins without complex process control systems, which the ribosome provides for all life.

Transfer RNA

Transfer RNA (tRNA) molecules are vital adaptors, shaped like four-leafed clovers, and are responsible for carrying individual amino acids to the site where they are added to a new protein. They comprise about 80 nucleotide letters, three of which are called the *anticodon*. The anticodon matches a corresponding three-letter *codon* on the mRNA. Thus the tRNAs add the right amino acids to the right place in the growing peptide chain.

Also, each amino acid must be *activated* to overcome an energy barrier that naturally prevents the linking up of adjacent amino acid in solution. The energy for this process comes from ATP (discussed below). Then, a special enzyme called *aminoacyl-tRNA synthetase* (aaRS) bonds each amino acid, in two steps, to the correct tRNA. There must be a minimum of 20 aaRSs, at least one for each type of amino acid. Any failure here would destroy the message, and thus the whole purpose of the genetic code.

The tRNA adaptor molecules must have exactly the right geometry to 1) hold the amino acids in a position where they can form a peptide bond and 2) place the anticodon in the right place on the mRNA. Correct geometry of the adaptors only works in the context of the ribosome (they either had to evolve together, which is problematic to the point of being impossible, or they were engineered together by a brilliant Designer). Any supposed pre-ribosomal life would not need the specific geometry, so where did the specific geometry come from? Also, the hypothetically evolving adaptors are likely to interfere both with each other

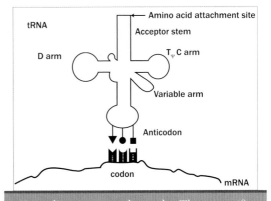

How the genetic code works. Three specific nucleotides on the mRNA (the codon) interact with their cognate nucleotides on the tRNA (the anti-codon). Since tRNAs with different anti-codons carry different amino acids, the sequence of nucleotides on the mRNA determines the order of amino acids in the final protein. Each tRNA is charged by an aminoacyl tRNA synthetase, using ATP (not shown).
creation.com/gencode

and with the mRNA.[29] The ribosome gives the cell a controlled environment, with a specific geometry, in which to perform a delicate yet necessary task.

Furthermore, the tRNA adaptors must be detachable once the amino acid has been joined to the end of the growing protein. The ribosome moves the mRNA along like a ratchet, and energy for detachment comes from another energy-storage molecule, GTP (guanosine triphosphate), which is in turn produced by a complex and tightly integrated and regulated machine.[30]

The take-home message is that this is an incredibly complex system. How could this come by chance from a random chemical reaction in a primordial soup? There are too many constraints placed upon the evolving system and too many objections to the process raised by an understanding of basic chemistry.

Double-sieves: advanced chemical machines

Aminoacyl tRNA synthetases (aaRSs) are special enzymes (protein machines) that perform amazing chemistry. They can even distinguish between amino acids that are very chemically similar (e.g. leucine and isoleucine, which are particularly difficult to separate in the laboratory).[31] But their small difference can still mean the difference between life and death in important biomolecules.

Yet the aaRS for isoleucine manages to distinguish them extremely well, with an error rate of only 1 in 40,000. It achieves this with a *double-sieve* mechanism: one sieve rejects amino acids too large, while the other rejects those too small.[32]

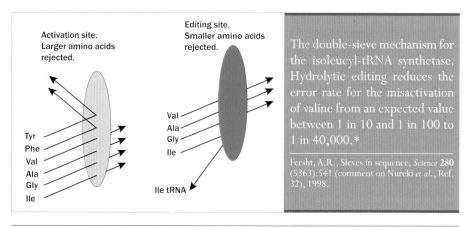

Activation site. Larger amino acids rejected.

Editing site. Smaller amino acids rejected.

Tyr
Phe
Val
Ala
Gly
Ile

Val
Ala
Gly
Ile

Ile tRNA

The double-sieve mechanism for the isoleucyl-tRNA synthetase. Hydrolytic editing reduces the error rate for the misactivation of valine from an expected value between 1 in 10 and 1 in 100 to 1 in 40,000.*

Fersht, A.R., Sieves in sequence, *Science* **280** (5363):541 (comment on Nureki *et al.*, Ref. 32), 1998.

29. Truman, R. and Borger, P., Genetic code optimisation: Part 1, *J. Creation* **21**(2):90–100, 2007; creation.com/gencode.
30. Truman, R. and Borger, P., ref. 29.
31. Sarfati, J., Decoding and editing designs: double-sieve enzymes, *J. Creation* **13**(1):5–7, 1999; creation.com/doublesieve; Karlson, P., (tr. Doering, C.H.), *Introduction to Modern Biochemistry*, 4th ed., Academic Press, London and New York, pp. 113, 145–146, 1975.
32. Nureki, O. *et al.*, Enzyme structure with two catalytic sites for double-sieve selection of substrate, *Science* **280**(5363):578–582, 1998.

Chaperones

Even the protein chain that forms in the ribosome is not the finished product. To perform its function in a cell, including the enzymes discussed below, a protein must be folded correctly into its own complex three-dimensional shape. The final protein configuration resulting from a particular DNA sequence is mainly determined by cellular machines called *chaperonins*, themselves barrel-shaped proteins that help other proteins to fold.[33] Without chaperonins, an important protein might mis-fold into a deadly prion, for example. This is the likely cause of the fatal brain conditions Creutzfeldt–Jakob disease and bovine spongiform encephalopathy (BSE), also known as mad cow disease.

Chaperonins also limit evolutionary 'progress', for they reject misfolded proteins, thus setting a limit to the amount of change allowed. In order for a new protein to evolve, it would necessarily go though conformational changes, some of them producing chaotic folds and bends in the structure. Yet, it would also need to escape or find a way around the chaperonin filter specifically designed to get rid of misfolded proteins. These protein-folding machines are ubiquitous in living organisms. How did the higher organisms evolve once chaperonins started to be used by early life? And how did the first chaperonins fold correctly without pre-existing chaperonins?[34]

The world's tiniest motor: ATP synthase

Another vital enzyme for life is ATP synthase, which makes the energy currency of the body, ATP (**a**denosine **tri**phosphate). Energy is essential for life, and all life uses ATP as its energy currency.[35] Yet, all living things, even bacteria and archaea, have ATP synthase motors.[36] This probably makes ATP synthase the most ubiquitous protein assembly on Earth.

In fact, the human body generates about its own weight of ATP every day, generated by many trillions of these motors. It is consumed very quickly, as it powers vital biochemical reactions, including DNA and protein synthesis, muscle contraction, transport of nutrients and nerve impulses. An organism without ATP is like a car without gasoline, and certain poisons (e.g. cyanide) work by stopping ATP production.

This motor squeezes two components of ATP (ADP and phosphate) at high enough energy to form ATP. Then it throws off the ATP and prepares to accept

33. Sarfati, J., DNA: marvellous message or mostly mess? *Creation* **25**(2):26–31, March 2003; See the animation 'DNA translation' at creation.com/message.
34. Aw, S.E., The Origin of Life: A critique of current scientific models, *J. Creation* **10**(3):300–314, 1996; creation.com/origin-of-life-critique.
35. Bergman, J., ATP: The perfect energy currency for the cell, *Creation Res. Soc. Q.* **36**(1):2–10, 1999; creationresearch.org.
36. Hiroyuki Noji *et al.*, Direct observation of the rotation of F_1-ATPase, *Nature* **386**(6622):299–302, 1997.

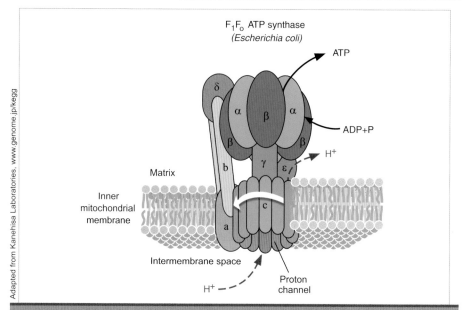

The whole ATP synthase machine with individually manufactured protein subunits each labelled with Greek letters. H+ ions (protons) flow through a special tunnel in ATP synthase, as the arrow indicates. This induces mechanical motion, forcing the axle and base to spin together like a turbine. Nearly 100% of the spinning momentum is converted to chemical energy in the formation of ATP molecules! Three ATPs are produced for every 10 protons.

new ADP and phosphate. This motor turns about 10,000 rpm, and each rotation produces three ATP molecules.

It's actually two motors in one. The top half (called F_1-*ATPase*) has three parts that are each ATP factories. The bottom half, F_O,[37] is the one directly powered by the electric current, which is positively charged (proton flow) instead of the negatively charged (electron flow) current that drives the motors we design.[38] But one more detail has been discovered since then, concerning the way these motors are connected, as well as how they are assembled.[39] And recent work shows that it's also the most efficient motor in the world—in fact as efficient as the laws of physics allow. The researchers conclude, "Our results suggested

---

37. Note that it is a subscript letter O *not* the number zero, for historical reasons: from 'oligomycin binding fraction'. The antibiotic oligomycin specifically blocks the proton channel on the F_O half of bacterial ATP synthase, with deadly effect.

38. Sarfati, J., Design in living organisms (motors), *J. Creation* 12(1):3–5, 1998; creation.com/motor. See also Thomas, B., ATP synthase, *Creation* 31(4):21–23, 2009; creation.com/atp-synthase. More details can be found in Sarfati, J., *By Design*, chapter 10, "Motors", available through creation.com.

39. Davies, K.M. *et al.*, Macromolecular organization of ATP synthase and complex I in whole mitochondria, *Proc. Nat. Acad. Sci. USA* **108**(34):14121–14126, 2011.

a 100% free-energy transduction efficiency and a tight mechanochemical coupling of F_1-ATPase."[40] So it's small wonder that even the strictly secular journal *Nature* called these motors, "Real engines of creation."[41]

Enzymes

ATP synthase and aminoacyl-tRNA synthetase are only two of the many types of proteins we call *enzymes*. These are biological catalysts that speed up vital chemical reactions without being consumed themselves. Life requires enzymes that are *extremely efficient* or survival would be impossible, as, without them, many reactions essential for life would be far too slow for life to exist.[42]

Super-catalysts

As a good example of an extremely efficient enzyme, Richard Wolfenden showed in 1998[43] that a reaction "'absolutely essential' in creating the building blocks of DNA and RNA would take 78 million years in water",[44] but was speeded up 10^{18} times[45] by an enzyme.[46] This enzyme needed a special, explicitly defined structure to work.[47]

In 2003, Wolfenden found a phosphatase, which catalyzes the hydrolysis (splitting) of phosphate bonds, that magnified the reaction rate 10^{21} times, a thousand times more than even that previous enzyme! This enzyme allows reactions vital for cell signalling and regulation to take place in a hundredth of a second. Without the enzyme, this essential reaction would take a trillion years, almost a hundred times even the supposed evolutionary age of the universe (about 15 billion years)![48] Yet, these enzymes, as well as all the other processes

40. Toyabea, S. *et al.*, Thermodynamic efficiency and mechanochemical coupling of F_1-ATPase, *Proc. Nat. Acad. Sci. USA* **108**(44):17951–17956, 2011.
41. Block, S.M., Real engines of creation, *Nature* **386**(6622):217–219, 1997 (perspective on Hiroyuki Noji *et al.*, ref. 32).
42. Catalysts do not affect the equilibrium, but only the *rate* at which equilibrium is reached. They work by lowering the activation energy, which means decreasing the energy of a transitional state or reaction intermediate. See diagram and explanation in Wieland, C. and Sarfati, J., Dino proteins and blood vessels: are they a big deal? 9 May 2009; creation.com/dino-proteins.
43. Miller, B.G. *et al.*, Anatomy of a proficient enzyme, *Proc. Nat. Acad. Sci. USA* **97**(5):2011–2016, 2000.
44. Meaning the reaction would take 78 million years to get half-way to completion. Using the half-life of a reaction is a common way to designate reaction rates in chemistry.
45. Cited in Lang, L.H., Without enzyme catalyst, slowest known biological reaction takes 1 trillion years: study, *UNC School of Medicine* **262**:30, 2003; unc.edu. See also Wolfenden, R. and Snider, M.J., The depth of chemical time and the power of enzymes as catalysts, *Acc. Chem. Res.* **34**:938–994, 2001.
46. This was orotidine 5′-monophosphate decarboxylase, responsible for *de novo* synthesis of uridine 5′-phosphate, an essential precursor of RNA and DNA, by decarboxylating orotidine 5′-monophosphate (OMP).
47. More detail can be found in Sarfati, J., World record enzymes, *J. Creation* **19**(2):13–14, 2005; creation.com/enzymes; and in Sarfati, J, *By Design*, ch. 11, available through creation.com.
48. Lad, C., Williams, N.H., and Wolfenden, R., The rate of hydrolysis of phosphomonoester dianions and the exceptional catalytic proficiencies of protein and inositol phosphatases, *Proc. Nat. Acad. Sci. USA* **100**(10):5607–5610, 2003.

listed above, must exist in the very first replicating cell in order for that cell to survive and pass on the DNA, and the DNA must code for the very proteins required for those processes!

Implications

Wolfenden said:

> Without catalysts, there would be no life at all, from microbes to humans. It makes you wonder how natural selection operated in such a way as to produce a protein that got off the ground as a primitive catalyst for such an extraordinarily slow reaction.[49]

But this is a curious blind spot. As pointed out earlier, natural selection could not have been operational until there was life, while, as he says, life could not have functioned without these enzymes to speed up vital reactions enormously. The origin of life was doomed from the start by the basic laws of chemistry!

Simplest possible life?

If that is not enough, *information*, rather than chemistry, is the main problem for the origin of life. Even the simplest imagined life would have enormous information content. The bacterium *Mycoplasma genitalium* has the smallest known genome of any known organism (a virus doesn't count because it is utterly dependent on the machinery of more complex cells for reproduction and assembly).[50] *Mycoplasma* contains 482 genes comprising 580,000 bases.[51] Of course, these genes are only functional with pre-existing translational and replicating machinery, a cell membrane, etc. But *Mycoplasma genitalium* has no cell walls, and can only survive by parasitizing more complex organisms (e.g. it lives in the cells of the respiratory system and urogenital tract of humans) that provide many of the nutrients it cannot manufacture for itself. Indeed, this organism seems to have arisen by *loss* of genetic information, making it dependent on a host.[52]

The mycoplasmas are very simple bacteria (although still quite complex). Could anything 'simpler' have arisen? A decade ago, Eugene Koonin, a researcher interested in making artificial biological organisms, tried to calculate the bare minimum required for a living cell. He based his work on the mycoplasmas, and

---

49. Lang, L.H., ref. 45.
50. Yet a virus has a powerful nano-motor to wind up DNA for packaging; Sarfati, J., Virus has powerful mini-motor to pack up its DNA, *J. Creation* 22(1):15–16, 2008; creation.com/virusmotor; Fuller, D.N. *et al.*, Single phage T4 DNA packaging motors exhibit large force generation, high velocity, and dynamic variability, *Proc. Nat. Acad. Sci. USA* 104(43):16868–16873, 2007.
51. Fraser, C.M. *et al.*, The minimal gene complement of *Mycoplasma genitalium*, *Science* 270(5235):397–403, 1995; perspective by Goffeau, A., Life with 482 genes, *Science* 270(5235):445–446. Other reports have different numbers, but all within the same ball park.
52. Wood, T.C., Genome decay in the Mycoplasmas, *Impact* 340, 2001; icr.org.

estimated how many genes even these simple cells could do without. His team came up with a result of 256 genes.[53]

They doubted whether such a hypothetical bug could survive for long, because such an organism could barely repair DNA damage, could no longer fine-tune the ability of its remaining genes, would lack the ability to digest complex compounds, and would need a comprehensive supply of organic nutrients in its environment.

It is not surprising that follow-up research has revised this number significantly upwards. This new hypothetical minimum genome consists of 387 protein-coding and 43 RNA-coding genes.[54]

A 2009 *New Scientist* article stated:

> There is no doubt that the common ancestor possessed DNA, RNA and proteins, a universal genetic code, ribosomes (the protein-building factories), ATP and a proton-powered enzyme for making ATP. The detailed mechanisms for reading off DNA and converting genes into proteins were also in place. In short, then, the last common ancestor of all life looks pretty much like a modern cell.[55]

In 2011, evolutionary biologists discussing this hypothetical *Last Universal Common Ancestor* (LUCA) likewise realized such a thing could not have been simple. Rather, it would have included a 'universal organelle' to store high energy compounds called pyrophosphates; previous dogma held that bacteria lacked organelles.[56] A report stated:

> New evidence suggests that LUCA was a sophisticated organism after all, with a complex structure recognizable as a cell, researchers report.[57]

No origin-of-life simulation approaches this bare minimum in the slightest.

Could this complexity have arisen by chance?

Natural selection can't operate without a self-sustaining, reproducing system. Therefore, it can't be invoked to explain this minimum level of complexity. All evolutionists have is chance. This is amenable to fairly simple probability calculations.

Information theorist Hubert Yockey calculated that, given a pool of pure, activated biological amino acids (a much more generous offer than the

53. Wells, W., Taking life to bits, *New Scientist* **155**(2095):30–33, 1997.
54. Glass, J.I. *et al.*, Essential genes of a minimal bacterium, *Proc. Nat. Acad. Sci. USA* **103**(2):425–430, 2006.
55. Lane, N., Was our oldest ancestor a proton-powered rock? *New Scientist* **204** (2730):38–42, 2009.
56. Seufferheld, M. *et al.*, Evolution of vacuolar proton pyrophosphatase domains and volutin granules: clues into the early evolutionary origin of the acidocalcisomes, *Biology Direct* **6**:50, 2011.
57. University of Illinois at Urbana-Champaign, ref. 1.

hypothetical 'primordial soup'), the total amount of information which could be produced, even allowing for a billion years of trial and error, as evolutionists posit, would be only a single small polypeptide, 49 amino acid residues long.[58] This is about 1/8 the size (therefore information content) of a typical protein, yet the *hypothetical* simple cell above needs *at least* 387 proteins (all pre-coded in DNA!), and that would only allow it to live in a very specific and invariant environment with a constant supply of high-level nutrients and biomolecules. And Yockey's estimate generously presupposes that the many *chemical* hurdles can be overcome, which is a *huge* assumption, as will be shown later.

Alternatively, one could calculate the probability of obtaining the DNA sequences for each of these proteins at random. Certainly there is some leeway in the sequence for many, but not around the *active sites*. However, even evolutionary writers implicitly concede that some sequences are essential. They call them 'conserved' (i.e. the sequence was so vital that natural selection conserved it by eliminating variants that appeared in evolutionary history). Conserved *whole* proteins include the histones that act as spools around which DNA wraps in chromosomes, ubiquitin which is *ubiquitous* in organisms apart from bacteria and essential for marking unwanted proteins for destruction,[59] and calmodulin, the ubiquitous calcium-binding protein which has almost all of its 140–150 amino acids 'conserved'.

The following calculation will be very generous to evolutionists. We will pretend that only 10 amino acids are conserved per enzyme and that there is some mechanism for joining amino acids in solution to form long chains (this is *overly* generous, as water constantly hydrolyses peptide bonds in solution):

- 20 amino acids
- 387 proteins for the simplest possible life
- 10 conserved amino acids on average

$$\therefore \text{ chance is } 20^{-3870} = 10^{-3870.\log 20} = \mathbf{10^{-5035}}$$

This is one chance in one followed by over 5,000 zeroes. So it would be harder than guessing a correct 5,000-digit PIN on the first go![60] Yet, without this entirely fortuitous assemblage, life is not possible. This is not a matter of slowly

58. Yockey, H.P., A Calculation of the probability of spontaneous biogenesis by information theory, *J. Theor. Biol.* **67**:377–398, 1977.

59. Truman, R., The ubiquitin protein: chance or design? *J. Creation* **19**(3):116–127, 2005; creation. com/ubiquitin. Aaron Ciechanover, Avram Hershko and Irwin Rose won the Nobel Prize in Chemistry in 2004 "for the discovery of ubiquitin-mediated protein degradation"; nobelprize.org.

60. Actually, for very low probability p of success, and d = 1/p, a good rule of thumb is: to have a 95% chance of at least one success, we need 3d trials. In this example, p is about 10^{-5000}, so d = 10^{5000}, so we would need about 3 × 10^{5000} trials for a 95% chance of obtaining all the needed enzymes. Personal communication from Dr Jim Davidson (North Carolina), 2012.

building up pre-living chemicals, for this is the simplest form of life *according to those who believe the origin of life is possible from a chemical soup.*

Many evolutionists have said that, given enough time, anything is possible. However, is time really 'the hero of the plot'? No. There are:

- 10^{80} atoms in the universe

- 10^{12} atomic interactions per second

- 10^{18} seconds since the origin of the universe, according to the fallacious big bang theory

  $\therefore$ only 10^{110} interactions are possible.

This is a huge number, but compared with the number of trials necessary to have a reasonable chance of obtaining the right sequence of *nucleotides* required to code for the necessary *proteins* required by the simplest conceivable life form, it is absurdly small. Even given these reactions, there would be but one chance in 10^{4925}. These numbers are so large as to be meaningless. The point is to illustrate the statistical impossibility (beyond 'improbability') of the origin of life from non-living chemicals.

The famous cosmogonist, Sir Fred Hoyle (1915–2001), abandoned his atheism when he considered the absurdly small probabilities:

> The likelihood of the formation of life from inanimate matter is one to a number with 40,000 naughts after it … It is big enough to bury Darwin and the whole theory of evolution. There was no primeval soup, neither on this planet nor any other, and if the beginnings of life were not random, they must therefore have been the product of purposeful intelligence. [61]

Self-replicating molecules?[62]

To try to grasp both horns of Popper's dilemma (introduced above), as well as the above analysis on the minimal complexity of life, some evolutionists have theorized that one type of molecule could perform both catalytic and reproductive roles. The choice is usually between the nucleic acids (RNA) and proteins.

However, even now, evolutionists have to admit that RNA is really a lousy catalyst, and proteins are lousy replicators. No RNA enzyme has approached anything like the efficiency of the proteinaceous enzymes needed for living creatures, such as those Dr Wolfenden analyzed, and life as we know it is impossible without those efficiencies. It is no use theorizing about alternate possible life forms either, for we have to explain life as we see it here on planet

61. Quoted in Major, E.L., Big enough to bury Darwin, Guardian (UK) education supplement, 23 August 2001; creation.com/hoyle-origin-of-life. See also Demme, G. and Sarfati, J., Big-bang critic dies, *J. Creation* **15**(3):6–7, 2001; creation.com/hoyle.
62. After Sarfati, J., Self-replicating enzymes? *J. Creation* **11**(1):4–6, 1997; creation.com/replicating.

earth, and that life defies naturalistic stories of origins. Evolutionists admit that ribozymes (RNA enzymes manufactured in laboratory experiments) are not efficient enzymes; they could never achieve the efficiencies of the enzymes necessary for life. Similarly, even Dawkins had to admit:

> Darwin, in his 'warm little pond' paragraph, speculated that the key event in the origin of life might have been the spontaneous arising of a protein, but this turns out to be less promising than most of Darwin's ideas. ... But there is something that proteins are outstandingly bad at, and this Darwin overlooked. They are completely hopeless at replication. They can't make copies of themselves. This means that the key step in the origin of life cannot have been the spontaneous arising of a protein.[63]

There are further enormous chemical difficulties with both RNA-first and protein-first models. Indeed, proponents of one are often the sharpest critics of the other. Actually, both sides are right in their criticism, *ergo*, life didn't evolve from chemicals at all!

The 'RNA World'

The very popular idea that life was based on RNA when it started out goes back to 1967, when Carl Woese suggested that RNA was not only reproductive, but could also act as a catalyst, and thus perform both roles.[64] Thomas Cech and Sidney Altman independently demonstrated that some sequences of RNA had catalytic effects. For "discovery of catalytic properties of RNA", they received the Nobel Prize in chemistry in 1989.[65]

The discovery of such *ribozymes* has led many evolutionists to postulate an *RNA World*. They propose that the first life consisted mainly of RNA, which could not only reproduce but also carry out many of the functions now carried out by enzymes. Richard Dawkins is sometimes a proponent of this idea.[66]

However, there are many problems for the RNA World hypotheses:[67]

- RNA is actually a very complex molecule. It is a flight of fantasy to claim that it could have arisen in a primordial soup.

- RNA is even less stable than DNA, and DNA is already extremely unstable (see below).

- Even the RNA building blocks (nucleotides) are themselves quite complex molecules, and could not have been produced in a primordial soup. The chemistry required to produce them in a laboratory is considerably complex.

63. Dawkins, R., ref. 19, pp. 419–420.
64. Woese, C., *The Genetic Code*, Harper and Row, New York, 1967.
65. Press Release: The 1989 Nobel Prize in Chemistry, 12 October 1989; nobelprize.org.
66. Dawkins, R., ref. 18, p. 421.
67. See also Mills, G.C. and Kenyon, D.H., The RNA world: a critique, *Origins and Design* **17**(1): 9–16, 1996; www.arn.org.

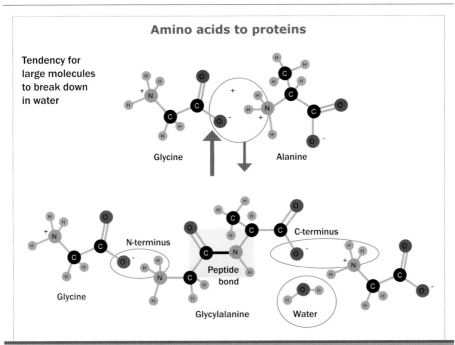

Amino acids to proteins

Tendency for large molecules to break down in water

Glycine   Alanine

Glycine   N-terminus   Peptide bond   C-terminus

Glycylalanine   Water

To form a protein, amino acids must link together to form a peptide bond, eliminating a water molecule. But there is a far greater tendency for the reverse to happen. This would be even more of a problem in water.

- Spark discharge experiments, like the Miller–Urey ones, do not produce the RNA/DNA base cytosine. Cytosine itself, even if it could be made, is too unstable to accumulate sufficiently to be useful, even over alleged geological 'deep time', as its half life for decomposition is 340 years at 25° C.[68]

- Even the simpler building blocks of RNA are unstable outside the cell. The half life of ribose is only 44 years at pH 7.0 and 0° C. It's even worse at high temperatures (e.g. 73 minutes at 100° C).[69] And RNA bases are destroyed very quickly in water at 100° C, a problem for 'warm ponds' or hydrothermal theories.[70] Adenine and guanine have half lives of about a year, uracil about 12 years, and cytosine only 19 days.[71]

- Like the amino acids discussed above, nucleotides do not spontaneously polymerize; they need to be *activated*. Furthermore, the conditions optimal

68. Shapiro, R., Prebiotic cytosine synthesis, *Proc. Nat. Acad. Sci. USA* **96**(8):4396–4401, 1999.
69. Larralde, R., Robertson, M.P. and Miller, S. L., Rates of decomposition of ribose and other sugars: implications for chemical evolution, *Proc. Nat. Acad. Sci. USA* **92**:8158–8160, 1995.
70. Sarfati, J., Hydrothermal origin of life?, *J. Creation* **13**(2):5–6, 1999; creation.com/hydrothermal.
71. Levy, M. and Miller, S. L., The stability of the RNA bases, *Proc. Nat. Acad. Sci. USA* **95**(14):7933–7938, 1998.

for promoting polymerization also promote the degradation of the ribozymes and templates needed to make the process work.[72] Even worse, due to the ubiquitous process of hydrolysis (breaking up of long-chain biomolecules), water in general is an enemy of polymerization.[73]

- The chemical reactions that create nucleotides produce *chiral* (mirror image) molecules. Any carbon-containing molecule with four side chains can have a 'left handed' and 'right handed' form (see diagram), and any reaction in the primordial soup would generate a 50:50 mixture of each.[74] To make a chain of nucleotides that can fold into a helix (necessary for stability and replication), the entire batch must be exclusively 'one-handed' (or *homochiral*). All five nucleotide bases (A, C, G, T, and U) are right handed, as are all the sugars used in the DNA backbone. Interestingly, all of the amino acids used in life are left handed. Due to the need for homochirality, even a small fraction of wrong-handed molecules terminates RNA replication in living and even artificial systems.[75]

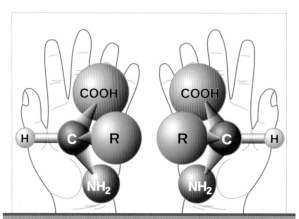

The two enantiomers of a generalized amino acid, where R is any functional group (except H)

- Even if such polymers *could* form, which first must have been without a pre-existing template, they would then have to be able to *replicate* themselves. This replication must be accurate, otherwise it would lose any information it managed to acquire by chance. Even 96.7% accuracy, as per one highly touted case,[76] would be nowhere near accurate enough—the result would be *error catastrophe*. Human DNA replication has an error rate of approximately one mistake every *billion*, thanks to the well-designed, sophisticated error correction machinery.

72. Johnston W.K. *et al.*, RNA-catalyzed RNA polymerization, *Science* **292**(5520):131925, 2001.
73. Sarfati, J., Origin of life: the polymerization problem, *J. Creation* **12**(3):281–284, 1998; creation.com/polymer.
74. Sarfati, J., Origin of life: the chirality problem, *J. Creation* **12**(3):263–266, 1998; creation.com/chirality.
75. Joyce, G.F. *et al.*, Chiral selection in poly(C)-directed synthesis of oligo(G), *Nature* **310**:602–604, 1984.
76. Johnston, ref. 74, admits that their ribozyme's copying accuracy is "still lower than the ≥0.996 fidelity seen with viral polymerases that replicate RNA by using RNA templates, and it is much lower than that seen for polymerases that replicate DNA."

- If they were the basis of the first life form, such self-replicating RNA molecules would have to have all the functions needed to sustain (maintain) an organism. Yet, RNA has not been shown to be able to do anything but a limited set of chemical reactions.

- On top of all that, how could such an RNA organism possibly give rise to a modern organism, with protein catalysts coded on reproducing DNA? This requires a whole new layer of decoding machinery[77] and would require an improbable switch from RNA to DNA/protein based information storage and usage.

- Because phosphate is an essential ingredient of nucleic acids, free phosphate ion (PO_4^{3-}) is essential, but the RNA world researchers typically use about a million times the concentration found in the sea today. In nature, phosphate is rapidly precipitated by the abundant calcium (Ca^{2+}) and magnesium (Mg^{2+}) ions, so it would be locked up into insoluble solids under all known and theoretical scenarios.[78]

It is no wonder that one of the leading researchers in 'RNA World' models, Gerald Joyce, wrote:

> The most reasonable assumption is that life did not start with RNA. ... The transition to an RNA world, like the origins of life in general, is fraught with uncertainty and is plagued by a lack of experimental data.[79]

Another chemical evolutionist, Robert Shapiro, stated after showing that one of the building blocks of RNA was an implausible component of a primordial soup, said:

> the evidence that is available at the present time does not support the idea that RNA, or an alternative replicator that uses the current set of RNA bases, was present at the start of life.[68]

The lack of any workable starting scenario for the origin of life is a painful Achilles' heel for evolutionary theory. It is not that we have missed something. It is not that, perhaps, there is something we still do not understand. While those things are certainly true, everything we *have* learned about physics, chemistry, and probability point *away* from the origin of life from inorganic chemicals.

Protein-first ideas

The older theory of chemical evolution proposed that proteins came first. This received an enormous propaganda boost from the famous Miller–Urey experiments in the 1950s.

---

77. Further chemical problems are found in Cairns-Smith, A.G., *Genetic Takeover: And the Mineral Origins of Life*, Cambridge University Press, 1982; see extract at creation.com/rna.
78. Schirber, M., A salt-free primordial soup? *Astrobiology Magazine*, 19 January 2012; astrobio.net.
79. Joyce, G.F., RNA evolution and the origins of life, *Nature* **338**:217–224, 1989.

Miller–Urey experiments

Stanley Miller (1930–2007), was a graduate student of Harold Urey (1893–1981), who had won the 1934 Nobel Prize for Chemistry for discovering deuterium (heavy hydrogen).[80] Miller and Urey filled a sealed glass apparatus with the *reducing* gases methane, ammonia and hydrogen (but excluded *oxidizing*

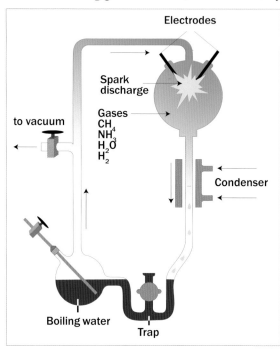

gases like oxygen). There was also a flask of boiling water, to supply water and drive the gases to circulate past a 60,000-volt sparking device designed to simulate lightning. The gas mixture also passed though a water-cooled condenser so that any reaction products could be collected by falling into a water trap below.

After a week, they found a red stain in the trap. Most of this was an insoluble, toxic, and carcinogenic mixture called *tar* or *resin*, a common product in organic reactions. In this tar, they found a small amount of amino acids.[81]

However, these were mainly the simplest amino acids glycine and alanine.[82] And the yields were a tiny 1.05% and 0.75%, respectively. Miller admitted, "The total yield was small for the energy expended."[82] Yet, there is no evidence that the situation would improve with longer time. The tiny yields of simple products seem to be as much as the simulation could ever achieve.[83]

80. Harold C. Urey—Biography, nobelprize.org.
81. Miller, S. L., A production of amino acids under possible primitive earth conditions, *Science* **117**:528–529, p. 528, 1953; Miller, S. L., Production of some organic compounds under possible primitive earth conditions, *J. Amer. Chem. Soc.* **77**:2351–2361, 1955.
82. Yockey argued in *Nature* (**415**(6874):833, 2002) that Stanley Miller wasn't the first. There were earlier experiments of Walther Löb (1913), Oskar Baudisch (1913), Edward Bailey (1922) and Harold Urey (1928, 1929). Yockey suggested that Miller merely augmented these previous experiments with modern separation and detection techniques such as two-dimensional paper chromatography. Coincidentally, the significance of these techniques was emphasized by my organic chemistry professor. A reply by Jeffrey Bada and Antonia Lazcano (*Nature* **416**(6880):475, 2002) defended the significance of Miller's experiments for chemical evolution, while Löb showed no interest in this.
83. Bergman, J., Why the Miller–Urey research argues against abiogenesis, *J. Creation* **18**(2):74–84, 2002; creation.com/urey.

It is ironic to look at the assumptions made, the repeated experimentation completed, and even the contraption manufactured to create a tiny yield of only a few amino acids that could not produce life in any sense, and proclaim 'no intelligence was required for the origin of life'! In effect, Miller and Urey discovered that random chemical reactions produce random chemicals. Yet, the chemicals produced were also simple. A random collection of simple molecules is the opposite of what life requires.

Chemistry: the mortal enemy of the spontaneous origin of life

DNA, the cell's information molecule, is actually a very unstable molecule. A recent paper on DNA stability estimates that, even when preserved in bone, DNA would have completely disintegrated in 22,000 years at 25°C, 131,000 years at 15°C, 882,000 years at 5°C; and 6.83 million years at –5°C.[84] Another article reported:

> "There is a general belief that DNA is 'rock solid' — extremely stable," says Brandt Eichman, associate professor of biological sciences at Vanderbilt, who directed the project. "Actually DNA is highly reactive."[85]

As mentioned in Chapter 2, on a good day about one million bases in the DNA in a human cell are damaged. These lesions are caused by a combination of normal chemical activity within the cell and exposure to radiation and toxins coming from environmental sources including cigarette smoke, grilled foods and industrial wastes.[86]

Because of this high level of daily damage, living creatures must have elaborate DNA repair machinery. University of Chicago biologist James Shapiro points out that:

> [A]ll cells from bacteria to man possess a truly astonishing array of repair systems which serve to remove accidental and stochastic sources of mutation. Multiple levels of proofreading mechanisms recognize and remove errors that inevitably occur during DNA replication. ... cells protect themselves against precisely the kinds of accidental genetic change that, according to conventional theory, are the sources of evolutionary variability. By virtue of their proofreading and repair systems, living cells are not passive victims of the random forces of chemistry and physics. They devote large resources to suppressing random genetic variation and have the capacity to set the level of background localized mutability by adjusting the activity of their repair systems.[86]

84. Allentoft, M.E. *et al.*, The half-life of DNA in bone: measuring decay kinetics in 158 dated fossils, *Proc. Royal Society B* **279**(1748):4724–4733, 2012.
85. Newly discovered DNA repair mechanism, *Science News*; sciencedaily.com, 5 October 2010.
86. Shapiro, J.A., A third way, *Boston Review*, p. 2, February/March 1997; Sarfati, J., New DNA repair enzyme discovered, creation.com/dna-repair, 13 January 2010.

Of course, the hypothetical primordial soup would not have contained these amazing repair systems. So even if DNA managed to form spontaneously somehow, it would not have survived long.

RNA is even more unstable than DNA. The instability of RNA is a major reason that many chemical evolutionists favour protein-first scenarios. However, proteins are *also* very unstable over the long term and so would be destroyed *anyway.* They are still subject to the second law of thermodynamics, so they will eventually break down because of random motion of the atoms and background radiation. For example, water tends to break proteins down into their constituent amino acids (hydrolysis),[87] and they would undergo destructive cross reactions with other chemicals[88] in the alleged primordial soup.[89] And, like the nucleotides discussed above, they would be produced as a mixture of left- and right-handed forms (a *racemate*) rather than with the homochirality (pure right-handed or pure left-handed forms only) required for biological enzymes.[90]

The most recent estimates place an upper limit of 2.7 Ma (million years) on collagen and 110 Ma for the bone protein osteocalcin at the freezing point (0°C). At a still cool 10°C, the upper limits are much less—180,000 years for collagen and 7.5 Ma for osteocalcin. At 20°C, the maximum lifetimes are even shorter: 15,000 and 580,000 years.[91] Since, in general, reaction rates increase *exponentially* with temperature (biological reactions generally double every 10 degrees Celcius),[92] this problem becomes insoluble for the warm pond theory. Actually, the instability of proteins is a strong argument against long ages: we find them in dinosaur bones, but if they were really >65 million years old, there should be no detectable protein remaining.[93] Furthermore, the problem for evolutionists has been further reinforced by the discovery of DNA in dinosaur bone. The experimenters ruled out contamination, and the DNA was intact enough to form small intact double helices.[94]

---

87. Sarfati, J., ref. 74.

88. E.g. the amino group ($-NH_2$) in the amino acid reacts readily with the carbonyl group (O=C<) in the sugar, releasing a water molecule (H_2O) to form an imine (HN=C<), which is useless for life. See Bergman, ref. 83.

89. If such a soup produced all the nitrogenous compounds required for life, why is there no trace of them in the 'earliest' rocks? Cf. Brooks, J. and Shaw, G., *Origins and Development of Living Systems*, Academic Press, London, UK and New York, 1973.

90. Sarfati, J., ref. 74.

91. Nielsen-Marsh, C., Biomolecules in fossil remains: Multidisciplinary approach to endurance, *The Biochemist*, pp. 12–14, June 2002. See also Doyle, S., The real 'Jurassic Park', *Creation* **30**(3):12–15, 2008; creation.com/realjurassic, and Thomas, B., Original animal protein in fossils, *Creation* **35**(1):14–16, 2013; creation.com/ancient-protein.

92. This is the simple Arrhenius rate equation $k = A \exp(-Ea/RT)$, where k is the rate constant, A is a temperature-independent constant (often called the frequency factor), exp is the exponential function, Ea is the activation energy, R is the universal gas constant, and T is the absolute temperature.

93. Sarfati, J., ref. 6., pp. 204–208.

94. Schweitzer, M.H. *et al.,* Molecular analyses of dinosaur osteocytes support the presence of endogenous molecules, *Bone* **52**(1):414–423, 2013; see also Sarfati, J., DNA and bone cells found in dinosaur bone, *J. Creation* **27**(1):10–12, 2013; creation.com/dino-dna.

Unacceptable investigator interference

Origin of life simulations purport to show that life could arise by time and chance. In reality, even the meagre results obtained are only possible because of the design of the experiment. A common procedure is to find a trace of compound *A* in a spark discharge experiment, and compound *B* in another simulation (sometimes with mutually incompatible conditions), then claim, "See, *A* and *B* can be produced under realistic primitive-earth conditions." They then obtain pure, homochiral, concentrated *A* and *B* from an industrial synthetic chemicals company, react them to form traces of the more complex compound *C*.[95] Then the news is trumpeted that *C* will form under primitive-earth conditions. But this doesn't show that *dilute A* and *B* can react that way, that they can be produced together, or that they won't react with contaminants *D*, *E* or *F* that were also formed in the first experiments. In short, the evolutionists' simulations have an unacceptable level of intelligent interference.[96]

Much of the evolutionary propaganda resembles the following *hypothetical* theory for the origin of a car:

> *Design is an unscientific explanation, so we must find a naturalistic explanation instead. Now, experiments have shown that one of the important building blocks of the car—iron—can be produced by heating naturally occurring minerals like hematite to temperatures which are found in some locations on Earth. What's more, iron can be shown to form thin sheets under pressures which are known to occur in certain geological formations. ...*

If the spontaneous origin of an automobile seems far-fetched, note that even the simplest possible self-reproducing cell has a vastly higher information content than a car, which does not even need to maintain internal homeostasis, let alone reproduce.

Life versus 'dirty' chemistry

Our biomolecules do not get their properties from their constituents, *per se*, but rather from the *arrangements* of those constituents, *i.e.* the information. These arrangements do not result from the physics and chemistry of these constituents, but are imposed upon them from a higher level. To restate what was said above, the properties of carbon, hydrogen, oxygen, nitrogen, phosphorus, and sulfur cannot be used to predict any specific macromolecular shape (there is an infinite number of possibilities). Rather, macromolecules were designed to perform a specific function by taking into account the properties of these simpler elements.

---

95. The evolutionist Cairns-Smith has raised the same objections against the typical 'origin of life' simulation experiments in ref. 79.
96. Thaxton, C.B., Bradley, W.L., and Olsen, R.L., *The Mystery of Life's Origin,* ch. 6, Philosophical Library Inc., New York, 1984.

Macromolecules were designed from the top, down; they did not evolve from the bottom, up. In living things, the machinery already present imposes this arrangement (information) upon the ingredients to make more copies, but this machinery itself arose in the same way from the previous generation, and so on. The machinery did not arise from the components any more than white noise can create a symphony.

The more we understand about *bio*chemistry, the more we learn how different it is from *abiotic* chemistry. The laws are the same, but chemistry outside the living cell is always 'dirty' mass action chemistry, while biochemistry is pure single-molecule chemistry.[97]

The term 'dirty' comes from chemical evolutionist and Nobel laureate, Christian de Duve. It is merely a statement of fact that chemistry in the non-living world involves many molecules at a time and invariably includes contaminants.[98] The theistic evolutionary paleontologist, Simon Conway Morris, called the product of typical origin-of-life experiments "muck", "goo" and "gunk",[99] echoing chemical evolutionist Graham Cairns-Smith's term "grossly contaminated gunks".[100]

Indeed, modern industrial chemistry, with carefully planned processes, can't normally achieve purities above 99.99%. This is largely because it deals with huge numbers of molecules at a time. But biochemistry can achieve better, because each enzyme manipulates one molecule at a time. Its products are then taken care of by the next enzyme, in the right shape and right place.

In the end, the chemistry of the cell is precise, constrained, controlled, and functional, and life could not exist without it being this way. The chemistry outside the cell is the opposite of what is needed for life to form. Abiotic chemistry is the antithesis of life. How, then, could it have led to the first living cell?

Unrealistic traps

All energy sources that produce biochemicals destroy them enormously faster. I have already mentioned the hydrolyzing effect of water that tends to break peptide bonds much faster than they are formed in solution. The energy sources would also be more destructive than constructive. For instance, on the hypothetical primordial earth, there would have been two forms of UV

97. Williams, A., Life's irreducible structure—Part 1: autopoiesis, *J. Creation* **21**(2):116–122, 2007; creation.com/autopoiesis.
98. De Duve, C., *Singularities: Landmarks on the Pathways of Life*, Cambridge University Press, Cambridge, 2005. See review by Williams, A., Great minds on the origin of life, *J. Creation* **21**(1):38–42, 2007; creation.com/singularities.
99. Conway Morris, S., *Life's Solution: Inevitable humans in a lonely universe*, Cambridge University Press, Chs 3–4, 2003. See review by ReMine, W., Evidence for Message Theory, *J. Creation* **20**(2):29–35, 2006; creation.com/lifes-solution.
100. Cairns-Smith, A.G., *Genetic Takeover and the Mineral Origins of Life,* Cambridge University Press, New York, 1982.

radiation. One is destructive (ionizing), short-wave ultraviolet (UV) light. The other is non-destructive, longer wave UV. Long-wave UV can be constructive in some cases. For example, it can be absorbed and used by chlorophyll.[101] Yet the destructive UV radiation is both more plentiful than the constructive UV radiation, and also more effective. This amounts to two strikes, so that the destructive effects are about 10^4–10^5 stronger than the constructive ones.[102]

The Miller–Urey experiments used strategically designed traps to isolate the biochemicals as soon as they formed so that the sparks (or UV radiation in later experiments) did not destroy them. Without the traps, even the tiny amounts obtained would not have survived. But this is not a realistic simulation of the primordial soup, which lacks a plausible prebiotic mechanism for rescuing the amino acids from the UV by quickly removing them from the atmosphere and even exposure to water. Note that you can be badly sunburned on a cloudy day and even under water in some cases as UV penetrates even tens of metres of clear liquid water.[103] So the traps were another case of *unacceptable level of interference from intelligent investigators.*

Chemical evolution: evidence or blind faith?

The non-creationist information theorist, Hubert Yockey, made a very revealing comment 30 years ago:

> Research on the origin of life seems to be unique in that the conclusion has already been authoritatively accepted … . What remains to be done is to find the scenarios which describe the detailed mechanisms and processes by which this happened.[104]

This is important to keep in mind when reading popular accounts of evolution, or in response to those who claim believers in design are "biased". Dr Yockey finished his paper with:

> One must conclude that, contrary to the established and current wisdom a scenario describing the genesis of life on Earth by chance and natural causes which can be accepted on the basis of fact and not faith has not yet been written.[105]

The Origin-of-Life Foundation currently offers a $1 million prize to anyone providing a chemically plausible naturalistic solution for the origin of the genetic code and life. The website states:

101.Photosynthesis is another irreducibly complex system, storing up the energy of four photons to split the strongly bound water molecule. See Sarfati, J., Green power (photosynthesis): God's solar power plants amaze chemists, *J. Creation* **19**(1):14–15, 2005; creation.com/greenpower.

102.Hulett, H.R., Limitations on prebiological synthesis, *J. Theor. Biol.* **24**:56–72, 1969.

103.UV-B penetrates 65 metres deep in clear Antarctic waters , according to Gieskes, W.C. and Kraay, G.W., Transmission of ultraviolet light in the Weddell Sea: Report on the first measurements made in Antarctic, *Biomass News.* **12**:12–14, 1990.

104.Yockey, H.P., ref. 58, p. 379.

105.Yockey, H.P., ref. 58, p. 396.

'The Origin-of-Life Prize' ® (hereafter called "the Prize") will be awarded for proposing a highly plausible mechanism for the spontaneous rise of genetic instructions in nature sufficient to give rise to life. To win, the explanation must be consistent with empirical biochemical, kinetic, and thermodynamic concepts as further delineated herein, and be published in a well-respected, peer-reviewed science journal(s).[106]

Thus far, there have been no awards and the more we know of the minimum requirements for life, the more unlikely it seems that any even remotely plausible materialistic explanation for the origin of life will be found. The problem is further from being solved than ever.[107]

Where is the evidence?

The above discussion has dissected the common chemical evolutionary ideas for the primordial soup, but few seem aware that there is not the slightest evidence that one ever existed. Such a soup was supposed to be the source of the essential nitrogen-containing amino acids and nucleotides. If it existed, evolutionary geologists should find some massive deposits rich in nitrogen in (what they claim are) very early rocks. Yet, there is hardly any nitrogen in what they call the earliest organic materials—only about 0.015%. Two geochemists point out:

If there ever was a primitive soup, then we would expect to find at least somewhere on this planet either massive sediments containing enormous amounts of the various nitrogenous organic compounds, acids, purines, pyrimidines, and the like; or in much metamorphosed sediments we should find vast amounts of nitrogenous cokes. In fact no such materials have been found anywhere on earth.[108]

Life from outer space?

To emphasize the desperation of chemical evolutionary theorists, some researchers have argued that life began in outer space. This is called *panspermia*, from Greek πάν (*pan*, all) and σπέρμα (*sperma*, seed), i.e. seeds of life are everywhere in the universe.

The classic branch of panspermia theory holds that seeds came to earth naturally, on comets perhaps. However, this really solves nothing and only throws the problem elsewhere. The chemical and informational problems are unchanged. Besides the improbability of surviving millions of years drifting across the cold, airless void and the trip towards our sun with its sterilizing

---

106. The Origin-of-Life Prize; www.us.net/life.
107. Smith, Calvin, Who wants to be a millionaire, creation.com/lifeprize, 15 Aug 2007.
108. Brooks, J., and Shaw, G., *Origins and Development of Living Systems*, Academic Press, London and New York, 1973.

levels of radiation, recent research shows that microbes could not survive the extreme heat produced from friction with the earth's atmosphere—the heat which produces 'shooting stars'.[109]

A newer version of the theory is called *directed panspermia*, which holds that *aliens* seeded life on earth. Its proponents include one of the co-discovers of the DNA double helix, Francis Crick (1916–2004), as well as Leslie Orgel.[110] Crick in particular was driven by his frustration with chemical evolutionary theories:

> An honest man, armed with all the knowledge available to us now, could only state that in some sense, the origin of life appears at the moment to be almost a miracle, so many are the conditions which would have had to have been satisfied to get it going.

> Every time I write a paper on the origin of life, I determine I will never write another one, because there is too much speculation running after too few facts.[111]

Once again, this merely puts the problem back a step; they would have to believe that these hypothetical aliens arose by chemical evolution in the first place.[112] One wonders how anyone could attack creation as 'unscientific' because it postulates an unobservable Creator, yet regard directed panspermia as 'science' despite the *ad hoc* theories of unobservable aliens. Note also that panspermia amounts to an 'evolution-of-the-gaps' argument and that directed panspermia postulates *design*.

Conclusions

The origin of life from non-living chemicals has been an article of blind faith, not science, and this has been true since the time of Darwin. The main problem with much chemical evolutionary theorizing is that the theorists consider life as an assembly of chemicals rather than an *information-processing* machine, and they never answer the question, "How did molecular hardware get to write its own software?"

Natural selection can't explain origin of *first* life. Machines are required to process this information. But this information includes instructions to build these machines. Thus, chicken-and-egg problems abound. These machines need energy, and this comes from the ATP synthase motor. But the motor can't be built without the instructions and reading machinery coded into DNA, and

109. Meteorite experiment deals blow to bugs from space theory, *Physorg.com*, 25 September 2008; Sarfati, J., Panspermia theory burned to a crisp: bacteria couldn't survive on meteorite, 10 October 2008; creation. com/panspermia.

110. Crick, F. and Orgel, L.E., Directed Panspermia, *Icarus* **19**:341–346, 1973.

111. Crick, *Life Itself, Its Origin and Nature*, pp. 88, 153, Simon and Schuster, 1981.

112. See also Bates, G., *Designed* by aliens? *Creation* **25**(4):54–55, 2003; creation.com/aliens.

the assembly machinery needs ATP to be assembled. This constitutes an egg-nymph-grasshopper problem.

Other enzymes are essential to speed up vital reactions that would take millions of years without them. Yet, enzymes alone would be destructive, e.g. an isolated ATP synthase would destroy ATP, not make it.

Proteins can't reproduce and would break down in nature. Long nucleotides and polysaccharides would also break down (in fact, they would never form) due to hydrolysis. RNA is a weak enzyme and is even more unstable than DNA. Some RNA building blocks have not been formed in chemical evolution 'simulation' experiments. Others are dilute, contaminated and/or unstable. Further, they would not be in the 'one-handed' form required for life.

Finally, there is no evidence in the 'earliest' rocks for the early and necessary stages of chemical pre-life.

In essence, the laws of physics, chemistry and probability disagree with the abiotic origin of life hypothesis. It is not biblical creationists who are appealing to a *god-of-the-gaps* argument here! In fact, our contention is that an intelligent, creator God who exists outside the universe and is the cause of the universe is the *only* reasonable conclusion when faced with what we have learned through centuries of experimental science.

Where does this lead?

This book started with an analysis of Darwin's main engine for evolution, natural selection, and found it wanting. We then dealt with genetics, of which Darwin was totally ignorant, even though it was necessary for a full understanding of evolution, and saw that evolution failed here as well. Those two chapters

Photo from wikipedia.org

Charles Darwin

make a nice couplet, as the topics are central to his theory. The present chapter on the origin of life can be paired with the next chapter by Dr Emil Silvestru on the fossil record. These are two topics that Darwin needed to be true, but he had to assume they would support his theory eventually, for the science was in its infancy. We saw that Darwin attempted to avoid discussing the ultimate origin of life, and for good reason! It turns out that he also avoided detailed discussion of the fossil record, for he knew that it did not support his ideas, according to the knowledge of the day. If evolution is true, first, it should be possible on chemical and statistical grounds (it is not), and second, we should see evidence for it in the fossil record. Was Darwin right to assume future discoveries would demonstrate slow change over millions of years? It turns out that the reality of the fossil record is yet *another* Achilles' heel of evolution.

Dr Emil Silvestru

Ph.D. Geology, Babes-Bolyai University, Romania

Dr Silvestru received his scientific training in communist Romania, where he became a world expert in cave geology and karst topography. Widely published in this esoteric field, he was the director of the world's first speleological institute, in Cluj, Romania. Emil became a Christian later in life and soon after began to re-think his previously held views on the age of the earth and evolutionary history. He is a natural choice to head up our chapter on the fourth Achilles' heel of Darwinian evolution, the fossil record.

See **creation.com/dr-emil-silvestru**

THE FOSSIL RECORD

Dr Emil Silvestru Ph.D. Geology
[Babes-Bolyai University, Cluj, Romania]

4

If the biological diversity of life today is the result of nearly 4 billion years of descent with modification through natural selection, the fossil record should provide the ultimate evidence for it. It turns out that one can hardly find a more factual example for the weaknesses of such a naturalistic view, making the fossil record a true Achilles' heel of evolution. Darwin knew it, and modern paleontologists know it.

What is the fossil record?

The use of the word 'record' in the term 'fossil record' suggests the fossils preserve some sort of history, but it is quite different from the historical records preserved by human observers. To the Darwinist, the fossil record is supposed to display the evolution of species over time. It has been known since ancient times that some rocks contain the remains of certain organisms, while others are barren of fossils. It was through the systematic study of a series of these layers over a large area of the

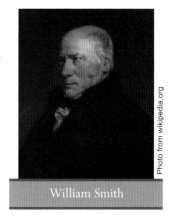

William Smith

Photo from wikipedia.org

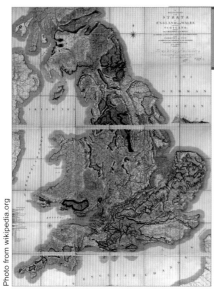

William 'Strata' Smith earned this nickname by his extensive mapping of the locations and extents of strata across much of England.

British Isles by William 'Strata'[1] Smith in the late 18th century that the concept of a consistent fossil succession emerged.

Within a century, a worldwide network of sites was being established, eventually becoming today's Global Boundary Stratotypes Section and Point (GSSP). These points are an attempt to correlate all fossiliferous strata into one planetary system, in which fossils are seen as continuously and consistently increasing in complexity (from 'primitive' to 'advanced') from the oldest to the youngest sediments. In the scientific world, the attempt to correlate the rock and fossil records is known as *biostratigraphy*. Its study is ultimately the extrapolation of modern taxonomy into the past. While that may seem harmless enough, it was pioneered and developed under the fundamental evolutionary assumption that later taxa are descended from older ones. Thus, this field of study produces decidedly evolutionary conclusions.

Taxonomy is simply the attempt to classify organisms, present and past, by their most fundamental common traits. As a science, it was pioneered by the remarkable Carl Linnaeus, a creationist. *Phylogeny* is a branch of taxonomy that builds tree-like structures that are supposed to represent relationships between

1	Domain	*Eukarya*	5	Order	*Primata*
2	Kingdom	*Animalia*	6	Family	*Hominidae*
3	Phylum	*Chordata*	7	Genus	*Homo*
4	Class	*Mammalia*	8	Species	*Homo sapiens*

Table 1: The human species within the Linnaean classification sytem: *Eukarya*: the cells that build the organisms have a nucleus; *Animalia*: animals (as opposed to plants); *Chordata*: with a supporting rod (in this case a backbone). *Mammalia*: warm blooded animals with hair that nurse their young. *Primata*: monkey-like creatures, with an emphasis on superiority. *Homonidae*: Man-like creatures. *Homo*: Man. *sapiens*: thinking.

---

1. He earned this nickname by his extensive mapping of the locations and extents of strata across much of England.

groups of organisms using taxonomic data. The results could be interpreted in either a biblical or evolutionary context, but the tree diagrams are most often used for evolutionary arguments based on their visual appeal. *Paleontology* is that branch of science that studies fossils. Again, the data can be used in either direction, but, since the majority of paleontologists are also evolutionists, the majority of interpretations in the field assume evolution.

Darwin's expectations from the fossil record

Carl Linnaeus laid the foundations of modern taxonomy in the 18th century, using a system of binomial nomenclature where every species has a two-word Latin name. For example, humans are called *Homo sapiens* ("man" + "thinking"). Since Linnaeus, the number of named species on Earth has constantly increased, with no end yet in sight. The biodiversity of our planet continues to surprise us.

But where does this diversity lie? There are millions of animal species but only 36 phyla! Many species in few phyla is also true of plants, fungi, bacteria, and Archaea. In other words, there are a relatively small number of basic designs that explain all life on earth. That was known in the time of Darwin, and one can see how he could imagine the origins of phyla by extrapolating into the past. A multitude of species could be collapsed into a small number of major groups, which could then be collapsed into several phyla, which could then be collapsed into a single ancestral form (or *forms*—Darwin suggested both single and plural in *Origin*).

Carl Linnaeus

Photo from wikipedia.org

Of course, if evolution from molecules to man covers most of the history of our planet, and if the sedimentary rocks have accumulated throughout all that period, the sediments should contain a good record of that evolution in the number and form of fossils, especially *transitional fossils* linking consecutive evolutionary stages. This is exactly what Darwin expected from the fossil record and one can only understand his frustration when he had to admit that:

> … why, if species have descended from other species by insensibly fine gradations, do we not everywhere see innumerable transitional forms? Why is not all nature in confusion instead of species being, as we see them, well defined?[2]

But in good Darwinian fashion, he dismisses the problem a few paragraphs later:

---

2. Darwin, C., *On the Origin of Species*, 1st ed., Chapter 6, p. 171, John Murray, London, 1859.

> ... and I will here only state that I believe the answer mainly lies in the record being incomparably less perfect than is generally supposed; the imperfection of the record being chiefly due to organic beings not inhabiting profound depths of the sea, and their remains being embedded and preserved to a future age only in masses of sediment sufficiently thick and extensive to withstand an enormous amount of future degradation; and such sediment can be accumulated only where much sediment is deposited on the shallow bed of the sea, whilst it slowly subsides.

There are numerous errors in this statement, including his belief that life did not exist in the depths of the sea, which was soon proven wrong. We shall see how his frustration would be much greater today since his excuse has been proven lame.

What biblical creationists expect to find

Since the centerpiece of creation geology is the Genesis Flood, geologists who believe in it have laid out certain expectations about the fossil record:

1. In the fossil record, which is mainly a record of the burial of creatures during the Flood, creatures should appear suddenly, generally with no precursors, exist for a given time and disappear without descendants, if not found alive today.

2. All major taxa (kingdoms, phyla, classes, and orders, perhaps some families and genera, and isolated, single-taxon species) should be present immediately before the Flood, existing as basic *kinds*, which would then re-radiate into many varieties (*species*) after the Flood.

3. The vertical order of fossils should reflect their habitat and flooding dynamics (both in terms of water movement and the organism's shape, size, and behaviour). The order should not be universal and organisms that live in one habitat should occasionally be found fossilized with organisms from a totally different habitat as a result of catastrophic flow and burial.

4. The majority of fossils in the record should be of marine organisms.

5. There should be few to no fossils of transitional forms, as all kinds (not species) were created in the beginning and present at the start of the Flood. There may be some forms difficult to classify (e.g. the platypus), even some that seem to fit between two other categories (e.g. the 'mammal-like reptiles'), but the rule should be a general absence of major transitions. We should not put a limit on God's creativity, so we make this statement *in general*.

6. There should be fossils and ichnites (trace fossils) made by land creatures capable of swimming or surviving on floating mats of vegetation in the early stages of the Flood. These should have arrived on areas of dry land that emerged periodically because of tides, tsunamis, storm surges, Coriolis

forces (due to the earth's rotation) acting on oceanic currents, and even movements of continental and regional tectonic plates.

We shall further see how these expectations are confirmed by the fossil record.

The fossil record as an icon

It almost appears that the fossil record has been turned today into an icon, a sacred image that is worshipped by a crowd of disciplined followers. When we read the list of 'golden spikes'[3] used to determine the geologic age for the Phanerozoic[4] rocks we see how much fossils are relied upon to make these calls, and this is despite the repeated claims to the contrary. Furthermore, like all icons, the fossil record is fiercely protected, so that no paleontological fact can blemish its fine, triumphant progression through time. From experience, it has gotten to the point that paleontologists often dictate where a fossil should be in that progression, and if found elsewhere it's firmly explained away. All new and challenging fossil finds are shoehorned to fit the icon while the ones that seem to confirm the paradigm are triumphantly popularized.

When we look at the way the history of life as revealed in the fossil record is presented today in textbooks and the media, we can often easily see big mysteries within, as clearly articulated by the late Stephen Jay Gould:

(1) Why did multicellular life appear so late? (2) And why do these anatomically complex creatures [Gould is referring to the Burgess Shale fauna] have no direct, simpler precursors in the fossil record of Precambrian times?[5]

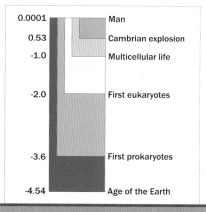

A stylized history of life on earth, according to evolutionary geologists

Indeed, multi-cellular life represents only a fraction of the evolutionary age of the earth's supposed 4.54 billion years. Since the oldest known form of life is believed to have originated some 3.4 billion years ago,[6] multi-cellular life represents only a fraction of the history of *life*. Strangely, if one considers the timing of evolutionary

---

3. 'Golden spike' is colloquial for Global Boundary Stratotype Section and Point (GSSP) which are physical markers decreed by the International Commission on Stratigraphy to define the boundaries between parts of the geologic column.
4. The Phanerozoic, from the Greek meaning 'visible life', covers the 'periods' in the evolutionary time scale with abundant fossil evidence of life. That is, it extends from Cambrian at the base of the Paleozoic to the most recent Quaternary.
5. Gould, S.J., *Wonderful Life*, W.W.Norton & Co., New York, p. 56, 1990.
6. Wavey, D. *et al.*, Microfossils of sulphur-metabolizing cells in 3.4-billion-year-old rocks of Western Australia, *Nature Geoscience* **4**:698–702, 2011.

events it would seem the more complex life became, the faster it evolved, but then the rate slowed dramatically once the main forms evolved.

While writing a review of a group of evolutionists skeptical of Darwinian processes, Walter J. ReMine pointed out:

> Stephen Jay Gould noted that the fossil sequence shows the most disparate (most different) biological designs tend to show up *first!* Followed by the slightly less-disparate designs. Followed by the still less different designs. Until, lastly, the last slight bits of interspecies biological diversity are filled-in at the very end of the process.[7]

Over evolutionary time, one would expect species to slowly diverge, eventually creating the higher taxonomic categories. Instead, the largest differences (kingdoms and phyla) appear first. After pointing out the obvious (evolutionary expectations are often opposite to what the fossil record tells us), ReMine continues:

> But it gets still worse. Recent discoveries in genetics are adding another interesting new challenge to the problem. Developmental biologists have observed a small set of genes coordinating organismal development of body plans—*and these are present across the multicellular kingdom, in the various phyla and classes.* Evolutionists call this the 'Developmental Genetic Toolkit'. According to evolutionary thinking, this complex toolkit *must* have originated in some common ancestor to all the phyla. But that common ancestor must have existed *prior to* first appearance of these phyla—in other words, prior to the Cambrian Explosion (the place in the fossil record where all phyla appear, fully formed, and suddenly, with no evolutionary precursors). The common ancestor (whose identity is still unknown) *must* have existed in the Pre-Cambrian—prior to the origin of multicellular life. In short, the genes that control body plans had to have originated when there were no bodies. The genes that control embryological development had to have originated when there were no embryos.

This is a major puzzle for those who believe in a naturalistic origin of life! As pointed out in Chapter 3, the Last Universal Common Ancestor (LUCA) must have been very complex indeed. But where is the evidence for LUCA? It has not been found in the rocks and genetics has thrown a curveball into the evolutionary game. Michael Syvanen, an evolutionist, discovered that a very large proportion of eukaryotic (everything more complex than bacteria) genes simply have no homologous gene among all bacteria.[8] This was not supposed to be true.

---

7. ReMine, W.J., Desperate attempts to discover 'the elusive process of evolution': A review of *The Altenberg 16: An Exposé of the Evolution Industry* by Suzan Mazur, *J. Creation* **26**(1):24–30, 2012; creation.com/review-altenberg-16.

8. Syvanen, M., Evolutionary implications of horizontal gene transfer, *Annual Review of Genetics* **46**:339–356, 2012.

By manipulating visuals and text, all these facts remain elusive to the student, who is often left with the general impression that the evolution of life has proceeded at a steady and consistent pace. The very image used to present this, known as the *tree of life*, another icon, uses a misleading analogy. What is visible on this tree is the trunk and branches. However, some evolutionists today are suggesting that this is not the case and the tree is more like an entangled bush. The reason for this is that the field of genetics has discovered

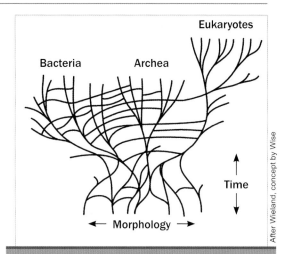

Revised evolutionary tree, depicting horizontal transfer among branches and a community of ancestral cells.

that there is no tree. Instead, diverse organisms share different genes, seemingly at random. This does not fit into the Darwinian 'Tree of Life' concept; it does not accord to the notion that all species are related through descent with modification from a common ancestor; so evolutionists have invoked *horizontal gene transfer* (HGT). That is, they believe ancient (bacterial) species shared different bits of DNA with each other and that this directly led to complete confusion at the roots of the tree.[9]

It is interesting to note that Darwin used the analogy of the tree of life in his *Origin*, although he drew it more like a vine (see Chapter 1). Now, since the fossil record is an archive of past life preserved in sedimentary rocks, its evolutionary interpretation should be a succession of discoveries revealing the continuous increase in complexity of living things over geologic time. More precisely, the 36 animal phyla we work with in taxonomy today should be ultimately traceable to the very first form of life believed to have emerged by natural causes from nonliving components. However, massive gaps were identified very early in the attempts to create such a straightforward succession, and fossils were found in rocks predating their theorized evolutionary origin, regularly causing significant revisions of the story.

Some fossil finds require such a drastic revision of the evolutionary story that there is a strong motivation to invoke a secondary hypothesis to explain their

9.   Jerlström, P., Is the evolutionary tree turning into a creationist orchard? *J. Creation* **14**(2):11–13, 2000; creation.com/creationist-orchard.

location and preserve the paradigm. These fossils are frequently labeled as 'derived', or 'reworked'. I prefer to think of them as *offset fossils*, meaning they were not found where they were supposed to be because some unknown (or hypothesized) geologic process removed them from their original (i.e. 'set') position and redeposited them in their present (i.e. 'offset') location.

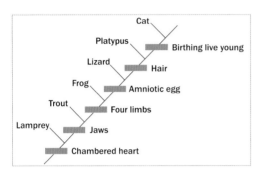

It became impossible to build a tree because of too many branches, and sections of the trunk are entirely missing. Instead, *cladograms* are now used.[10] Evolutionists draw nested boxes of shared and unshared characters, and branching tree diagrams from these. But these are esoteric representations of ideas unhindered by many paleontological facts! Thus a cladogram may contain nodal points labeled with fancy names representing a category of *undiscovered* creatures! The figure shown here is a simplified branching tree diagram representing of the origins of life, based on many sources and highly sophisticated cladograms.

There are a number of conclusions we can draw from the fossil record. First, far from continuous, the increase of complexity over time (if it happened at all) is discontinuous and sudden. Second, there are many groups of animals which do not seem to have evolved over very long periods of geologic time, a phenomenon noted and dubbed *evolutionary stasis*. The most stubborn example involves stromatolites: colonies of cyanobacteria that have not changed over allegedly 3.4 billion years, except that the most complex colony forms are in the most ancient past![11] Third, the most relevant evolutionary steps occurred in creatures that have not been discovered (evolution is in the gaps!). Fourth, if fossils are found outside the evolutionary order, the whole evolutionary history collapses. As Richard Dawkins once said, echoing J.B.S. Haldane before him:

> However, if there was a single hippo or rabbit in the Precambrian, that would completely blow evolution out of the water. None have ever been found.[12]

Hippos and rabbits may not have been found in the Precambrian but guess what? Many other similar fossils have been found, as far as their evolutionary significance is concerned. Did they "blow evolution out of the water"? No,

10. Doyle, S., Cladistics, evolution and the fossils, *J. Creation* **25**(2):32–39, 2011; creation.com/cladistics.
11. Other sources place this at 3.5 billion years; give or take 100 million years, which is commonplace at this scale.
12. Wallis, C., The evolution wars, 7 August 2005; time.com.

because evolution is a worldview that is used to interpret all evidence, no matter what is found. It cannot be falsified by a fossil find. The fossil is simply reinterpreted to make it look like it proves evolution all along.[13]

We shall now analyze some well-documented cases of what I have called 'offset fossils', but, before we do that, let us summarize: the 'big picture' offered by the fossil record is that of discontinuity and stasis. These facts are much more consistent with a creationist interpretation.

'Offset fossils'

The Salt Range Formation, Pakistan

Located at the foot of the Karakorum Mountains, between the Indus and Jhelum rivers in northeastern Pakistan, the Salt Range Formation has attracted

a lot of controversy since the 19th century. The salt deposits are located underneath the Kehwra Sandstone (previously known as the Purple Sandstone) which is of *Cambrian* age (supposedly between 542 and 488 million years old).[14] As early as 1927, the presence of botanical remains in the salt deposits was brought to the attention of geologists.[15] Since the plant fossils were of modern oak, the Salt Range Formation was assigned a *Tertiary*[16] age.

The Salt Range Formation in the Punjab province of Pakistan

Wikimedia commons: Khalid Mahmood

In 1944, Sahni[17] mentioned a wide range of fossils found in the salt layers: shreds of angiosperm (flowering plant) wood, gymnosperm (non-flowering plants like pines) tracheids (fluid-carrying vessels) and at least one good, winged, six-legged insect with composite eyes. Fossils were also found in the dolomite sequences in the salt. The age assigned by Sahni was Eocene (supposedly 56 to 34 million years ago, post-dating the extinction of the dinosaurs). Yet, detailed field studies by many geologists showed that the Kehwra Sandstone is Cambrian in age and that the underlying Salt Range Formation was in a normal position

13. Walker, T., Slow fish in China, *Creation* 22(3):38–39, 2000; creation.com/slow-fish-in-china.

14. Sameeni, S.J., The Salt Range: Pakistan's unique field museum of geology and paleontology, in Lipps, J.H. and Granier, B.R.C. (eds), PaleoParks—the protection and conservation of fossil sites worldwide, *Carnets de Géologie/Notebooks on Geology*, Brest, Book 2009/03, 2009.

15. Anderson, R.V.V., Tertiary stratigraphy and orogeny of the northern Punjab, *Bull. Geol. Soc. America* **38**:665–720, 1927.

16. The Tertiary is the third major section on the evolutionary geologic column, after 'the time of the dinosaurs'.

17. Sahni, B., Age of Saline Series in the Salt Range of the Punjab, *Nature* **153**:462–463, 1944.

(i.e. no overthrust) and hence must be of Precambrian age.[18] Sahni continued with very cautious and rigorous investigations, finding a piece of carbonized wood inside a dolomite block. He even demonstrated the extraction of new fossils (wood tissue) from dolomite in front of participants to a geological gathering in Great Britain.[19] His efforts of attributing this anomalous (offset) stratigraphic position to an overthrust failed, as they would have questioned some of the basic principles of geology and he admitted:

> Quite recently, an alternative explanation has been offered by Mr. Gee. The suggestion that the angiosperms, gymnosperms and insects of the Saline Series may represent a highly evolved Cambrian and Precambrian flora and fauna! In other words, it is suggested that these plants and animals made their appearance in the Salt Range area several hundred million years earlier than they did anywhere in the world. One would scarcely have believed that such an idea would be seriously put forward by any geologist today.[20]

Throughout the 1950s, fossil discoveries in the Salt Range Formation continued to be reported. Yet silence suddenly descended and, although modern investigations assign this formation to the *Eocambrian* (Late Precambrian),[21] I have only found one recent paper that mentions the discovery of wood fragments in the Khewra salt mines, but it dismisses them as intrusive, totally ignoring Sahni's massive evidence for *in situ* placement.[22] It is symptomatic that a more recent geological document published in 2009, which seeks the protection of fossil sites, describes the Salt Range Formation as Precambrian in age but makes absolutely no mention of any fossils![23]

The Roraima Formation, Venezuela

In 1966, Stainforth announced the discovery of pollen in the Roraima Formation, a quartz sandstone of which the famous *tepuis*—table mountains— of Venezuela are made.[24] Famous as the location of Arthur Conan Doyle's fictional *Lost World* and also the world's highest waterfall (Angel Falls), this spectacular landscape is infamous for evolutionists because of Stainforth's

18. Coates, J. *et al.*, Age of Saline Series in the Punjab Salt Range, *Nature* **155**:266–277, 1945.
19. Sahni, B., Microfossils and the Salt Range Thrust, *Proceedings of the National Academy of Sciences, India*, Section **B**, vol. **16**:i–xlx, 1946.
20. Sahni, ref. 19, pp. xlv–xlvi.
21. Yeates, R.S. *et al.*, Late Quaternary deformation of the Salt Range of Pakistan, *Geol. Soc. of Am. Bull.* **95**:958–966, 1984; Jaumé, S.C. and Lillie, R.J., Mechanics of the Salt Range-Potwar Plateau, Pakistan, *Tectonics* **7**:57–71, 1988.
22. Butler, R.W.H. *et al.*, Salt control on thrust geometry, structural style and gravitational collapse along the Himalayan Mountain Front in the Salt Range of Northern Pakistan; in Lerche, I. and O'Brian, J.J. (eds), *Dynamical Geology of Salt and Related Structures,* Orlando, Academic Press, pp. 339–418, 1987.
23. Sameeni, S.J., ref. 14.
24. Stainforth, R.M., Occurrence of pollen and spores in the Roraima Formation of Venezuela and British Guiana, *Nature* **210**:292–294, 1966.

Angel Falls, Venezuela

discovery. The 'unanimously' accepted, radiometrically-assigned evolutionary age of the formation is 1.8 billion years, placing it in the Paleo-Proterozoic, at a time when, according to the evolutionary scenario, green (photosynthetic) plants did not exist! Desperate efforts were made to explain this problem away, to no avail,[25] leaving Stainforth's conclusion perfectly pertinent, "We offer no solution to the paradox and this remains a highly intriguing problem."

The Ediacara vertebrate

The town of Ediacara in South Australia's Flinders Range is the site of the 'earliest' (Late Precambrian) assemblage of multicellular organisms, significantly different from more 'recent' ones (in the evolutionary dating scheme). Although the first fossil belonging to this age and biota, *Aspidella terranovica*, was found in Newfoundland in 1868, it was at Ediacara that the full range of strange creatures was discovered. Now the Late Precambrian is called *Ediacaran*. Tubular and feather-shaped invertebrates represent the bulk of the fossils, without apparent modern equivalents.

The Ediacaran fossil *Dickinsonia costa*

Photo from wikipedia.org

Then in 2003 various news outlets announced the discovery of the earliest vertebrate (chordate) within the same assemblage.[26] Deemed "the deepest part of the tree of life",[27] the creature has no name and conveniently faded away almost

25. Silvestru, E. and Wieland, C., Pollen paradox, 27 June 2011; creation.com/pollen-paradox.
26. Oldest vertebrate fossil found, *Discovery News*, 23 October 2003; dsc.discovery.com.
27. Farmer's fossil find excites, *BBC News*, 24 October 2003, news.bbc.co.uk.

Evolutionary timescale (Millions of years ago)		
1.8	QUARTERNARY	CENOZOIC
65	TERTIARY	CENOZOIC
145	CRETACEOUS	MESOZOIC
199	JURASSIC	MESOZOIC
251	TRIASSIC	MESOZOIC
299	PERMIAN	PALEOZOIC
318	PENNSYLVANIAN (CARBONIFEROUS)	PALEOZOIC
359	MISSISSIPPIAN (CARBONIFEROUS)	PALEOZOIC
416	DEVONIAN	PALEOZOIC
443	SILURIAN	PALEOZOIC
488	ORDOVICIAN	PALEOZOIC
542	CAMBRIAN	PALEOZOIC
4600	PRECAMBRIAN	

Geologic column

immediately! After initially creating a bit of a stir, the scientific community was so perplexed that it deliberately stopped speaking about the fossil. Unlike in other situations when a challenging offset fossil was found, there was no plethora of debunking articles in the mainstream science media. The fossil stands generally ignored, which can mean only one thing: it is a real challenge to the evolutionary scenario of the origins of life. That is because it pushes the evolution of the first vertebrates much farther into the past, leaving an unreasonably short time for pre-chordate evolution. To make things even worse, there is nothing in terms of fossils to connect this vertebrate to earlier times. It looks like vertebrates simply popped onto the scene of life from no discernable or even imaginable ancestry!

Vascular plants in the Cambrian

Standard present-day paleobotany holds that the first land-based vascular plants evolved in the Upper Ordovician (450 million years ago), despite early evidence from East Siberia that they already existed in the Cambrian (540 million years ago).[28] Similar evidence was found in Sweden and Estonia.[29] Since pollen was already found in Paleo-Precambrian rocks and vascular plants in the Late Precambrian, vascular plants in the Cambrian should not be a surprise, except that it would push the evolution of plants very far back and into an area of the sedimentary record notorious for its scarcity of fossils. These fossils also put an abrupt end to a media darling and much-talked about paleoclimate hypothesis, the Snowball Earth,[30] which posits an ice-covered planet in the Upper Precambrian. Somehow this caused, as it came to an enigmatic end just before the Cambrian, a true explosion of organisms with a shocking diversity of designs.

28. Leclerq, S., Evidence of vascular plants in the Cambrian, *International Journal of Organic Evolution* **10**(2):109–114, 1956.
29. Jacob, K. *et al.*, Evidence for the existence of vascular plants in the Cambrian, *Current Science* **22**:34–36, 1953.
30. Hoffman, P.F. *et al.*, A Neoproterozoic snowball Earth, *Science* **281**:1342–1346, 1998.

Animals fossilized in abnormal environments

There is another category of 'offset fossils', seldom spoken about: fossils of animals that lived in a completely different environment than the one in which they were fossilized.

1. Hadrosaurs (duckbilled dinosaurs) have been found in marine sediments in Montana's Bearpaw Shale.[31] Although discovered in 1900 and reported in 1902, the discovery has been overlooked by the absolute majority of paleontologists (land creatures buried in marine sediments are not exactly what they expected!) until 1979. Today these discoveries are still seldom mentioned, even if their inventory has grown significantly, which essentially rules out accidental burial in the open sea.

2. Nodosaurus (armored dinosaurs) fossils have been found lying upside down in marine sediments (including chalk) in western Kansas.[32] The first was discovered in 1870 by the famous O.C. Marsh, the discoverer of Apatosaurus.[33]

3. In 2011, the skeleton of an Ankylosaurus was discovered in the tar sands near Fort McMurray, Alberta,[34] another big surprise since the sands are marine sediments which have already yielded fossils of marine reptiles (mosasaurs).

These are only a few out of many possible examples. The frequency and large geographic extent of such finds point to a major watery catastrophe rather than accidental transport of carcasses hundreds of kilometers out into the open sea.[35] This is especially true since even large carcasses, including bones, are rapidly consumed by many oceanic critters, as evidenced by the absence of fish and whale skeletons on the ocean bottom!

Thus, the general picture of the fossil record is not what Darwin and Darwinists since Darwin want it to be. Offset fossils and a lack of natural explanations (other than Noah's Flood) for fossil accumulation are a serious challenge to evolution.

The Cambrian explosion

During his last summer break from college, Darwin performed field work in Wales with Adam Sedgwick. It was Sedgwick who was famous for naming the

31. Horner, J.R., Upper Cretaceous dinosaurs from the Bearpaw Shale (marine) of South Central Montana, with a checklist of Upper Cretaceous dinosaur remains from marine sediments in North America, *J. Paleontology* **53**(3):566–577, 1979.

32. Bakker, R.T., *The Dinosaur Heresies*, Zebra Books, New York, p. 40, 1986.

33. Everhard, M.J. and Hamm, S.A., A new nodosaur specimen (Dinosauria: Nodosauridae) from the Smoky Hill Chalk (Upper Cretaceous) of western Kansas, *Transactions of the Kansas Acadamy of Science* **108**:15–21, 2005.

34. *Drumheller Mail*, April 1st, 2011.

35. Horner, J.R., ref. 31.

Cambrian system (after the ancient name for Wales, *Cambria*). Darwin was well aware of something strange in the Cambrian: a number of fossils found in Cambrian strata seemed to pop into the fossil record with nothing more primitive to connect to in the Precambrian layers below. As he stated in *Origin*:

> To the question why we do not find records of these vast primordial periods, I can give no satisfactory answer. Several of the most eminent geologists, with Sir R. Murchison at their head, are convinced that we see in the organic remains of the lowest Silurian [Cambrian] stratum the dawn of life on this planet.[36]

Murchison was referring to Creation and that must really have frustrated Darwin as he admitted a few paragraphs later:

> The case at present must remain inexplicable; and may be truly urged as a valid argument against the views here entertained.

Darwin's ultimate solution was an escape to the future, when the fossil record will yield evidence to prove him right and Murchison wrong. Well, in one of those ironic twists of historical science, Murchison was proved wrong when life was discovered in the Precambrian, but so was Darwin! While some Precambrian fauna has been discovered, it too seems to have 'exploded' onto the scene, and nothing in it connects to or explains the Cambrian explosion. As Gould put it:

> … and the problem of the Cambrian explosion has remained as stubborn as ever—if not more so, since our confusion now rests on knowledge, rather than ignorance, about the nature of the Precambrian life.[37]

He was certainly right since the only known Precambrian fauna (the Ediacaran fauna, see above), although it turned out to have a global distribution, represents, according to evolutionists, a failed experiment. The Ediacaran fossils are not considered ancestors of the Cambrian and later life forms.

Why did the simplest life forms, which reproduce so quickly, remain alone for so long, evolving over the longest time into something only a little more complex, only then to explode into the most diverse life forms that have ever lived? All-in-all, there appears to be a strange and weak correlation between Darwinian evolution and geologic time. Since it represents such a serious challenge, the Cambrian explosion is presented in most evolutionist circles in any way that can make it seem more palatable, and more difficult for Darwin skeptics to use. The most common approach today is to refer to it as the Cambrian 'slow fuse'. As more fossils come to light, they have been wrestled into ordered positions

---

36. Darwin, C., ref. 2, Ch. 9.
37. Gould, S.J., ref. 5, p. 57.

within the Cambrian, leaving many to believe that there was no explosion and that the rate of change was no greater during this time period than in most other periods of life on earth. However, blue-green algae supposedly remained unchanged for over two-and-a-half *billion* years (not to mention the next half-billion years, since they appear morphologically unchanged today), and then nearly all phyla emerged within a window of about 100 million years. Considering the evolutionary innovation that must have been occurring, this is a geological blink of an eye.

We shall consequently take the facts and list them, leaving the reader with the task of drawing the conclusions. We shall also ignore the 'offset' fossils presented above, especially the Precambrian insects, so that the case is argued exclusively on the accepted evolutionary data.

After the Ediacaran, at the very beginning of the Cambrian, another strange fauna entered the stage. Known after the East Siberian location where it was first discovered, the Tommotian fauna marks the first appearance of mineralized (shelly) animals: brachiopods, trilobites, archaeocyathids (the first 'reef' builders, but not corals), mollusks, echinoderms and a number of problematic creatures with no modern equivalent. Soon after, in the mid-Cambrian, the real 'explosion' took place when incredibly diverse faunas suddenly appear. The first to be discovered (1909), and still a most famous location, is the Burgess Shale in British Columbia's Yoho National Park. Later, similar faunas were discovered at Sirius Passet in Greenland and Chengjiang in China's Yunan province.

The Burgess Shale has yielded a total of 9 new phyla and 13 unique arthropods never found in sediments before or after.[38] None of these can be derived (in an evolutionary sense) from previous fossils. What is also shocking (to the Darwinist) is that most of these new creatures had body plans that do not exist today. Creatures with 5 eyes (*Opabinia*) and some with an odd number (7) of pairs of appendices (*Hallucigenia*) were not oddities in those days. Neither did they become oddities later, as they completely vanished from the fossil record. Today, all creatures that have pairs of appendices have an even number of them. The same is true for the eyes.

What is really remarkable about the Burgess Shale fauna is that, although it is the first assemblage of virtually all known phyla, no new phylum has appeared since. It has a diversity of body designs never again found in the fossil record. Gould called this "decimation and diversification". In his view, life appears to start with an abundance of designs, most of which are subsequently eliminated.

---

38. Gould, S.J., ref. 5, pp. 210–211.

This is supposedly enough to account for all the biodiversity ever seen,[39] but is also the very antithesis of Darwinian evolution. Descent with modification should progress from simple to complex. Instead, the greatest evolutionary innovations appear suddenly, with no precursors, and no new major innovations are made while several of the originals go extinct.

Neo-Darwinian evolutionary biologists have tried to explain the Cambrian by invoking 'an absence of competition'. This inference is based on the idea that since virtually all ecological niches were open, there for the taking, most every experiment of life (i.e. any odd or less odd outcome of mutations) could be successful, as serious competition was still far in the future. That of course would have required an incredibly high potential for rapid and continuous change, an opportunity never again achieved afterwards. Gould was skeptical about it:

> The Cambrian explosion was too big, too different, and too exclusive. I just can't accept that if organisms always have the potential for diversification of this kind—while only the odd ecology of the Lower Cambrian ever permitted its realization—never, not even once, has a phylum arisen since Burgess times.[40]

Gould and other proponents of the *punctuated equilibrium model* (sudden big evolutionary jumps in small, marginal populations, as opposed to neo-Darwinian small mutations over long periods of time) invoke a much higher "genetic flexibility" in those first complex organisms, a flexibility lost subsequently by the "aging of the genetic system."[41] Of course, anything can be inferred by them as long as the grand icon of evolution is preserved. The possibility that all phyla were created by God during the unique event of Creation, drastically tested and filtered through a global Flood is utterly rejected by secular scientists, even though it is a simpler and more complete explanation. When geological and paleontological facts visibly support this explanation, they are subtly made invisible by academia and the media.

Fossils that should not be there: the case of exceptional preservation

For many years it was a commonplace belief that, since fossils represented mineralized remains of ancient dead creatures, only the hard parts of those organisms would stand any chance to fossilize without sudden burial. The bulk of the fossil record is made of shells of marine invertebrates and one would expect that the small percentage of fossils of terrestrial organisms would not have fossilized soft tissues surviving over millions of years.

39. Gould, S.J., ref. 5, p. 46.
40. Gould, S.J., ref. 5, p. 230.
41. Gould, S.J., ref. 5, pp. 230–231.

That may explain why the exceptional preservation of the soft-bodied marine organisms of the Burgess Shale came as a big surprise. To this day the chemical intricacies of the fossilization process remain a mystery, for slow and gradual processes. Yet one discovery after the other has left paleontologists and biochemists perplexed. The real shocker, a paradigm-changer, was the discovery of preserved soft, non-bony tissue from an unfossilized *T. rex* bone by Dr Mary Schweitzer.[42] That initial discovery has been followed up by careful work to confirm and expand the initial findings. Multiple individual dinosaurs from several species, including theropods, hadrosaurs, and ceratopsids[43] have now been found with non-fossilized organic remains, including recent claims of evidence for dinosaur DNA. If soft tissues and blood vessels can survive for 65 million years or more, the whole concept of fossilization needs to be revised. That is not a pleasant prospect for paleontologists. An immense frustration is associated with it since it implies that, over hundreds of years of paleontological exploration and discovery, preserved soft tissues may very well have been unknowingly discarded with the rock matrix surrounding the bones.

No wonder the evolutionary establishment has desperately tried to explain away Schweitzer's "dangerous discovery" (as the media dubbed it), claiming, among other things, that it was simply a bacterial film ("biofilm") mimicking soft tissue.[44] But Schweitzer's answers to the challenges have been firm and convincing, leading paleontologists to make surprising statements:

> "I'd call it a milestone," says paleontologist Hans Larsson of McGill University in Montreal, who was not part of the studies. "Dinosaurs will enter the field of molecular biology and really slingshot paleontology into the modern world."[45]

Soft tissue fossils of cephalopods (such as squid) were found as far back as 1841, including mantle, ink sac, arms with suckers and hooks.[46] This was in the Jurassic Oxford Clay Member of England near Christian Malford and Trowbridge (Wiltshire), during the works on the Great Western Railway. Sporadically mentioned in the scientific literature since, this amazing fossil site became the focus for taphonomic studies[47] after 2000. Phosphatization, that is

---

42. Schweitzer, M. *et al.*, Soft-tissue vessels and cellular preservation in *Tyrannosaurus rex*, *Science* **307**:1952–1955, 2005.

43. Armitage, M.H. and Anderson, K.L., Soft sheets of fibrillar bone from a fossil of the supraorbital horn of the dinosaur *Triceratops horridus*, *Acta Histochemica* **115**(6):603–608, 2013.

44. Kaye, G. *et al.*, Dinosaurian soft tissues interpreted as bacterial biofilms, *PLoS ONE* **3**(7):e2808.

45. Vergano, D., Yesterday's *T. rex* is today's chicken, *USA Today*, 12 April 2007; usatoday.com.

46 Pearce, J.C., On the mouth of ammonites, and on fossils contained in the laminated beds of the Oxford Clay discovered in cutting the Great Western Railway, near Christian Malford in Wiltshire, *Proc. Geol. Soc. London* **3**:592–594, 1841.

47. Taphonomy is the study of the processes involved in fossilization, from death to the recovery of the fossil.

the replacement of the organic matter with phosphate minerals, is now believed to be the cause of the exceptional fossilization.[48] In 2007 the fossils became a media sensation as the ink from a well-preserved sac of *Belemnotheutis antiquus* was 'reactivated' with ammonia allowing paleontologists to draw the shape of the squid![49] This was actually an old trick, but the location of the source of these fossils was lost for a hundred years or more. What is really remarkable and still not fully understood is how phosphatization could occur so rapidly, in order to prevent the decay of soft tissues and the easily-degradable melanin, the substance that makes up the dark ink pigment.

The well-preserved fossil of *Darwinius masillae* (a.k.a., "Ida"), the subject of an orchestrated media campaign of hype. Ida was almost identical to modern lemurs.[50]

In Germany, locations with exceptionally preserved fossils are frequent enough to have acquired a name of their own: Lagerstätten (German for "storage place"). This term is used today for similar locations around the world. Ida[50], the Eocene primate whose purported ancestry drove the media crazy[51] not too many years ago (and drove many scientists crazy about the media's haste in reporting it) came from such a site, the Messel Pit in Germany.

The frequency and extent of Lagerstätten around the world makes exceptional preservation a general rule rather than an exception. Thus, it is a fundamentally irresolvable contradiction of the Darwinian view of the fossil record. It also makes the view that the earth and fossils are young perfectly reasonable.

Transitional fossils

Now that we have documented several evolutionary Achilles' heels inherent in the fossil record, including the sudden appearance of major taxonomic groups and the many out-of-place fossils, let us examine some of the latest and greatest claims for evolutionary transitions.

48. Wilby, P.R. *et al.*, Taphonomy and origins of an accumulate of soft-bodied cephalopods in the Oxford Clay Formation (Jurassic, England), *Paleontology* **47**(5):1159–1180, 2004.
49. Ink found in Jurassic-era squid, *BBC News*, 19 August 2009; news.bbc.co.uk.
50. Franzen, J.L. *et al.*, Complete primate skeleton from the Middle Eocene of Messel in Germany: morphology and paleobiology, *PLoS ONE* **45**(5):e5723, 2009.
51. Batten, D., Darwin fossil hyper-hype, 23 May 2009, creation.com/ida.

First, we must understand that the vast majority of fossils used as evidence for evolutionary transitions display small-scale variation only, what can be described as variation within a basic kind. Thus, they fit into the common creationist idea that God created multiple, independent kinds of animals, each with a rich genetic diversity and the capacity to moderately change in order to adapt and survive in different environments. This change would include physiological adaptation through selection on designed genetic variation as well as variation due to mutations.

Therefore, when considering some of the small changes that occurred within a certain lineage, this is non-discriminating evidence. That is, it cannot be used as proof one way or the other. This is one reason why biblical creationists have consistently attempted to make the argument about things like big changes (and the absence of evidence for them), the origin of life, and the origin of the information content inherent in that life. Those are significantly large changes and offer a better test of evolutionary theory.

Regarding the difficulties of placing the bones, tracks, or traces of extinct animals into discrete evolutionary categories, Professor Maciej Henneberg once wrote:

> There is no precise way to test whether Julius Caesar and Princess Diana were members of the same species, Homo sapiens.[52]

One can then ask, "How does one define a 'transitional fossil'?" The evolutionist's answer is rather simple, "A transitional fossil is an organism that shares common characteristics with both its precursors and its descendants." The next question will then be, "How does one know which are the precursors and which are the descendants?" And the answer goes, "A precursor lived before (is found in layers dated older than the transitional fossil) and had more primitive features. A descendant lived after (in layers dated younger than the transitional fossil) and had or has more advanced features."

Well, that may be the situation at any given moment, but subsequent discoveries may change the transitional status of any fossil. In the history of paleontology this has happened many times. In addition, the boundaries between fossil species are extremely mobile, as we shall further see. To make the situation even more complicated, who establishes where a fossil is placed on the evolutionary ladder? Fossils can be moved up and down according to discoveries and theories. Of course, that is more of a professional secret, and the average consumer of paleontological data is unaware of.

Henneberg's observation above is sobering; if we cannot *test* if two humans separated by only 2,000 years were members of the same species, how can we

---

52. Henneberg, M., *The Hobbit Trap*, Wakefield Press, Kent Town, Australia, p. 25, 2008.

do that with creatures allegedly separated by millions of years? This is a huge problem in reality, but the evolutionary paleontologist blithely treats it as minor, and feels free to arrange and rearrange fossils separated by millions of years in any sequence that will yield an evolutionary series and narrative (ultimately a cladogram, as mentioned before).

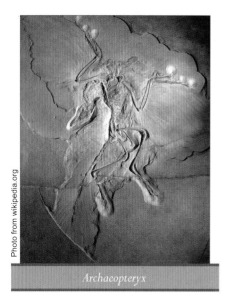

Archaeopteryx

Photo from wikipedia.org

Archaeopteryx and the dinosaur-to-bird transition

Archaeopteryx is the first fossil claimed to be a transitional form from dinosaurs to birds. It later became an ancestral bird, but as recently as 2011, after the discovery of yet another Chinese fossil, *Xiaotingia*, *Archaeopteryx* was demoted to a dinosaur similar to the theropod, *Deinonychus*,[53] before being reinstated by another group who challenged the conclusions of the first. As for *Deinonychus* itself, it has also undergone an interesting transformation, summarized by the signage next to its reconstruction at a feathered dinosaur exhibition:

These sculptures were originally made between 1986 and 1989 with a scaly hide based on fossil skin impressions from other dinosaurs. When *Deinonychus* was first discovered in 1969, it was thought to be a bird-like dinosaur and a possible ancestor of birds. Now it is known that *Deinonychus* itself had ancestors that flew—flying dromeosaurs—which makes it a form of flightless bird instead of a dinosaur. Had *Deinonychus* been found after the discovery of fossil flying dromeosaurs in China, scientists could not have thought of it as a scaly dinosaur, but as a bird that has lost its ability to fly.[54]

This is as far from empirical science as one can get, isn't it? How can the skeleton of a dinosaur (and there is an abundance of *Deinonychus* fossils) be interpreted once as a dinosaur, then as a flightless bird? There are many anatomical details preserved in the bones of fossils, so many that separating a bird from a dinosaur should be rock solid (pun intended). What happened, however, is that the boundary between birds and dinosaurs has been deliberately blurred so that almost any future discovery can be 'retrofitted'.

---

53. Xu, X. *et al.*, An *Archaeopteryx*-like theropod from China and the origin of Avialae, *Nature* **475**:465–470, 2011.

54. *Feathered Dinosaurs*, The Dinosaur Museum, Blanding, UT, USA– exhibition at Royal Ontario Museum, 2005.

Photo from wikipedia.org

Even though *Sinosauropteryx* was the original 'poster child' for the dinosaur-to-bird transition, the fibers that were originally described as feathers are quite clearly under the skin.

The simplest explanation (according to Occam's razor) is not part of the evolutionary biologists' mindset: all feathered fossils are fossils of birds and all bird-like featherless fossils belong to dinosaurs. In other words, the presence of feathers should be the definitive criterion to separate birds from dinosaurs. In fact, a recent study of another famous 'feathered' dinosaur, *Sinosauropteryx*, has demonstrated, quite clearly, that the 'feathers' were part of a thick subcutaneous layer. The study authors said:

Quite extraordinarily, Currie and Chen (2001) describe only the filamentous tissue in NIGP 127587 (as protofeathers) despite the fact that the dermal tissue distal to and overlying it comprises the greater part of the external tissue, extending as a continuous band from the head to the tail (Figs. 1, 6). This is quite unmistakable. The description presented here shows that the filamentous structures were internal support fibres …[55]

There are other issues (e.g. warm blooded vs cold blooded, and reptile lung vs bird lung) that need to be considered as well. Dinosaurs were reptiles, but they were a distinct group of reptiles with unique features. They are also extinct, whereas most all other reptile groups were buried with dinosaurs but are still alive today. There may be certain characteristics that make them more similar to modern avians, but this is not enough to demonstrate dinosaur-to-bird evolution.

Another possibility is that, in fact, dinosaurs had feathers. Whether or not birds evolved from dinosaurs is a second question. While it is true that evolutionists have nested (pun intended) birds within the theropod dinosaurs, creationists have no prior commitment to dinosaurs with or without feathers or to whether or not birds group with dinosaurs in a nested hierarchy. This is true because the Bible makes no specific prediction about where birds are to be grouped and does not even mention dinosaurs (by name). Even though the father of

55. Lingham-Soliar, T., The evolution of the feather: *Sinosauropteryx*, life, death and preservation of an alleged feathered dinosaur, *J. Ornithology* **153**(3):699–711, 2012. This author also made prior claims that the supposed melanosomes (which would be indicative of coloration in feathers) discovered in certain dinosaur fossils was a magnification artifact inherent in the microscope used. See also Sarfati, J., 'Feathered' dinos: no feathers after all! 24 July 2012; creation.com/featherless.

taxonomy (Linnaeus) was a creationist, this does not mean his categorization system is sacrosanct, and it is true that diverse groups can be lumped together based on shared features (e.g. humans fall within mammals, along with monkeys and marmosets). Yet, the evolution of birds from dinosaurs is the evolutionary 'order of battle'.

Tiktaalik

When *Tiktaalik roseae* was discovered in 2004 on Ellesmere Island in Northern Canada,[56] it joined the minuscule club of so-called transitional fossils with great media drum beating. The end of creationist arguing against evolution was considered imminent because this 'legged' fish (a.k.a. 'the fishapod'),

Tiktaalik

was 'definitely' a transitional form from fish to tetrapod (an animal with four legs). It was dated as mid-Devonian (383 million years ago), before the first known tetrapods.

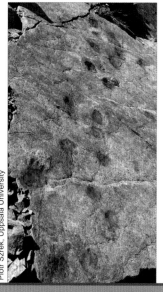

Limestone slab from Poland with fossil footprints.

Piotr Szrek, Uppsala University

Yet, it only took 6 years to join the fate of *Deinonychus*, *Sinosauropteryx* and many other previous candidates for transitional status, because true tetrapod footprints were found in Poland and dated at 10 million years before *Tiktaalik*![57] By the evolutionists' own reasoning, the poor fishapod is considered a mere relic, its supposed transitional features having to have evolved at least 400 million years ago (prior to the tetrapod that made the tracks and in a creature still undiscovered).

The absence of transitional fossils within the fossil record is not an argument *per se* against their existence, of course. So the evolutionary excuse that the fossil record only preserves *moments in time* while transitional forms represent *periods of time* is not completely absurd. However, it is absurd and outright unscientific to claim that *absence* cannot be used as argument against the

56. Daeschler, E.B. *et al.*, A Devonian tetrapod-like fish and the evolution of the tetrapod body plan, *Nature* **440**:757–763, 2006. See also Sarfati, J., *Tiktaalik roseae*—a fishy 'missing link', 2006; creation.com/tiktaalik.
57. Niedzwiedzki, G. *et al.*, Tetrapod trackways from the early Middle Devonian period in Poland, *Nature* **463**:43–48, 2010. See also Walker, T., Is the famous fish-fossil finished?; creation.com/tiktaalik-finished.

very concept of transitional forms, especially since the story that the fossil record presents is far from satisfying to evolutionary paleontologists:

> No wonder paleontologists shied away from evolution for so long. It seems never to happen. Assiduous collecting up cliff faces yields zigzags, minor oscillations, and the very occasional slight accumulation of change over millions of years, at a rate too slow to really account for all the prodigious change that has occurred in evolutionary history. When we do see the introduction of evolutionary novelty, it usually shows up with a bang, and often with no firm evidence that the organisms did not evolve elsewhere! Evolution cannot forever be going on someplace else. Yet that's how the fossil record has struck many a forlorn paleontologist looking to learn something about evolution.[58]

Paradoxically, the very few examples of transitional forms Darwin had in mind were not in use in the time of the Scopes Trial (1925), and the triumphalist list we saw in the 1960–1970s quickly deflated to a precious few today, and none of the remainder are without serious problems.

Of course, popular websites have drafted long lists of transitional forms, but they fail to point out the major difference between variations within the same kind (i.e. a basic group like 'family') and transition from one kind to another. Who would argue that a Schnauzer dog with a size between the standard and the miniature breeds is a transitional form? Yet they all belong to the Schnauzer breed! In the fossil record, we see many variations within certain limits, and very few forms intermediate between major groups of animals and plants. Thus, the greatest leaps in evolutionary history, those that required the greatest degree of innovation and which would have consumed innumerable experimental evolutionary prototypes, are spanned by the fewest number of intermediate forms. The reality is exactly the opposite of what Darwin predicted!

Puijila

In 2009, a fossil named *Puijila darwini* was announced as the latest 'missing link'.[59] It was the first evidence claimed for the evolution of the pinnipeds (seals, sea lions, and walruses) from a land mammal. Richard Dawkins jubilantly exclaimed:

> *Puijila* neatly straddles the gap between land and water in the ancestry of pinnipeds. It is yet another delightful addition to our growing list of 'links' that are no longer missing.[60]

58. Eldredge, N., *Reinventing Darwin*, Orion Publishing, London, p.95, 1996.
59. Rybczynski, N., Dawson, M.R., and Tedford, R.H., A semi-aquatic Arctic mammalian carnivore from the Miocene epoch and origin of Pinnipedia, *Nature* **458**:1021–1024, 2009.
60. Dawkins, R., *The Greatest Show on Earth*, Bantam Books, New York, 2009, p. 173. Dr Jonathan Sarfati dealt with other fossils that Dr Dawkins claimed to be transitional in chapter 8 of *The Greatest Hoax on Earth*, Creation Book Publishers, 2010 (available through creation.com). See also, creation.com/fossils.

Puijila Skeleton
Pinniped or Otter?

Although scientists who support evolution refer to *Puijila* as a "walking seal" [3] or an otter with a seal's head,[22] its skeletal appearance is very similar to a river otter, as shown in the photographs below.

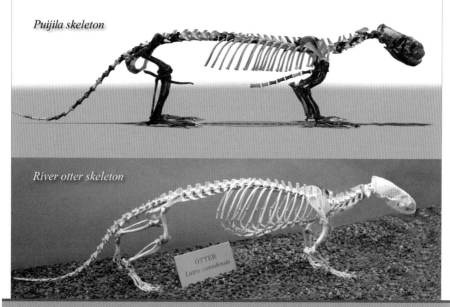

Puijila skeleton

River otter skeleton

OTTER
Lutra canadensis

A page from Appendix E of Dr Werner's *Evolution: the Grand Experiment, 2nd edition*, showing the skeletons of the supposed transitional fossil (top) and the North American river otter (bottom). Other than *Puijila* standing flat-footed, it is hard to see much difference.

There is one major problem with evolutionary interpretations of *Puijila*, however, for the skeleton is almost identical to that of the living North American river otter, *Lontra canadensis*.[61] Hence, not only is *Puijila* not a transitional fossil, but it is a fossil of a known living species and the pinnipeds still have no evolutionary history. This is despite the fact that more than 15,000 fossil pinnipeds have been discovered to date.[62]

---

61. Batten, D., Another major 'link' fails: *Puijila*, claimed ancestor of pinnipeds is an otter, *Creation* **35**(1):51–53; creation.com/puijila. For a more detailed refutation, see the supplement to this article: Werner, C., Analysis of the 'family tree' published for *Puijila* in *Nature* 2009, creation.com/puijila-s.
62. Werner, C., *Evolution: the Grand Experiment*, vol. 1, New Leaf Press, Green Forest, Arkansas, p. 225, 2007 (available through creation.com).

Whales

Whale evolution is a hot topic today. Unknown just a few decades ago, a huge array of ancient whale and whale-like creatures are now available, arranged in what is claimed to be an evolutionary sequence. The whale evolution story depends on three fossils to link the 'first' true whales (Basilosaurids) to land animals: *Pakicetus*, *Ambulocetus,* and *Rodhocetus,* but all three have now failed, as revealed by Dr Carl Werner, author of *Evolution: the Grand Experiment.*[63]

With *Pakicetus*, Dr Philip Gingerich imagined an incomplete fossil skull to be that of a whale-like creature, displayed as such on the cover of *Science*, in 1983. When the rest of *Pakicetus* was published in 2001, it proved to be a land animal.[64] In a *National Geographic* documentary in 2009, Dr Gingerich still claimed that *Pakicetus* should be classed with whales, based on its ear-bone. However, the ear-bone is not at all like a whale, which has a finger-like projection (sigmoid process). No, this one is plate-like, like land animals known as artiodactyls.

Dr Hans Thewissen claimed that eight features showed *Ambulocetus* was a whale ancestor. Dr Werner recorded Dr Thewissen admitting that a key 'evidence' of whale ancestry, the sigmoid process of the ear-bone, was actually nothing like a whale's. Dr Werner says, "All eight characters he reported as whale features are disturbingly non-whale features."

Rodhocetus was claimed to be an aquatic mammal that was developing flippers and a whale-like tail—well on the way to becoming a whale. However, there was no fossil evidence for a tail or flippers.[65] When pressed on this issue, Gingerich

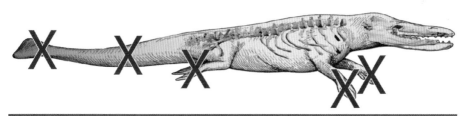

Rodhocetus at the Museum of Natural History, University of Michigan, USA. Original fossil evidence overlaid on the museum's illustration from Dr Carl Werner, *Evolution: the Grand Experiment Vol.* 1 DVD. Red Xs added to emphasize the imagination involved in the illustration.

63. Batten, D., Whale evolution fraud: Another evolutionary icon bites the dust; creation.com/whale-evolution-fraud, 12 April 2014.
64. Williams, A., and Sarfati, J., Not at all like a whale, *Creation* **27**(2):20–22, 2005; creation.com/not-at-all-like-a-whale.
65. Batten, D., *Rodhocetus* and other stories of whale evolution, *Creation* **33**(3):54–55, 2011; creation.com/rodhocetus.

admitted that, based on later finds, he no longer believes that *Rodhocetus* had a fluked tail or flippers.[64] So the key animal in the transitional sequence for whale evolution is not what it is claimed to be.

There are many other problems with whale evolution, even though the story is portrayed as clear-cut. Evolutionists cannot even agree on which land animal gave rise to the whales. Based on fossil similarities of teeth, some paleontologists favoured hyena-like animals (*Pachyaena*), while other preferred a cat-like animal (*Sinonyx*). However, based on recent comparisons of DNA evidence, molecular biologists decided hippos were the closest to a whale ancestor. But there are huge problems with converting a hippo into a whale (like how a land animal gains the ability to give birth and nurse young underwater!).

Living fossils

The impression we get from the evolutionary history of the world—at least its media and textbook versions—is that descent with modification, filtered through natural selection, is an unstoppable and omnipresent feature of the entire universe, of which the living world is just a small portion. It therefore comes as a surprise to the diligent student that there is an abundance of cases of *evolutionary stasis* (an oxymoron by all definitions). In fact, there are innumerable examples of organisms that have not changed or have changed very little over extremely long geologic times.

The standard answer to this apparent incongruence is that evolution only happens when needed (e.g. "The organism did not need to evolve since it was perfectly adapted to its environment."). In other words, natural selection will only cull those modifications that are not best adapted to a given environment. If the environment does not change, that *already selected* best modification, or best variation, will be what is propagated through time. There are serious problems with such a reductionist solution though, including the fact that so-called living fossils have supposedly survived through major world catastrophes (e.g. the End-Permian extinction that supposedly occurred 252 million years ago and that killed off most of the then-living species, and the hypothesized meteor strike 65 million years ago at the Cretaceous-Tertiary boundary that killed off the dinosaurs). These events are associated with dramatic climate change in evolutionary models. Thus, precious few micro-environments are thought to have remained constant. How could anything have remained "perfectly adapted"? Also, how can a species remain in one place when other species are evolving to compete with and/or eat it? Evolutionists themselves have admitted the problem:

> But stasis was conveniently dropped as a feature of life's history to be reckoned with in evolutionary biology. And stasis had continued to be

ignored until Gould and I showed that such stability is a real aspect of life's history which must be confronted—and that, in fact, it posed no fundamental threat to the basic notion of evolution itself. For that was Darwin's problem: to establish the plausibility of the very idea of evolution, Darwin felt that he had to undermine the older ... doctrine of species fixity. Stasis, to Darwin, was an ugly inconvenience.[66]

Gould and Eldredge believed that punctuated equilibrium—evolution through sudden big jumps after long periods of stasis—was the true pattern of evolution. But they were not even attempting to explain from whence such a massive addition of genetic information could have come. Thus, after Gould's passing away, punctuated equilibrium lost popularity and gradualistic neo-Darwinism became the ruling dogma in academia again. Consequently, the problem of evolutionary stasis has followed the fate of other embarrassing issues and they tend to paper over the problem with fancy Greek words and phrases.

Stromatolites

The 'oldest' fossils on earth (supposedly 3.5 billion years), stromatolites are interpreted as the remains of blue-green algae (cyanobacteria) colonies. While blue-green algae are still around today, it came as a surprise that colonial forms of these microorganisms known from the fossil record, called stromatolites, are also alive today and virtually unchanged! Such cases are popularly known as *living fossils*, because the fossils were found before the living animals. Linguistically, this phrase is as nonsensical as the word 'undead'.

Stromatolites represent the epitome of evolutionary stasis, no doubt, yet the problems are many with such an interpretation. First, since neo-Darwinian dogma maintains that mutations are the engine of evolution, it stretches logic beyond recognition to believe that 3.5 billion years of mutations in sedentary prokaryotes have not affected them in a more visible way! After all, according to neo-Darwinism, the simpler the creature the faster its evolution should be, since any mutation is significant and simple creatures pass on those mutations to the next generation in a short time. When we consider the sheer number of inevitable random mutations in stromatolites/blue-green algae in the alleged 3.5 billion years, their stasis defies logic.

Studying living stromatolites in the Bahamas and Australia has shown that their fossil forms are identical to the living versions.*

Figure 3 from Awramik, S.M., Respect for stromatolites, *Nature* 441:700–701.

66. Eldredge, N., *Time Frames: The Rethinking of Darwinian Evolution and the Theory of Punctuated Equilibria*, Simon & Schuster, New York, pp. 188–189, 1985.

Second, as mentioned before, according to the evolutionary history of the planet, the world environment has been affected by many massive changes. And since stromatolites are found alive on opposite sides of the world today, in Australia and the Bahamas, we can confidently infer they have been subjected to serious environmental challenges throughout geologic time—all the more reason for evolution. Yet it did not happen.

Horseshoe crab

The 'earliest' known member of the *Limulus* genus comes from central and northern Manitoba, Canada, and its fossils have been found in Late Ordovician sediments, said to be 445 million years old—very early in the evolutionary history of multicellular organisms. Other than being smaller, and size may simply be a matter of age at death of the fossilized creature, the fossil is virtually identical to the present horseshoe crab. The discoverers' own words are revealing:

> Understanding how horseshoe crabs adapted to this ecological niche very early on, and then remained there through thick and thin, can give us insights into how ocean and shoreline ecosystems have developed through deep time.[67]

Again, given the extent of environmental changes since the Ordovician (according to the evolutionists themselves), the unchanged survival of this creature is a miracle and challenges gradualistic neo-Darwinism. But they don't see the contradiction to their long-age worldview because they believe in it so absolutely. Within their worldview every anomaly becomes an 'amazing' discovery.

The Coelacanth

From their first discovery as fossils in Australia in 1839, the coelacanths were believed to be a transitional evolutionary form between fish and tetrapods—four-legged land animals. Fossils of this group of lobed-finned fish were found in sediments from the Devonian to the Late Cretaceous, when it was believed to have gone extinct. Its muscular fins were seen as the precursors to legs.

In 1938, a living coelacanth was caught off the east coast of South Africa. This was a huge shock, for not only was this fossil fish alive and well, but it was essentially unchanged for supposedly 400 million years, including the 65 million years since its 'extinction'. Since then, living coelacanths have been found at many locations, and even filmed in their natural habitat near the Comoros Islands.

---

67. Oldest horseshoe crab fossil found, 445 million years old, *ScienceDaily*, 8 February 2008; sciencedaily. com.

It turns out that these deep-water fish are not in any way evolving legs. Besides the fact that the natural habitat is far from any shoreline, those muscular fins are used to artfully navigate their underwater lair, allowing them to deftly follow currents or to remain in place in those currents when they like. Their fins are used for ... swimming! Another species of the genus has been found extant in the 1990s and turned out to be a delicacy at Indonesian fish markets. Farewell missing link; hello new (and yummy) living fossil.

Scorpions and dragonflies

The earliest land scorpion found in the fossil record comes from Upper Devonian sediments from China,[68] supposedly more than 360 million years old. Although incomplete, the fossil closely resembles modern scorpions. A huge scorpion, *Pulmonoscorpius kirktonensis,* was found in younger Carboniferous sediments of Scotland,[69] nearly 300 million years ago according to evolutionary dating. Most of its anatomical features are identical to modern scorpions, the only major difference being its size. It was up to 70 cm (27 inches) long, whereas the largest living scorpions are about 20 cm (8 inches).

Photos from istockphoto

It is interesting that among arthropods (to which scorpions belong) there are other cases of gigantism in the Carboniferous: *Meganeura*, a dragonfly with a wingspan of 75 cm (nearly 30 inches) and *Arthropleura*—a centipede over 2 meters (6.5 feet) long. Such gigantism is believed by many, incorrectly, to be caused by a higher atmospheric concentration of oxygen in the 'Carboniferous times'. Since the basic anatomy of scorpions and dragonflies has been preserved virtually unchanged over 320 million evolutionary years, they can also be classified as living fossils.

The Wollemi pine

In 1994, a most surprising discovery added a new plant to the list of living fossils. In a deep gorge in the Blue Mountains, New South Wales, Australia, just west of Sydney, a grove of Wollemi pine trees was discovered. It was growing in a small area of about 5,000 square metres (1.2 acres). The tree is not actually a pine but a relative of the monkey puzzle tree (Araucaria family) and it was known as a fossil from the Jurassic period. When first announced, the discovery triggered a sensational reaction from the media and scientists, saying

68. Wallosek, D. *et al.*, A scorpion from the Upper Devonian of Hubei Province, China (Arachnida, Scorpionida), *N. Jub. Geol. Paläont. Mh.* **H3**:169–180, 1990.
69. Jeram, A.J., Phylogeny, classification and evolution of Silurian and Devonian scorpions, *Proceedings of the 17th European Colloquium of Arachnology,* Edinburgh, 1997; european-arachnology.org.

it was "like finding a dinosaur in your backyard". Some suggested prudence, saying it was "a new genus" and too early to be called living fossil.[70] But no one mentioned that the find was incongruous to evolutionary theory. Today the plant has earned a permanent position in the list of living fossils. Further, they are widely cultivated and available for sale in garden nurseries, although the government-supported project to propagate them was terminated due to poor sales.[71]

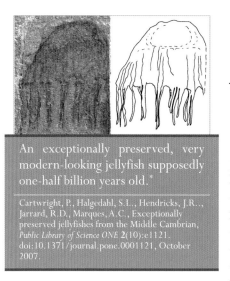

An exceptionally preserved, very modern-looking jellyfish supposedly one-half billion years old.*

Cartwright, P., Halgedahl, S.L., Hendricks, J.R., Jarrard, R.D., Marques, A.C., Exceptionally preserved jellyfishes from the Middle Cambrian, *Public Library of Science ONE* 2(10):e1121. doi:10.1371/journal.pone.0001121, October 2007.

Living jellyfish

One of the best examples of a 'living fossil' comes from rocks in Utah. This jellyfish is not only beautifully preserved, but, since very similar animals exist today, it is thought to have remained essentially unchanged from about 505 million years ago.[72] Half a billion years puts this into the middle of the Cambrian Era, when multicellular life was first evolving. Thus, this jellyfish has remained unchanged through the entire evolutionary history of multicellular life on earth, while one of its cousins went on to evolve into people! Can you see that, if evolution, on the one hand, claims to explain radical changes over time while, on the other hand, also claims to explain radical stasis over time, there is no evidence one can submit as a test of evolutionary theory? Truly, it is more philosophy than science.

Trace fossils

Traces of animal activity (foot prints, tail drags, nests, burrows, etc.) have been known from the fossil record for a long time. Known scientifically as *ichnites* (Greek for 'footprint') they have spawned a new branch of paleontology, called *ichnology*. Each of the different appearing tracks, nests, etc. was assigned a fancy Latin name within the binomial nomenclature system, even though the animals that made them were unknown. This created a great deal of duplication of species names. In the vast majority of cases, an ichnologic item, well named as it may be, has an unknown source, which means that on the same layer we can find a track of footprints belonging to an unknown creature, and also

70. Anderson, I., Pine 'dinosaur' lurks in gorge, *New Scientist* **1957**:5, 1994.
71. Catchpoole, D., 'Dino tree' project ends, 2 July 2009; creation.com/dino-tree-project-ends.
72. Cartwright, P. *et al.*, Exceptionally preserved jellyfishes from the Middle Cambrian, *PLoS One* **2**(10):e1121, 2007. See also Catchpoole, D., Exceptionally preserved jellyfishes, *Creation* **30**(4):21, 2008; creation.com/epjelly.

fossilized remains of a known creature that cannot be irrefutably linked to the track.[73] In other instances, later discoveries linked the trace to a known fossil. For example, tracks from the giant centipede, *Arthropleura* (mentioned above), were given the ichnotaxon name *Diplichnites cuithensis*.[74] That's a fancy name for a centipede footprint! Many other complicating elements can be added. For example, the fact that three-toed prints can be produced by bipedal theropod dinosaurs (carnivores) as well as bipedal herbivores, and birds.[75] This at least doubles the volume of paleontological information garnered from three-toed tracks, without necessarily making it more accurate or illuminating.

A puzzling feature is that the earliest dinosaur tracks are found in Early Triassic sediments (supposedly around 200 million years ago),[76] while the earliest dinosaur bones date from the Middle Triassic, some 20 million evolutionary years later. This, of course, is rather disturbing for the ruling dogma of gradualistic evolution, because it pushes the origins of dinosaurs into the Permian and makes them somehow able to survive the greatest extinction event in evolutionary history, the one that supposedly occurred at the Permian/Triassic boundary. Because of this, some paleontologists have chosen to reject the dating of the tracks (considering them synchronous with the first dinosaur remains), while some simply stretched dinosaur ancestry, introducing a new biological taxon, *Archosaurs*, from which dinosaurs allegedly evolved. *Archosaurs* are believed to have created tracks virtually undistinguishable from dinosaur tracks, and they present the handy characteristic of having no fossil remains and being able to accommodate any addition and subtraction of uncertain fossil forms.

In some cases, tracks of dinosaurs have been found on several consecutive layers, which is seen by many as a solid refutation of the global Flood described in Genesis. That of course depends on the flooding scenario with which one starts. A global flood generated by rapidly rising waters will have violent episodes as well as calm ones. It is reasonable to assume that after entire areas were covered with freshly deposited, unbound sediments, relative changes in sea level cause the sediments to emerge, allowing some dinosaurs to land.[77] Prolific creationist author Michael Oard has coined the term BEDS (Briefly Exposed

73. Lockley, M.G. *et al.*, *Dinosaur Lake: The story of the Purgatoire Valley Dinosaur Tracksite Area*, Colorado Geological Survey Special Publication **40**, Denver, CO, USA, p. 35, 1997.
74. Hunt, A. *et al.*, The giant *Arthropleura* trackway *Diplichnites Cuithensis* from the Cutler Group (Upper Pennsylvania) of New Mexico, *The Geological Society of America* 2004 Denver Annual Meeting; gsa.confex.com.
75. Lockley, M.G. and Meyer, C, *Dinosaur Tracks and Other Fossil Footprints of Europe*, Columbia University Press, New York,, 2000.
76. Lockley, M.G. *et al.*, *Dinosaur Lake: The story of the Purgatoire Valley Dinosaur Tracksite Area*, Colorado Geological Survey Special Publication **40**, Denver, CO, USA, pp. 67–69, 1997.
77. Oard, M.J., *Dinosaur Challenges and Mysteries*, Creation Book Publishers, Atlanta, GA, USA, pp. 113–128, 2011 (available through creation.com).

Diluvial Sediments) to explain the phenomenon.[78] This temporary emergence of sedimentary beds would result either in repeated ichnites or instant burial of the animal in thick, soft, water-laden sediments. A superimposed sequence of track-bearing sediments would later result. It is therefore most likely that nearly all ichnites worldwide were subject to rapid covering by wet sediments, in agreement with a global Flood.

Ape-like progenitors of man

Out of all the major sequences of Darwinian evolution, the evolution of man is the nearest to us in time and should, therefore, be backed by an abundance of fossils. It isn't. In fact we have many more dinosaur fossils to study than we have putative human ancestors. Even worse, most of the fossil evidence is in the form of teeth, not skeletons or even individual bones.

Over the last 50 years, the story of the evolution of *Homo sapiens* has changed drastically, from the classical tree diagram, to a tangled bush, then to an orchard. None of these visual representations offers a clear, even if fragmentary, descent (or, more appropriate to the evolutionist, 'ascent') of man. Every such representation abounds with uncertainties and many possible alternative evolutionary paths, and representations have shifted radically over the decades. We are left with the impression that any path from multiple candidates can be chosen, according to preference, since they all 'prove' that man evolved from "ape-like progenitors" as Darwin put it.[79] As in the case of *Deinonychus*, various interpretations of which have included both 'dinosaur' and 'bird', various fossils related to the alleged evolution of man have been going up and down the ladder to make room for new discoveries. And most new discoveries are, in fact, old samples kept in drawers for decades, only to be rediscovered by new researchers at a later date. Anthropology, more than most other areas of science, craves the limelight, which facilitates funding.

Ape-men of the past

Zinjanthropus boisei, a.k.a. Nutcracker Man, was once a very popular 'proof' that humans evolved from apes. Discovered in 1959 by the famous paleoanthropologist, Mary Leakey, it was heavily promoted by the evolutionary establishment for well over a decade, before being pushed off to the side. Renamed *Paranthropus*, it is now seen as a more distant relative and part of the australopithecine apes, that group of extinct, robust apes that includes the famous Lucy.[80]

---

78. Oard, M.J., Is the K/T the post-Flood boundary?—part 2: paleoclimates and fossils, *J. Creation* **24**(3):87–93, 2010; creation.com/kt-boundary-flood-2.
79. Darwin, C., *The Descent of Man, and Selection in Relation to Sex*, ed 1, John Murray, London, p. 86, 1871.
80. See Myth-making: The power of the image, *Creation* **21**(4):4, 1999; creation.com/myth-making. Also Grigg, R., Missing the mark: How a missionary family gave rise to the top name in 'apeman' research (Louis leakey)! *Creation* **26**(3):24–27, 2004; creation.com/leakey.

Ramapithecus was another popular and powerful example of the ape ancestor of humanity that has also been pushed off to the side. Based on skull fragments and teeth discovered in Nepal in the early 1930s, it was triumphantly portrayed as 'proof positive' of human evolution. Yet, following more recent finds in the 1970s, *Ramapithecus* has been renamed *Silvapithecus* and is now considered an extinct ape only, possibly the ancestor of orangutans.

Besides *Zinjanthropus* and *Ramapithecus*, we could list well over a dozen ape-like taxa that were once promoted as part of the human linage but are now relegated to the dust bin. Where, then, is the evidence?

Ape-men of the present

The australopithecines, including *A. afarensis*, *A. africanus*, *A. sediba*, are promoted heavily as the link between man and apes. However, distinguished evolutionary anatomist Charles Oxnard, recipient of the Charles R. Darwin award for physical anthropology, does not accept them as ancestral to people. When all their anatomical coordinates are compared with humans and modern apes, they fall further from both groups than these are from each other.[81]

Another important icon in the evolutionary line is *Homo habilis*. Although it is promoted as an ancestor, it is much more problematic. Many regard it as a phantom taxon into which a jumble of different fossil pieces belonging to different species has been placed. And what are we to think of *Homo erectus* and the many other ape-men claims? Space does not allow a full discussion of these, but the reader is encouraged to visit creation.com/anthropology for detailed articles on each of these fossil claims.

Neanderthal

Ever since *Neanderthal* man was discovered in 1829 in Belgium, 1848 in France, and 1856 in Germany (the type specimen) it was claimed to be an ancestor of modern humans. Then, after the discovery in 1998 of a hybrid 4-year old child skeleton at Lagar Velho in Portugal,[82] the possibility of *Homo sapiens* and *Homo neandertalensis* being the same species was raised by anatomists. The majority of geneticists strongly rejected such a possibility, based on their beliefs about the evolutionary history of the human genome. Further similar discoveries, like the one in Romania's Peştera cu Oase (The Cave with Bones)[83] did not change the geneticists' position.

---

81. Oxnard, C.E., The place of the australopithecines in human evolution: grounds for doubt? *Nature* **258**:389–395, 1975.
82. Duarte, C. *et al.*, The early Upper Paleolithic human skeleton from the Abrigo do Lagar Velho (Portugal) and modern human emergence in the Iberian Peninsula, *Proceedings of the National Academy of Sciences, USA* **96**(13):7604–7609, 1999.
83. Trinkaus, E. *et al.*, An early modern human from Pestera cu Oase, Romania, *The Proceedings of the National Academy of Sciences, USA* **100**:11231–11236, 2003.

However, starting in 2006, the Neanderthal Genome Project (NGP) brought more and more genetic evidence that indeed Neanderthals and humans interbred.[84] As these discoveries further complicate (to use a mild word) the much desired gradual transition of human ancestry, a flurry of articles contesting the validity of the NGP followed, which of course triggered responses and counter-responses. The anthropological establishment today is torn between various visions regarding the position of Neanderthals in the evolutionary sequence of hominids. This is based on the study of not only bone remains but also DNA. There is no genetic information, though, for alleged human ancestry predating the Neanderthals, and it seems the consensus has been to bring Neanderthals into the human family.[85]

As a general feature, all respectable charts of human origins present a list of individual discoveries by their stratigraphic position, most of them unconnected. If any connection is suggested, it is with dotted lines—a clear admission of uncertainty. The story changes drastically in the media, however, where the human family story is narrated in such detail it seems to almost match family details found in TV series family sagas!

Ape men that never were

The influence of Darwinian evolution on the public understanding of the origin of humanity cannot be understated, especially since it has fuelled various justifications for colonialism and racism of all sorts, as evolutionists themselves admitted.[86] Perhaps this is why hoaxes have stained the face of anthropology from its inception—the ape men that never were. The first major hoax was Piltdown Man (*Eoanthropus dawsoni*), presented with pomp at the Geological Society of London in 1912 as pieces of a recent human skull. Enthused scientists discovered more fragments and a jaw in the same gravel pit at Piltdown, close to the Darwin residence in England. The remains were considered by the elite of British scientists as the 'earliest Englishman':

> Piltdown also buttressed some all too familiar racial views among white Europeans. In the 1930s and 1940s, following the discovery of Peking man in strata approximately equal in age with the Piltdown gravels, phyletic trees based on Piltdown and affirming the antiquity of white supremacy began to appear in the literature ... If Piltdown, as the earliest Englishman, was the progenitor of white races, while other hues must trace their ancestry to *Homo erectus*, then whites crossed the threshold

84. Green, R.E. *et al.*, A draft sequence of the Neandertal genome, *Science* **328**:710–722, 2010; Than, K., Neanderthals, humans interbred—first solid DNA evidence, *National Geographic Daily News*, 6 May 2010; news.nationalgeographic.com.
85. Carter, R.W., Neandertal genome like ours (There may be Neandertals at your next family reunion!), 1 June 2010, creation.com/neandergenes.
86. See Chapter 8: Ethics and Morality.

to full humanity long before other people. As longer residents in this exalted state, whites must excel in the arts of civilization.[87]

In 1923, the German anatomist Frantz Weidenreich pointed out that the skull fragments were human but the jaw was of an orangutan with filed teeth! It took the scientific community 30 years after that to admit he was right.[88] That was the accepted science of the day, later proved wrong.

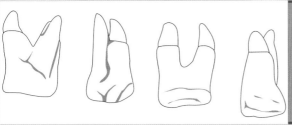

A drawing of the Nebraska-man tooth. From left to right; posterior, outer, anterior and inner perspectives.*

Smith, G.E., *Hesperopithecus*: the ape-man of the Western world, *The Illustrated London News*, p. 944, 24 June 1922.

William Jennings Bryan. The false identification of the Nebraska tooth was used by Osborn to attack Bryan's integrity.

Photo from wikipedia.org

Another infamous example involved a tooth discovered in Nebraska, in the US, described as belonging to *Hesperopithecus haroldcookii*, better known as Nebraska Man.[89] The discovery was part of the background behind the famous Scopes (Monkey) Trial in 1925. Although no actual evidence for evolution was presented at the trial, the scientist Henry Fairfield Osborn who described it in 1922 felt at liberty to mock the defender of the biblical position, William Jennings Bryan:

It has been suggested humorously that the animal should be named *Bryopithecus*, after the most distinguished Primate which the State of Nebraska has thus far produced [as a politician, Bryan's home district was in Nebraska]. It is certainly singular that this discovery is announced within six weeks of the day (March 5, 1922) that the author advised William Jennings Bryan to consult a certain passage in the Book of Job, "Speak to the earth and it shall teach thee," and it is a remarkable coincidence that the first earth to speak on this subject is the sandy earth of the Middle Pliocene Snake Creek deposits of western Nebraska.[90]

Two years after the trial, the respected journal *Science* acknowledged that the tooth (from which a whole human being was 'reconstructed') belonged in fact

---

87. Gould, S.J., *The Panda's Thumb*, Norton Press, New York, p. 117, 1980.
88. White, A.J., The Piltdown man fraud, 24 November 2003; creation.com/the-piltdown-man-fraud.
89. Sibley, A., A fresh look at Nebraska Man, *J. Creation* **22**(2):108–113, 2008; creation.com/nebraska2.
90. Osborn, H.F., The earth speaks to Bryan, *The Forum* **73**:796–803, 1925.

to an extinct peccary (a pig).[91] Again, the accepted science of the day used to mock biblical creation was later proved wrong. Yes, it is true that science is often self-correcting, but these two false examples did much to further evolution in the public mind.

In August 1972, *National Geographic* published a major article about the discovery of a Stone Age tribe (the Tasaday) in the jungles of Mindanao Island, Philippines. A famous documentary was produced by *National Geographic* which was screened in movie theatres around the world. In 1986 a Swiss journalist and anthropologist, Oswald Iten discovered the Tasaday were in fact an elaborate hoax. It was perpetrated by the former head of a government agency for the protection of cultural minorities, Manuel Elizalde,[92] who wanted to raise money to improve the life of the real Tasaday, which was not a Stone Age tribe, money which he eventually embezzled. It took 14 years to correct the lie. This is a minor example, but how many people were influenced to accept the evolutionary history of man in the meantime, thinking it was soundly based scientific fact?

In 2005, a huge scandal led to the forced retirement of Professor Rainer Prtosch von Zieten who fabricated and plagiarized data in order to show a link between humans and Neanderthals.[93] Although his 'discoveries' were accepted by the scientific community for nearly 30 years, when the scandal erupted, many anthropologists tried to save face, claiming they didn't really trust Protsch's research, even if in fact they referenced it. Again, that was the accepted science of the day (and a much more recent example of blatant bias in academia).

These are just a few of the many cases that could be cited. It makes us wonder why the need for so much fraud if the evolution of humans is certain?[94] The answer is obvious: fossils do not support the evolution of humans and apes from a common ancestor. It is this absence of evidence that forces frustrated anthropologists to explore every possible way to compensate for the lack of fossils. The frauds themselves are not an Achilles' heel for evolution, but they do highlight an interesting problem: all the data used *historically* to support human evolution has since been rejected. This rejection (happily) includes the fraudulent material but also the ape-men examples from the 19th and 20th centuries (as described earlier).

91. Gregory, W.K., *Hesperopithecus* apparently not an ape nor a man, *Science* **66**:579–581, 1927.
92. Iten, O., Die Tasaday: Ein Philippinischer Steinzeitschwindel, Neue Zurcher Zeitung, Zurich, pp. 77–89, 12 April 1986.
93. For example, see Harding, L., History of modern man unravels as German scholar is exposed as fraud, *The Guardian*, 18 February 2005; guardian.co.uk.
94. Bergman, J., Why the epidemic of fraud exists in science today, *J. Creation* **18**(3):104–109; creation.com/science-fraud-epidemic.

It is obvious that only a fraction of all the evidence presented as current science is fraudulent. However, the changing stories demonstrate that interpretations fluctuate, so we should be cautious when various facts are being touted as the 'evidence' for the evolutionary paradigm of the descent of man. It would be nice to think that modern geologists, paleontologists, and paleoanthropologists have become wiser before making their announcements. However, these folks are not blameless in their quest for evolutionary proselytizing, as demonstrated by the way they supported the media frenzy surrounding their announcements of Ida (a lemur and yet another example of a 'living fossil')[95] and Ardi (a fossil well known for more than a decade prior to its 'announcement'),[96] not to mention the hype surrounding old Lucy (an ape).

Why are no human fossils found buried with dinosaurs?

It has always been held as indisputable that the worldwide fossil record has a consistent vertical order that moves from simple to complex. Part of this mindset is that humans evolved about 60 million years *after* dinosaurs vanished from the earth. That, according to this view, is why dinosaur and human fossils are not found within the same geologic formations.

There is little doubt that a consistent fossil order is real, but the existence of offset fossils prevents such an order from being turned into a geologic and biologic axiom. Well, it should prevent it if logic and common sense were not trumped by ideology! There is, of course, another way to look at the order of the fossils which allows room for offset fossils: order of burial in a universal hydraulic catastrophe.

First, since rapid burial is the obvious fact of fossilization, marine creatures would have the highest chance to fossilize as a result of a global flood, especially bottom dwellers, particularly the sedentary ones. As mentioned before, a large percentage of the fossil record is represented by the shells of such creatures. In modern marine habitats, most bottom dwelling metazoans (multicellular animals) are simpler organisms, while most of the more complex creatures tend to live closer to the surface. While there are of course exceptions for both cases (simpler creatures floating on the surface [zooplankton] and mammals [sperm whales] diving very deep), in terms of sheer density of biota, bottom dwellers are predominantly simpler creatures (clams, corals, sea stars, sea squirts, etc.).

Second, some of the surface dwellers, especially marine mammals, would have survived the Flood, and the ones that were killed stood less chance to fossilize as they would decompose without being buried if they lived through the major

95. Batten, D., Ida: Darwin fossil hyper-hype, *Creation* 32(1):44–46; creation.com/ida.
96. Wieland, C., *Ardipithecus* again: a recycled ape-man, 5 Oct 2009, creation.com/ardipithecus-again.

sediment-depositing episodes. They would thus be present mostly in the upper sections of the fossil record, but exceptions (like the offset fossils presented above) are to be expected.

Third, the geographical distribution and size of the antediluvian human population would have played a major role in determining where and when and how many humans should be buried in the fossil record. Yet, we know little about the topography of the earth prior to the Flood, we do not know where humans lived (on the shore or far from the sea?), and we do not know how many people were alive when the Flood came. It seems the earth may have had a significant amount of low-lying, swampy terrain, as evidenced from the many plants and animals thought to have lived in that type of environment. In this case, people may have tended to live at higher elevations far from the sea, also far from the range of herbivorous dinosaurs, who would not fit in well with human agricultural pursuits. However, this is something we simply cannot know for certain.

Regarding the number of people alive when the Flood came, this is also impossible to know. Various estimates have ranged from a few hundred thousand to upwards of a billion. Being that human fossils are rare in or absent from most sedimentary layers, lower numbers are more likely. There were ten male generations and over 1,500 years from Adam to Noah. This gives ample room for a large human population, but the Bible also describes a world filled with violence (Genesis 6), so perhaps the population was not as large as it could have been without said violence.

Fourth, land mammals would have tended to flee to higher ground (depending on how fast the floodwaters came upon the land), and many of these (unlike things like clams and barnacles) can swim to varying degrees. Thus, they might be assumed to be among the last creatures to be overwhelmed by the waters, and one of the last creatures to be buried as the floodwaters were rising. After the floodwaters reached their peak, the water began to flow from the continents into the oceans, eroding the present landscape of the continents. This period of erosion has been well recognized by geologists, who have called it in some places the 'great denudation'. In places, miles of overlying sediment have been eroded away. Much of the remains of creatures buried late in the Flood would have been eroded away with the sediments in this time.

Fifth, the question can easily be turned around and it can become quite uncomfortable for the evolutionist. For example, we know that whales and coelacanths are living in the ocean today, but no whales have been found buried with coelacanth fossils. Actually, there are no coelacanth fossils in sediments younger that the supposed 65 million years between the time they disappear from the fossil record to today. Why do we not see them buried with *any* marine organism that lived sometime during all those years? The answer from the evolutionary community is telling: "The fossil record is spotty." But why, then, is it not okay for the biblical creationist to say, "The Flood did not perfectly record the world before the Flood?"

I am quite convinced though that if ever human skeletons will be found in say, dinosaur fossil-bearing layers, evolutionists will come up with some yet-to-be-determined explanation for such a problematic find.

Conclusions

Throughout this chapter I have looked at the fossil record with more than one paradigm in mind. While the interpretation based on evolutionary assumptions has enjoyed countless outlets, and man-hours of research and significant funding, the creationist diluvial interpretation has been marginalized for over two centuries. For the last half-century it has become a target for incessant, well-orchestrated and aggressive attacks. Given the absolute dominance of the evolutionary media, the general public is not usually presented with any real creationist argument, just alarm that creationists still exist. If arguments are mentioned, they are usually distorted and outdated, or in terms of logical fallacies, they are called 'straw man' arguments. On the very few occasions when a geologist who believes in a young earth and Noah's Flood is allowed a little spot in the media, they usually feel obliged to include an evolutionary geologist on the program to offer the opposite views. But the opposite does not seem to apply, that young-earth geologists have been asked to present their views to counter evolutionary geologists in the media.

There is still much for biblical geologists to research in the fossil record in order to understand the effects and progress of the global Flood. It has not been all worked out. This is a good thing, for it leaves ample work for future generations. It is also a fact that, unless biblical geologists have physical access to the important geological sites, such as those that define the 'golden spikes', they will be forced to reinterpret data collected by evolutionary geologists, which is laden with evolutionary interpretations. After Francis Bacon proposed in his *Novum Organum* (1620) that data should be collected without any bias and interpreted inductively, it became obvious that such an approach is unrealistic, for all 'data collectors' have earned the title by accumulating a bias, a.k.a. education! Reinterpretation through revisitation of the geological field sites is necessary, but it is a slower process.

In a metaphorical way, one may say that fossils are the letters geologists use to decipher the rocks in which they are found. Such a statement would be rejected by most modern geologists, yet it is their very 'bible' that reluctantly admits it:

> ... even today it is an article of faith for many Earth scientists that divisions of the developing international stratigraphic scale are defined by the fossil content of the rocks. To follow this through, however, leads to difficulties: boundaries may change with new fossil discoveries; boundaries defined by particular fossils will tend to be diachronous; there will be disagreement as to which taxa shall be definitive.[97]

In other words, the rocks continue to be defined by their fossil contents, even if that leads to difficulties. To the evolutionary geologist, the difficulties resulting from not using fossils to define them are simply a risk not worth taking because it opens wide the floodgates (literally!). It would allow many rock formations to be compressed into shorter time frames, by simple use of sedimentology. In fact the last decade has seen a major shift in the way sedimentation is interpreted:

> Second, we have to be aware of longer-term hiatuses in sedimentation and the fact that in most environments areas of non-deposition and erosion are both more widespread and persistent than those of net deposition ... . Even in the deep sea, where once we thought in terms of the unrelenting snowfall of pelagic sediments, we now recognize major breaks in deposition or even erosion.[98]

In other words, as rocks go, most of the geologic time is in the gaps between layers and, therefore, fossils are a most welcome 'time anchor' (and relief to the evolutionist). Without the fossils, the geologic column will be a dry, uninteresting list of rocks piled on top of rocks and here and there intruded by some other rocks.

So we conclude our brief discussion of out of place fossils, the lack of serious candidates for transitional forms, and the failure of evolutionary science to come up with examples of human ancestry from apes that can withstand the test of time. From this we can see the fossil record is as much an Achilles' heel of evolutionary theory today as it was in Darwin's time.

Where does this lead?

The first two chapters worked together and dealt with the centerpiece of Darwinism: natural selection, and its corollary, genetics. The third chapter, on the chemical and statistical constraints that apply to all origin-of-life models, worked hand-in-hand with this one on the fossil record. Not only is the origin of life from non-living matter conceptually difficult, and not only is it chemically and physically impossible, but its diversification through time is not reflected in the fossil record!

---

97. Gradstein, F.M. *et al.*, Chronostratigraphy: linking time and rock; in Gradstein, F.M., Ogg, J.G. and Smith, A.G. (eds), *A Geologic Time Scale 2004,* Cambridge University Press, p. 20, 2004.
98. Reading, H.G. and Levell, B.K., Controls of the sedimentary rock record; in Reading, H.G.(ed.), *Sedimentary Environments: Processes, Facies and Stratigraphy*, Blackwell Science, p. 18, 2002.

Even after that initial spark of life supposedly occurred, there is no record of the vast experiments that would have been required for life to have evolved to its current state. And, according to the first chapters on natural selection and genetics, there is also no mechanism in the physical world that could have led to the vast diversity and complexity of life on earth today.

The first two chapters dealt with what Darwin *thought* was true. The second two dealt with what Darwin *assumed* was true and thought future discoveries would prove. From here, we will look at what Darwin *needed* to be true, specifically long ages. From the fossil record, we move to a discussion on the rock record and whether or not it gives Darwinism the *time* he knew he needed.

Dr Tasman Walker

Ph.D. Mechanical Engineering,
University of Queensland, Australia

Dr Walker's experience centers on the coal industry, having worked extensively as an engineer with coal-fired power-generating plants, and the mines that supplied them, in Australia over several decades. Not content with his Ph.D., however, he went back to school for additional training and received a Bachelor of Science in Earth Science, with a focus on geology, including stratigraphy, petrology, paleontology, and geophysics. He then went on to obtain an Honors Degree (the US equivalent of a Masters) in that same field. Thus, Tas is no lightweight when it comes to evaluating the next Achilles' heel of Darwinian evolution, the geologic record.

See **creation.com/dr-tas-walker**

THE GEOLOGIC RECORD

Dr Tasman Walker, Ph.D. Engineering
[University of Queensland] | **5**

The fossil record vs. the geologic record

The term *geologic record* relates to the arrangement of the rocks on Earth through time, while the *fossil record* speaks of the way plants and organisms have been preserved within the rocks that contain those fossils. The rocks and strata connect to the idea of geological evolution, while the fossils are supposed to record biological evolution. The fossil record was dealt with in the last chapter, but here we will address the geologic record, yet another Achilles' heel for evolution.

The use of the term *record* here is convenient but misleading because it gives the impression that the rocks and fossils are ordered and can be read as a historical document to provide a valid *history*. It has given geological interpretations priority over ancient documents and affected the way human history is interpreted.

But rocks and fossils cannot be read like a book. The so-called 'histories' that are derived from this evidence are based upon preexisting assumptions that are brought to bear when interpreting the layers. It may come as a surprise to some, but the rocks are often described as ambiguous, because they can support multiple interpretations. Geologists are well aware of this, and many find it amusing to see their colleagues argue different scenarios about the past while observing the same rock outcrop. You may think that is a bit of a stretch, but keep reading.

Geology has long been considered the solid foundation for evolution. Indeed, Darwin, who was primarily a geologist early on, built his theory of biological evolution squarely on then-current theories of geology, especially the work of his contemporary, Charles Lyell. The so-called geologic record has given the historical sciences an earth 'history' of billions of years that allows unobservable biological evolution to seem plausible. Without eons of time, evolution would be dead in the water.

How can a scientist reject the long ages of secular geology?

After I completed my Ph.D. research in mechanical engineering, I became involved with geological issues professionally when I worked with the electricity industry in Queensland, Australia. Most of the power stations were fuelled by black coal and I helped manage this resource. As part of my duties I visited many coal mines in Queensland to inspect their operations and discuss the mining and coal-preparation processes.

After many years in industry, I undertook extended studies in geology, enrolling in a Bachelor of Science degree, specializing in earth science. That helped bring me up-to-date on a range of fields in earth science, including stratigraphy, petrology, paleontology, and geophysics. I also studied related subjects such as cell biology, evolution, zoology, botany, astronomy and geomorphology. After the bachelor's degree, I enrolled in an honors degree (the equivalent of a master's degree in the US) in earth science where I studied geochemistry and I applied geochemical techniques to a layered igneous intrusion near Brisbane.

During these years of training I realized that, contrary to popular belief, the eons of time provided by geology are not based upon discoveries that geologists make, but flow out of assumptions that were accepted within the discipline over 150 years ago. In Darwin's time, these assumptions seemed plausible, were culturally attractive, and did work in some situations (especially with the data then available). However, our geological understanding of the earth has increased a thousand fold and more since then. It is rapidly becoming apparent that uniformitarian assumptions do not match the geological observations.

A fundamental re-evaluation of historical geology is necessary. However, this is such a daunting task that the geological establishment has been unwilling to face the upheaval. The corporate responses of the various professional geological societies have been to censor discussion and issue policy statements meant to marginalize alternative views.[1] But, the evidence is accumulating and it is becoming clearer that there is a problem. It does not seem possible that geologists can avoid it forever.

First, let's see how geology arrived at this millions-of-years position, and some of the problematic evidence that has been accumulating.

A brief history of geology

These days, the idea that the earth is millions of years old is presented everywhere as an accepted fact. It has become, in a sense, part of our culture. Visit Natural Bridge in Virginia, USA, and the interpretive sign will say it is at least 500 million years old. Tour Peggy's Cove in Nova Scotia, Canada, and the signs will tell you that 800 million years ago the granite rocks were molten magma. I'm sure you have seen dozens of such signs in your travels. Where did that idea come from and how soundly based is it?

The founders of modern geology did not view the world like that. One of the first pioneers was Nicolaus Steno (1638–1686) whose *Prodromus* is still considered a geological classic. In this "introduction", as he called it, he formulates a number of the principles of stratigraphy, still taught today in geology courses and used by geologists in the field. He also solved a mystery of his time, the origin of certain solid objects found within rocks. These had long puzzled the ancients, some suggesting they were just "sports of nature" and others saying they grew from ocean spores trapped in cracks.

Natural Bridge, Virginia, USA

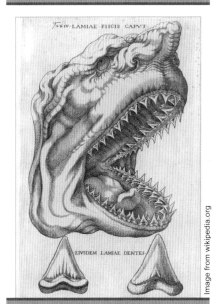

Image from wikipedia.org

The creationist geologist Nicolaus Steno showed that the mysterious things called "Glossopetra" were actually fossilized sharks teeth.

1. Walker, T., The Geological Society of Australia seeks to censor creation, intelligent design and Flood geology, 27 December 2008; creation.com/gsa-censor; Walker, T., The Geological Society of London uses bully tactics, 13 May 2008; creation.com/geological-society-bully.

Left to right: Nicolaus Steno, Isaac Newton and Johannes Kepler.

A few even suggested they were placed there by the gods to confuse mortals. Because of his training in anatomy, Steno recognized these as the remains of animals that were once alive. We call them fossils. He showed that the objects called *Glossopetra* in his day were actually sharks' teeth, and he attributed their burial to Noah's Flood.

Steno was the first person ever to have described the geological history of any area on the earth, and he did this for Tuscany, Italy where he lived at the time. He explained it within the framework of biblical history and particularly noted that the timeframe observed within the rocks was consistent with Scripture.[2]

Steno was not alone in using a biblical framework in his scientific studies. Sir Isaac Newton (1642–1727) and Johannes Kepler (1571–1630), famous for their discoveries about gravity and other things, considered the Bible reliable and they meticulously developed biblical chronologies. Likewise for Robert Hooke (1635–1703) and Lazzaro Moro (1687–1764), who published on earthquakes. Thomas Burnet (~1635–1715) and William Whiston (1667–1752) were two more pioneers of science who wrote volumes on theories of the earth and cosmogony. John Woodward (1665–1728) pioneered paleontology. These scientists all believed the Bible and used it as their interpretive framework.[3] Their writings made up the key books in the field, ones that researchers focusing on geology would have studied late into the 1700s and early 1800s. To these geological pioneers, the rocks did not demand a history extending for unimaginable eons of time. Rather they spoke of rapid catastrophism and were seen as consistent with the history of the Bible.

During the so-called *Enlightenment* period (starting in the 18th century), the mood in academic Europe changed. There was growing desire to dispense with the Bible as a source of knowledge and discover truth independently, from nature and reason alone. Part of this was in reaction to a misuse of the Bible and multiple claims for miraculous explanations in the Middle Ages, but it was also convenient for those with other agendas. The idea was that we should clear our minds of old beliefs, begin with a clean slate, and give new ideas a fair chance.

---

2. Walker, T., Geological pioneer Nicolaus Steno was a biblical creationist, *J. Creation* **22**(1):93–98, 2008; creation.com/steno.
3. Not surprisingly, they didn't agree with each other in all their interpretations of the rocks or the Scriptures. Nor would modern creationists agree with them on every point. But they were doing their scientific work within a Christian worldview.

The problem was that the Bible was simply thrown out without a proper evaluation. On the surface, a purely deductive approach seems reasonable. After all, if the Bible is true, should not deductive reasoning reveal evidence for things like Noah's Flood? What is often missed, however, is that it is impossible to separate theory, presupposition, and assumption from models of geological history. When the tide turned during the Enlightenment, this was conveniently swept under the rug.

One of the earliest to propose a new scheme was the Scottish physician, James Hutton (1726–1797), who published his *Theory of the Earth* in the late 1700s. Hutton's ideas were picked up and popularized by Charles Lyell (1797–1875) in his highly influential *Principles of Geology,* first published in 1830. Lyell was a trained lawyer and his book is a masterpiece of persuasion. His thesis, a restatement of Hutton's philosophy, is set forth in the subtitle of Volume 1: "Being an attempt to explain the former changes of the earth's surface with reference to causes now in operation."

Note that Lyell presented his case as "an attempt to explain". In other words, his primary aim was not so much about reporting observations and geological facts, but a way of explaining them—an interpretive framework.

That framework is about explaining what happened on the earth in the past (e.g. "the former changes"). Note how Lyell proposed to explain the past "… with reference to causes now in operation." In other words, he advocated we should only use what is happening geologically on the earth now. For example: frost and ice weathering the rocks, rivers transporting sediment across the landscape, oceans moving sediment along the shore, and earthquakes changing the level of the land. He argued that, given enough time, these present causes are entirely sufficient to explain all geological features, and that there is no need to resort to any great catastrophe.

This philosophy dismisses biblical history from consideration because the Bible describes two significant catastrophic events that we do not see happening today. No one alive today observed the global Flood; neither did anyone alive today witness the original Creation events. With a wave of the hand, Lyell dismissed these key events of biblical history, allowing them no place at the table of ideas. According to Lyell, we cannot use the biblical Flood as an explanation for anything, no matter what geological evidence we observe.

This concept has been called *uniformitarianism*. It's the idea that geological forces at work in the present day—barely noticeable to the human eye—are responsible for the immense geological features we observe on the earth. It has been encapsulated in the pithy phrase, "The present is the key to the past." It's obvious that for such an idea to work, enormous lengths of time would be required—hence the need for an earth of unimaginable age. In other words, the idea of billions of years is not an observation but a consequence of this belief.

Most geologists today prefer the term *actualism* over *uniformitarianism*. However, the two ideas are similar in that actualists accept the uniformitarian conclusion that the earth is billions of years old while allowing for catastrophes to have occurred periodically throughout this time. The word *actualism* gives the impression of something real and tangible, but it is a plastic philosophy not easily defined. Their acceptance of catastrophe means that most rocks present on the earth are now recognized to have been deposited quickly. Yet, by holding to an old earth they have a time problem—where to put the time if it is not within the rocks. This will be discussed below, especially in the section on flat gaps.

Often without knowing it, modern geologists owe their current old-age position to the lawyer turned uniformitarian geologist, Lyell. With this principle of seeming eternal continuity between present and past, Lyell gave geologists a technique by which they could invent their own 'history' solely from observing rocks in the *present*. He liberated geologists from the constraints of biblical history, based as it is on observations by eyewitnesses recorded in ancient documents and corroborated by independent lines of evidence. His philosophy has been a powerful force for over a century, but most of the public does not know that many secular geologists have moved on to a new form of catastrophism (actualism).

Lyell was clear about what he wanted to achieve, as he revealed to a colleague in his correspondence. He said his aim was "to free the science [of geology] from Moses".[4] Clearly his was not an unbiased approach, following the evidence wherever it leads. Rather, he was pursuing an agenda. And geologists jumped at the opportunity he provided and have been using this to explain rocks all around the world. For over one hundred years, Lyell's uniformitarianism (based, as it were, on other uniformitarians before him) has formed the fundamental philosophy of the earth sciences, and the great age of the earth was part of the deal.

A three-cord rope

Like a rope woven from three cords, Lyell's philosophy is composed of three main strands. The *first* is to dismiss the biblical account of earth history from consideration. The *second* is to believe that all geological features can be interpreted in terms of slow-and-gradual processes—no matter how unlikely or difficult that may seem. And the *third* makes much of geological features that seem to demand long periods of time to form.

4. Mortenson, T., *The Great Turning Point*, Master Books, Green Forest, AR, USA, pp. 225–226, 2004, citing Brooke, J., The natural theology of the geologists: some theological strata, in Jordanova, L. and Porter, R., *Images of the Earth*, British Society for the History of Science, Monograph 1, 1979, p. 45.

In the second half of the twentieth century, each of these cords began to unravel due to accumulating geologic evidence. It is now widely acknowledged that Lyell's approach is not supported by the geological evidence. Geologists are distancing themselves from the term 'uniformitarianism'. Truly, geology is an Achilles' heel of evolution.

We will consider these strands of the uniformitarian rope, in reverse order, looking first at some of the geological features that geologists have claimed take long periods of time to form.

Cord #1: Geological features do not demand millions of years

Although many geological features are widely believed to take millions of years to form, recent findings have shown this to be wrong. This belief has taken geologists down wandering paths and distracted researchers from understanding what is really happening. Here we will describe a few of the many examples that could be cited.

Fossils

Fossils are explained from a uniformitarian perspective as a product of the normal processes that we see happening today. The formation of a fish fossil is often depicted with the fish dying and sinking to the bottom of the ocean. There it is slowly covered by sediment that is gradually eroded from the continent and carried to the sea.

This popular view is widely presented in encyclopedias and text books. Yet geologists since Charles Darwin (1809–1882) have recognized that fossilization is rarely observed in the present. Animals that die are quickly scavenged and their remains are removed from the environment by natural processes. Beaches, lakes and waterways are rapidly cleared of dead and rotting carcasses. Thus, contrary to popular beliefs, uniformitarian geologists end up having to invoke abnormal and catastrophic processes to explain fossilization, describing it as a rare event and speaking of the "imperfection of the fossil record".

Indeed, the fossils we find on the earth do speak of unusual and catastrophic processes. And the fact that we find them on all the continents on earth signals the global nature of these processes. Here are a few examples.

Dinosaur National Monument: Visitors to the Douglass Quarry Dinosaur National Monument, Utah, USA, can see hundreds of dinosaur bones, large and extra large, exposed in the original rock formation that forms a viewing feature of the interpretive centre.[5] Under what conditions today and in what

---

5. Strand, H., Earl Douglass and Dinosaur National Monument, National Parks Service; bridgerlandaudubon. org, accessed 6 October 2011.

sort of an environment would the remains of so many large land animals be buried together within such a thick deposit of sediment? The visitor centre has a fanciful story of hundreds of dinosaurs dying in a drought and then being buried in an enormous flood. But the dinosaur graveyard points to watery catastrophe on a large scale and not to causes "now in operation".[6]

Queensland Plesiosaur: In Queensland, Australia, two decades ago, a farmer found a skull on his property, hundreds of kilometers from the ocean.[7] He contacted the Queensland Museum and, when palaeontologists were dispatched to investigate, it turned out to be a plesiosaur, a marine reptile, over 4 meters long. They excavated the fossil, which was lying on its back. Amazed at its excellent preservation, they concluded that it must have been buried in sediment in a large local catastrophe. The fossil is now on display at the museum in Brisbane, and almost all the bones of the creature, even those in its flippers, are preserved. To completely bury such a large animal so quickly, the 'catastrophe' would have had to be quite large, meaning it would not have been just a local affair.

Photo supplied by Cathy Mobbs

Paleontologists Mary Wade and Cathy Mobbs excavating the Richmond plesiosaur.

Dead Dinosaur Posture: Many dinosaur fossils, and even other animals such as birds, exhibit a characteristic *dead dinosaur posture*.[8] The back and neck of the animal are arched, the head tilted, the tail curved and the feet pointed outwards. Why so many fossils exhibit this posture has troubled palaeontologists for more than a century.

Recently, Marshall Faux and her palaeontologist colleague Kevin Padian of the University of California have claimed that there's only one possible explanation: death throes. She and other vets affirm that animals go into the "opisthotonic posture" shortly *before* they die (not after) because of muscle spasms resulting from severe malfunction of the central nervous system. In short, it's due to a shortage of oxygen after being buried alive. A more recent paper claims the characteristic arching of the

Image from wikipedia.org

6. O'Brien, J., Dinosaur disarray, *Creation* **34**(2):28–31, 2012; creation.com/dinosaur-disarray.
7. Walker, T., Deluge disaster, *Creation* **26**(3):28–31, 2004; creation.com/deluge-disaster.
8. Catchpoole, D., Death Throes, *Creation* **31**(3):42–44, June 2009; creation.com/death-throes.

neck, back and tail is not opisthotonis but because of tension on a tendon (the *ligamentum elasticum*) that runs down the spine. The reason the animals are arched is due to the fact that they drowned. The tendon that supports the weight of the neck and tail on land causes curving when buoyed by water.[9] Either explanation, opisthotinos or buoyancy, give us dramatic evidence for watery catastrophe, for thousands of dinosaurs (and many birds) have been fossilized in this position.

Fossil Jellyfish: In keeping with the mindset of uniformitarianism, Charles Darwin did not expect that soft-bodied animals would be fossilized. He is famously quoted as saying, "No organism wholly soft can be preserved," in Chapter IX of the *Origin of Species*. This explains the derision and disbelief of a scientific conference when, in 1946, geologist Dr Reg Sprigg presented a find of jellyfish fossils from the Ediacara Hills, South Australia. He was so angry at the way his colleagues derided his find that he went back to the spot, collected 300 more and returned to Adelaide and showed them.[10]

More recently, paleontologist James Hagadorn and colleagues reported jellyfish fossils from rocks in Wisconsin, USA, classified as upper Cambrian, which they described as stranded on an ancient shoreline.[11] Another recent find was from Utah, USA, where geologists found three different types of jellyfish, all with exquisite preservation, supposedly from half a billion years ago.[12] The problem with their assigned age is that each has a relative alive today almost indistinguishable from its fossil form—no change over the entire evolutionary course of multicellular life on earth?

The preservation of fossils of soft-bodied creatures is a huge problem for all uniformitarian views.

Dinosaur Herd, Inner Mongolia: In 2009, scientists reported a herd of dinosaurs buried and fossilized in western Inner Mongolia.[13] More than 25 dinosaurs were excavated within the same layer of mudstone, generally facing the same direction and remarkably well preserved.[14]

9. Reisdorf, A.G. and Wuttke, M., Re-evaluating Moodie's opisthotonic-posture hypothesis in fossil vertebrates Part I: Reptiles—the taphonomy of the bipedal dinosaurs *Compsognathus longipes* and *Juravenator starki* from the Solnhofen Archipelago (Jurassic, Germany), *Palaeobiodiversity and Palaeoenvironments* **92**:119–168, 2012. See also creation.com/featherless.

10. Fossil jellyfish greeted with derision, *Creation* **12**(4):21, 1990; creation.com/jelly-fossils.

11. Hagadorn, J.W., Dott, R.H., and Damrow, D., Stranded on a Late Cambrian shoreline, *Geology* **30**(2):147–150, 2002; see Catchpoole, D., Hundreds of jellyfish fossils! *Creation* **25**(4):32–33, 2003; creation.com/jellyfossils.

12. Cartwright, P. *et al.*, Exceptionally preserved jellyfishes from the Middle Cambrian, *PLoS One* **2**(10):e1121, 2007.

13. Young dinosaurs roamed together, died together, *Eurekalert*, 16 March 2009; eurekalert.org.

14. Varricchio, D.J. *et al.*, Mud-trapped herd captures evidence of distinctive dinosaur sociality, *Acta Palaeontol. Pol.* **53**(4):567–578, 2008.

Most of the dinosaurs were in a crouching posture and, even more surprisingly, their limbs were plunging down into the underlying mud. Their hind legs were often still bent indicating that they were struggling to escape. Two of the skeletons were found one over the other where they apparently fell.

The thick layer of mud in which the animals were trapped was still soft when the animals disturbed it. There was an absence of bioturbation (such as burrowing by worms or crustaceans) in the mud, indicating it had been only recently deposited when the animals became mired. Also, the overlying sediments were deposited soon after the animals were trapped, burying the animals before their soft parts had a chance to rot away.

So promptly were the animals buried that the delicate bones in the eye (sclerotic rings) of some were preserved. The team interpreted the site as a "catastrophic miring of an immature herd"[15] and indeed it is.

Does not explain or predict: The fossils being recovered from around the world are providing a growing body of evidence that uniformitarianism does not work. The philosophy popularized more than 150 years ago, does not predict or explain much about fossils discovered since that time.

Finely laminated sediments

Thinking in terms of slow-and-gradual processes, geologists have automatically assumed strata with finely laminated sediments took long periods of time to form. The layers are routinely called varves and supposedly record time, with each pair of layers representing a year of sedimentation, similar to the way tree rings can indicate annual growth with the alternation of light and dark bands. Since there are hundreds of thousands of layers (some even quote millions) in some deposits, they supposedly confirm the vast age for the earth.

However, this idea was dealt a blow with the eruption of Mount St Helens in Washington State, USA, in 1980. That eruption deposited eight meters (25 feet) of finely layered sediment in a single afternoon! In other words, fine layers do not automatically mean long periods of time.

Laboratory tests have confirmed these results. Guy Berthault and other researchers studied sedimentation in a laboratory flume using different sized sand particles. They demonstrated that a mixture of grains deposited from moving water automatically sorts into thin layers according to the nature of the particles, such as the size of the grains.[16] They observed that the layers would build sideways beneath the moving water, like sand dunes in a desert wind,

15. Varricchio et al., ref. 14, p. 570.
16. Snelling, A., Sedimentation experiments: *Nature* finally catches up! *J. Creation* **11**(2):125–126, 1997; creation.com/sednature.

and that many layers would form at the same time, all growing sideways in the direction of the water flow.

So, contrary to the long-age assumptions, finely layered rock does not need long periods of time to form but can form very rapidly.

Diamonds

Diamonds are a form of carbon where the atoms are arranged in a tight 3D lattice, creating a hard mineral. It is popularly believed that diamonds take millions of years to form deep within the earth.

However, there is a commercial company called LifeGem that can turn carbon into diamond within a few months. They can use carbon from the remains of your pet, or from the hair of your

Photo: chomikuj.pl/kariba

loved one. Their advertising has said, "A diamond that takes millions of years to occur naturally can now be created from the carbon of your loved one in about twenty-four weeks."

An even faster method of producing diamonds has been developed by a company in Florida called Gemesis, founded in 1996. A carbon *seed* is placed within a thick, multi-walled steel container and subject to a process that includes high temperature and pressure. After four days the new diamond has grown and is removed from the chamber. Currently, Gemesis can produce up to 40 artificial diamonds a day.

Clearly these new technologies developed to manufacture diamonds prove experimentally that diamonds do not *need* millions of years to form. And diamonds point to catastrophe in another way—how they were emplaced in the earth. Some geologists now envisage that natural diamonds were blasted into place within seconds, when volcanic explosions created enormous, carrot-shaped 'pipes' called kimberlites.

Opals

Opals are attractive gems with beautiful, iridescent colors, ranging from white to pink, turquoise, blue and black. Opal is a form of silica that has absorbed extra water molecules into its structure, forming arrays of microscopic spheres that break the light into a spectrum of glorious colours.

The popular belief is that opals take millions of years to form. However, Len Cram, who prospects for opals in Lightning Ridge, South Australia, has long known how to produce opals artificially. In his make-shift bush laboratory, he places some sediment from the area into a jar and adds various liquids that he has developed. The distinctive colouring of opal appears within the sediment after a few weeks, although it still needs time to harden.[17]

A number of other processes for creating artificial opals have been developed commercially and details of these can be found on the internet.

The idea that opals form rapidly is going mainstream. A report on opal formation by the Geological Survey of New South Wales said:

> The time taken for the formation of opal is therefore probably of the order of weeks to months and not the hundreds of thousands of years required by the conventional weathering model.[18]

It was the long-age *geological* beliefs that fostered the idea of "hundreds of thousands of years". However, it is now realized that the evidence points to "weeks to months" instead.

Stalactites and stalagmites

Caves, often adorned with stalactites and stalagmites that form picturesque spires, columns and shawls, are popular tourist destinations. Almost without exception, the tour guides describe the cave decoration as forming over hundreds of thousands, even millions of years. The same story is told in geology textbooks, which also report that radioactive dating has measured these immense ages precisely.

Sometimes a humorous situation will arise during a cave tour as the guide is explaining the great age of the stalactites. A tourist may notice fresh growths on a hand rail, light fitting or discarded drink can.

Photos by Gary Livesay

17. Snelling, A.A., Creating opals: Opals in months—not millions of years! *Creation* **17**(1):14–17, 1994; creation.com/creating-opals.
18. Watkins, J.J., Behr, H.J., and Behr, K., Fossil microbes in opal from Lightning Ridge—implications for the formation of opal, *Quarterly Notes* **136**, Geological Survey of New South Wales, June 2011.

When Gary Livesay and his family visited the deserted Mollie Kathleen Gold Mine in Colorado, USA, they found stalactites and stalagmites growing from the ceiling, floor, and walls.[19] The fine 'straws' were hollow inside and dominated many parts of the mine, many having grown all the way from the roof to the floor.

An old wooden chair had stalagmites sitting on it. A small stalagmite was even growing up from a discarded explosives container. In places, the columns were profuse, like bars in a jail or pipes on an organ. Some were up to 2.7 meters (9 feet) tall and 10–12 centimeters (4–5 inches) in diameter.

At most, this cave decoration had only been growing for twenty years, since mining operations ceased and the airflow to the tunnels was shut off. Some formations were only five or ten years old. While still relatively small, they will not need vast amounts of time to reach appreciable size.

The formations in the Mollie Kathleen Mine are just one of scores of examples that prove stalactites and stalagmites do not need hundreds of thousands of years to form as commonly believed. We cannot know the growth rates for most of the world's cave formations, but we do know that many formations have grown relatively quickly. Thus, the only reason tourist placards at cave entrances say anything about vast periods of time is because the authorities who create the signs are predisposed to slow and gradual explanations.

Mudstone

For more than a hundred years, geoscientists have *assumed* that long periods of quiet water conditions are required for the deposition of mud. However, new research documents how mud can deposit from rapidly flowing water.[20]

Using specially designed laboratory equipment, Juergen Schieber and colleagues have shown that fine particles from muddy water will deposit under much higher current velocities than previously thought.

19. Livesay, G., Mollie Kathleen's marvellous mysteries, *Creation* **23**(3):44–46, 2001; creation.com/mollie-kathleens-marvellous-mysteries.
20. Schieber, J., Southard, J., and Thaisen, K., Accretion of mudstone beds from migrating floccule ripples, *Science* **318**(5857):1760–1763, 2007.

They used extremely fine kaolinite clay (80% finer than 0.005 mm), as well as calcium montmorillonite and natural lake muds. According to conventional geological wisdom, clay material should not settle from rapidly moving water. However, after only a short time the mud was moving along the bottom of the flume. According to Schieber, "They accumulated at flow velocities that are much higher than what anyone would have expected."[21]

Macquaker and Bohacs said of this research:

> The results call for critical reappraisal of all mudstones previously interpreted as having been continuously deposited under still waters. Such rocks are widely used to infer past climates, ocean conditions and orbital variations.[22]

These mud experiments overturn long-held geological beliefs and challenge all previous interpretations of mudstone deposits.

A waterwheel showing remarkable concretions have formed in little more than 60 years.

Petrification

Another long-held belief in long geological ages is the idea that fossils and rocks take millions of years to petrify. However, research at a hot spring in Japan is another one of many examples that show how wood can turn into stone faster than previously thought.

Scientists led by Hisatada Akahane studied a small lake in central Japan where a mineral-rich solution gushes from the bottom and cascades over the edge.[23] The scientists found the naturally fallen wood in the overflow, less than 36 years old, was hard and heavy because it was petrified.

As an experiment, they wired pieces of fresh wood in the lake. After seven years the wood had turned into stone, petrified with silica. Under a powerful

Petrified teddy bear

21. As waters clear, scientists seek to end a muddy debate, December 13, 2007; phys.org.
22. Macquaker, J.H.S. and Bohacs, K.M., On the accumulation of mud, *Science* **318**(5857):1734–1735, p. 1735, 2007.
23. Akahane, H. *et al.*, Rapid wood silicification in hot spring water: an explanation of silicification of wood during the earth's history. *Sedimentary Geology* **169**(3–4):219–228, 15 July 2004.

Petrified roll of fencing wire

A longitudinal cut surface, clearly showing the lengths of wire. Photo inset: the surface of where the specimen fractured, showing the circular cross-sections of the wire.

Photos by Steve Cardno

microscope, they saw that the silica had deposited to fill the pore spaces in the wood and cover the cell walls.

Their study confirmed that, under suitable conditions, wood can turn to stone in 10 years or less. There are many other examples of rapid petrification from contemporary sources.[24] They prove that the millions of years still taught in standard geology books are not needed to explain petrified fossil remains.

Coal formation

It is widely thought that it takes millions of years for vegetation to change into coal, but this is not so. It can be transformed in just 1–9 months using simple ingredients. Put some wood in a strong sealed container with water and a catalyst (such as clay). Heat it to 150°C to get brown coal.[25] Turn up the temperature for black coal. It just takes heat and pressure. Vast amounts of time are not a prerequisite.

Sandstone

Sandstone is a sedimentary rock composed of grains held together with a cementing agent. The grains may be fragments of other rock, or minerals such as silica or calcite. People imagine that it needs a long time to form, but under the right conditions, this rock can also be formed rapidly.

For one couple, their long-age belief was dispelled by a walk along the beach. On the shore at Victoria Point, near Brisbane, Australia, Chris and Sandra Barnes noticed a rock that looked like an ordinary lump of rounded sandstone. But when they kicked it over, they were amazed to discover that a toy

24. creation.com/geology#petrify
25. Hayatsu, R., McBeth, R.L, Scott, R.G., Botto, R.E., and Winans, R.E., Artificial coalification study: Preparation and characterization of synthetic mecerals, *Organic Geochemistry* **6**:463–471, 1984.

car was encased inside. The sand had been cemented around the car on the beach. The rock could only have been ten or twenty years old, but most would think it looked much older because of pre-held beliefs that such things take long periods of time.[26]

When natural rock at construction sites is poorly cemented, engineers find that building foundations subside and embankments collapse. To address this problem some Australian scientists developed a new chemical process that transforms loose sediment into rock within days.[27] Solutions sprayed onto the porous sand seep into the material and form calcite crystals on each grain. The calcite cements the grains together creating rock-hard strength.

The speed of the reaction can be controlled to take from one to seven days. This research dramatically demonstrates that rocks do not need millions of years to form.

Of course very large sedimentary deposits would require lots of cementing chemicals to percolate through the mass in order to solidify it. This is interpreted as taking very long periods of time. However, slow percolation might be expected to lead to uneven hardening as the leading edge received more of the active solution. It is still an open area of debate and experimentation, but quickly laying down sediments with a mineral-rich solution already filling the pore spaces is a recipe for rapid solidification. This is a better explanation for uniform hardening than some uniformitarian models. Thus, even thick rock layers are not the challenge for rapid petrification they are thought to be.

The first cord is unraveling

Geological features do not demand millions of years. This cord of the uniformitarian rope is unraveling. When the icons of long ages are examined in detail—fossils, diamonds, opals and the like—it turns out that they do not need long ages to form. Under suitable conditions they can form very rapidly indeed. Thus, they do not provide a reason in themselves to dismiss the biblical account of a recent creation.

Cord #2: Slow-and-gradual interpretations do not work

We now come to the second strand of the uniformitarian rope: Lyell's claim that causes, or processes, now in operation would be sufficient to explain *all* geologic evidence. However, geological exploration is revealing a picture of

26. Walker, T., Toy car rocks million-year belief, *Creation* **29**(4):49, 2007; creation.com/toy-car-rocks-million-year-belief.
27. Kucharski, E., Price, G., Li, H., and Joer, H.A., Laboratory evaluation of CIPS cemented calcareous and silica sands, *Proceedings of the 7th Australia New Zealand Conference on Geomechanics,* South Australia, pp. 102–107, 1996; Kucharski, E., Price, G., Li, H., and Joer, H.A., Engineering properties of sands cemented using the calcite in situ precipitation system (CIPS), *Exploration and Mining Research News* **7**:12–14, January 1997.

massive catastrophism on all continents, as we will see. As this picture emerges, geologists are losing faith in uniformitarianism and are working to find an alternative interpretive philosophy. We will look at a few examples of evidence that have led geologists to accept catastrophic interpretations.

Coal deposits

Vast deposits of coal are found on all continents and provide energy for our modern lifestyle. Geologists say that coal formed in a swamp over millions of years.

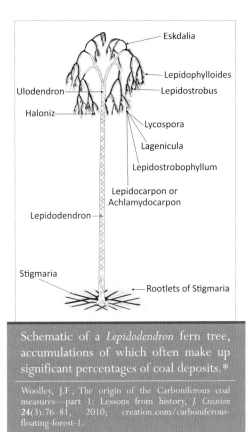

The characteristics of the coal vary from deposit to deposit and from mine to mine. However, it is not uncommon to find the remains of trees, leaves, shells and even fish in the seams. Coal measures often have coalified vegetation with delicate, fern-like leaves and leaf-scarred trunks with a scaly appearance such as *Calamites* and *Lepidodendron*.

In places, the trees and brush are heaped up as if they were dumped beside a flooding river. In other places large tree trunks are found 20 or 30 meters long. Usually coal seams are sandwiched between layers of sediment, including sandstone, laid down by flowing water.

Schematic of a *Lepidodendron* fern tree, accumulations of which often make up significant percentages of coal deposits.*

Woolley, J.F., The origin of the Carboniferous coal measures—part 1: Lessons from history, *J. Creation* 24(3):76–81, 2010; creation.com/carboniferous-floating-forest-1.

When the coal is cut from the seam, methane gas usually hisses from the fresh coal face, suggesting the coal is not hundreds of millions of years old as claimed. In such a long time we would expect gas under pressure would long ago have leaked away.

When geologists say coal forms in a swamp, they will often describe the environment as a vast, featureless coastal swamp extending for hundreds of miles and barely rising above sea level. Why a swamp? That idea comes directly from Lyell's uniformitarian philosophy. When considering "causes now in operation", a swamp is the only way that geologists can imagine lots of vegetation could accumulate in one place. Normally, vegetation disintegrates, even in a rainforest. The idea is that the slightly acidic, oxygen-free swamp water would prevent the vegetation from decaying.

Geologists won't say the vegetation *washed* into place, because that would require a flood of biblical proportions, which is far too catastrophic. So, unable to appeal to a large flood, they are only left with a large swamp. However, we have no modern examples of coal forming in any of the many swamps across the world, even though we know it can form quickly. Thus, the model lacks contemporary examples.

Not only that, but there are huge problems with the swamp explanation. For it to work, the swamp has to be just above sea level—too low and it would drown; too high and it would dry out. It has to cover the whole area, hundreds of miles across. It has to sink gradually, over hundreds of thousands of years, at *exactly* the same rate that the vegetation accumulated. And it has to stay level all that time—no tilting or folding.

Other problems with the swamp idea include:

- There is usually no soil *under* coal layers, as would be expected if the vegetation grew in place.[28]

- Strata above and below coal seams usually show evidence of being deposited by flowing water, such as sandstone deposits with cross-bedding in the strata.

- Thin clay bands run through most coal, often extending for miles. Fine clay would not deposit in such extensive thin layers in a swamp. Even if fine, thin layers were present, burrowing organisms, plant growth, and water movement would destroy the structure.

- Fossils immediately above and below coal layers are often well preserved, indicating rapid burial.

- There are sharp contacts between coal layers and the sand/silt above and below. The structure with a swamp, or with soils, would be blurred and indistinct.

- Broken fossil trees are occasionally found in a vertical orientation above, below, and sometimes *through* a coal layer, pointing to rapid burial of the layers and not gradual or slow accumulation.

Coal deposits have long been a problem for the uniformitarian philosophy, adverse as it is to large watery catastrophes. And the efforts expended to develop plausible explanations over the years since Lyell have not solved the problem.

---

28. Wieland, C., Forests that grew on water, *Creation* **18**(1):20–24, 1995; creation.com/forest, shows that fossil 'roots', called stigmaria, are not *in situ*.

Polystrate fossils

Derek Ager (1923–1993), for many years professor of geology at the University College of Swansea, Wales, was trained under Lyellian uniformitarianism and aware that geological catastrophes were not welcome. However, over the course of his working life he came to see that uniformitarianism did not work.

Ager wrote two books advocating a return to catastrophism.[29] In *The New Catastrophism*, he presents an example of two fossil tree trunks 10 meters high, crossing through coal measures in Swansea, Wales. Trees cutting across many strata like this are common and have been called polystrate fossils. Examples are found in Nova Scotia, at Joggins, in Australia, at a place also named Swansea, and many other locations. Ager recognized that these trees were not gradually buried over many thousands or hundreds of thousands of years because the top exposed part would have rotted away before it could be protected by sediment. They point to rapid burial. Commenting on this, Ager says:

An old print showing fossil trees that appear to be in growth position at Nant Llech in the Swansea Valley, South Wales, UK. The trees are now preserved outside Swansea Museum.*

Ager, ref. 30, Fig 4.5, p. 48.

Photo by Ian Juby

If one estimates the total thickness of the British Coal Measures as about 1000 m, laid down in about 10 million years, then, assuming a constant rate of sedimentation, it would have taken 100,000 years to bury a tree 10 m high, which is ridiculous. Alternatively, if a 10 m tree were buried in 10 years, that would mean 1000 km in a million years or 10,000 km in 10 million years (i.e. the duration of the coal measures). This is equally ridiculous and we cannot escape the conclusion that sedimentation was at times very rapid indeed and at other times there were long breaks in sedimentation, though it looks both uniform and continuous."[30]

29. Ager, D.V., *The Nature of the Stratigraphical Record*, Macmillan, London, p. 46–47, 1987; Ager, D.V., *The New Catastrophism*, Cambridge University Press, p. 49, 1993.
30. Ager, D.V., *The New Catastrophism*, Cambridge University Press, p. 49, 1993.

In spite of his training, Ager could see that the geological evidence pointed to rapid sedimentation. It's interesting to follow his argument. He recognized that sedimentation *looked* 'uniform and continuous', but he assumed that there had to be 'long breaks'. Why? It was to preserve the idea of millions of years—in spite of the evidence. Although Ager recognized that uniformitarianism does not work and was prepared to advocate rapid geologic processes, he was not prepared to abandon the idea of millions of years necessary for the General Theory of Evolution. Modern geologists have widely embraced Ager's new catastrophism, a philosophy that is sometimes linked with Actualism, but they are still to come to grips with the fact that it is an *ad hoc* philosophical position contrary to the evidence.

Vast sedimentary blankets on the continents

Another remarkable feature of the geologic record is the blankets of sediment that cover immense areas of the continents. These provide evidence for vast continental flooding in the past. In fact, when considering the effects of Noah's Flood, it should be noted that one major prediction would be that the rapidly rising muddy water should leave behind vast extents of mostly flat layers across large continental areas, and this is exactly what we find.

Ager in *The Nature of the Stratigraphical Record*[31] marveled at the way sedimentary layers, thin compared with the area they cover, persisted across continents for thousands of kilometers.

He mentioned the chalk beds that form the famous White Cliffs of Dover in Southern England and explained that they are also found in Antrim (Northern Ireland), and can be traced into northern France, northern Germany, southern Scandinavia, then to Poland and Bulgaria, and eventually to Turkey and Egypt. He described many other cases, yet even after that he said, "There are even more examples of very thin units that persist over fantastically large areas ...".

Various vantage points on Earth provide glimpses of these blankets. One is on the rim of Grand Canyon in western USA, where you can peer across the abyss and see the horizontal rock layers in the walls. It has the same pattern on both sides of the canyon. With so little vegetation in the area, the layers stand out and can be traced into the distant haze. In fact, these sedimentary formations have been recognized over thousands of kilometers across North America, both east-west and north-south.[32]

For another example, Echo Point west of Sydney, Australia, provides visitors with a panoramic view of The Three Sisters—remains of a sandstone outcrop,

31. Ager, D., *The Nature of the Stratigraphical Record*, MacMillan, pp. 1–13, 1973.
32. Sloss, L.L.(ed.), *The Geology of North America, Vol. D-2, Sedimentary Cover—North American Craton: U.S.*, The Geological Society of America, ch. 3, pp. 47–51, 1988.

teetering on the edge of a wide valley. In the distance you can see the same sedimentary strata in vertical cliffs that stretch as far as the eye can see. These sedimentary layers also travel out-of-sight under the earth—100 km east to the Pacific Ocean, 200 km north and 200 km south.[33] They form part of the Sydney basin, a geological structure where layers of sediments accumulated more than 3 km deep.[34]

The Three Sisters, near Sydney, Australia, provides powerful testimony for the Flood.

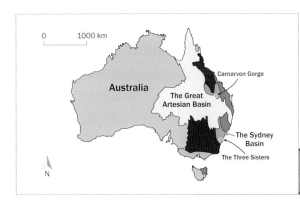

The major geologic features of eastern Australia.

Even more extensive is the Great Artesian Basin, which covers most of Eastern Australia. Its individual strata run continuously for thousands of kilometers.[35]

One formation within this basin is the Hutton Sandstone, a rock layer that is easily-recognized. It is buried 2 km deep in the middle of the basin but exposed at the surface at the edges, at places like Carnarvon Gorge in Queensland.

A curious feature of these sedimentary blankets is that they contain evidence of rapid and energetic deposition. Geologists describe various strata as deposited in a "fluvial environment" or a "high energy braided stream system".[36] This is just another way of describing large volumes of fast-flowing, sediment-laden water that covered a very large area.

Layers of sediment covering huge areas of the continents and stacked up like pancakes point to something unusual happening in the past. They are

33. Jones, D.C. and Clark, N.R., *Geology of the Penrith 1:100,000 sheet 9030*, NSW Geological Survey, Sydney, p. 3, 1991.
34. Branagan, D.F and Packham, G.H., *Field Geology of New South Wales*, Department of Mineral Resources, Sydney, p. 38, 2000.
35. *Assessment of Groundwater Resources in the Broken Hill Region*, Geoscience Australia, Professional Opinion 2008/05, ch. 6, 2008; www.environment.gov.au.
36. Day, R.W. *et al.*, *Queensland Geology: A Companion Volume*, Geological Survey of Queensland, Brisbane, pp. 127–128, 1983.

a contradiction of Lyell's philosophy, where causes now in operation are considered adequate to explain the past. We don't see blankets of sediments deposited across vast areas of the continents today. If they were it would be difficult for humans to survive. Rather, sedimentation is localized, confined to the deltas of rivers, lake beds, and along the narrow strips of coastline (when they are generally not eroding). Sedimentary blankets point to a watery catastrophe that affected all the continents, something that Lyell was wanting to ignore.

Flat gaps

This image shows the contact of two of the geological formations visible in the Grand Canyon—the light coloured Coconino Sandstone on the top and the dark coloured Hermit Shale underneath. Notice that the contact between the two formations is remarkably straight and flat, yet there is supposed to be a 12 million year time gap between the two.

This is an example of a *flat gap*. The sedimentary layers above and below the 'gap' are parallel, but layers of sediment supposedly representing many millions of years are absent. Flat gaps can persist for great geographical distances.

In all the time that is supposed to be indicated by the gap there should have been a great amount of erosion that removed a great depth of sediment. In fact, most geologists today would tell you that it took less than 12 million years to carve the entire Grand Canyon (although some advocate a longer time). Today, erosion carves canyons and gorges, creating an uneven land surface. But the contacts at the flat gaps are remarkably flat.

Flat gaps are common around the world and are very difficult to explain by processes we observe today. Just within the layers exposed at Grand Canyon, there are multiple flat gaps, with age gaps, based on evolutionary beliefs, ranging from 10 to 100 million years. Most people don't realize that, when looking at the rock record, most of the time for the evolutionist is in the gaps. Yet, when they look at the gaps, there is usually no evidence of time! Flat gaps severely conflict with the million-year timeframe proposed by geologists for the slow deposition of the strata. Rather, they suggest that the sedimentary layers formed rapidly as would be expected by catastrophic watery deposition.

Thick sandstone formations

When uniformitarian geologists encountered the Coconino Sandstone, visible as a 20-meter-thick layer below the rim of Grand Canyon, they assumed the enormous volume of quartz sand had been deposited in a windy desert. They described the large cross-beds (i.e. the enormous wave patterns in the sand) as desert sand dunes.

They opted for a desert interpretation, because to say the formation was deposited from water so far inland would require a flood of biblical proportions. But there is much evidence that the Coconino Sandstone was indeed deposited in a watery environment.

The sandstone formation is bounded, top and bottom, between formations that are obviously from a marine environment.[37] What forces lifted the continent above the ocean and then lowered it again after millions of years, multiple times, without the slightest tilt?

Such a switch in environments from marine to desert and back would create chaotic beach deposits at the upper and lower contacts, but none are found. We would also expect to find an uneven surface due to prolonged erosion, but the contacts at the top and bottom are remarkably straight and flat.

Another problem sandstone deposit is found in Australia. The Hawkesbury Sandstone in the Sydney area is of quartz sand and typically 50 meters (160 feet) thick. The prominent horizontal strata display large cross beds.

Over the years, geologists have suggested many different environments but these have fallen from favour one after the other:[38]

- Marine (1844)

- Partly glacial (1880)

- Desert (1883)

- Desert and lake (1883)

- Freshwater lake (1920)

- River (1964)

- Marine barrier and tidal delta (1969)

- Braided alluvial (1975, 1980, 1983)

- Catastrophic bursting of ice dams (1994)[39]

- Stream dominated fluvial fan (2003)[40]

37. Austin, S.A., Interpreting strata of Grand Canyon, in Austin, S.A. (editor), *Grand Canyon—Monument to Catastrophism*, Institute for Creation Research, Dallas, TX, p. 30, 1994.
38. Jones, D.C. and Clark, N.R. (eds.), *Geology of the Penrith 1:100,000 Sheet 9030*, New South Wales Geological Survey, Sydney, pp. 10, 14, 1991.
39. Woodford, J., Rock doctor catches up with our prehistoric surf, *The Sydney Morning Herald*, p. 2, 30 April 1994.
40. Blake, P., Creationist weds Three Sisters: evidence that creationists don't know which bed they are in, *The Skeptic* **24**(1):49–51, 2004.

That the environmental interpretations keep changing demonstrates how present processes are not adequate to explain thick deposits of sandstone containing large 'sand dune' patterns. Such deposits are found all over the world, and are a major problem for uniformitarianism, but they are easily explained if we allow the possibility of a large-scale watery catastrophe. But notice that this most obvious explanation is excluded on philosophical grounds.

Large igneous provinces

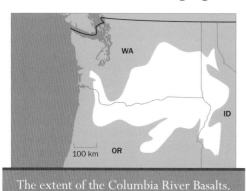

The extent of the Columbia River Basalts.

In the past, some volcanic eruptions covered enormous areas, such as the Columbia River Basalt Group in north-western USA. Here, as many as 300 individual lava flows engulfed some 163,000 km² (63,000 sq. miles) of the countryside to a depth of more than 1.8 km (1.1 miles).[41] The lava gushing from the earth was so hot and runny that it flowed across the landscape for vast distances. In places sediment, as well as petrified wood and gravel, have been deposited between some lava flows. The individual flows followed each other so quickly that there was not much erosion between them. After the lava finally stopped, the surface of the complex was eroded to form deep valleys.[41]

Features like this are very difficult to explain by the slow-and-gradual processes we observe on the earth today. Enormous volcanic deposits like this have been called *Large Igneous Provinces* (or LIPs). Contrasting with today's volcanoes, LIPs are usually found within the earth's plates instead of along their edges.

Because LIPs are so much larger[42] than today's volcanoes, long-age geologists are puzzled. What could have produced the titanic volume of magma, and how was so much lava erupted so quickly? They suggest that mantle plumes, large upward movements of hot rock from deep in the earth, were responsible. But the puzzle remains. What caused the plumes? Why are there no plumes of this magnitude beneath volcanoes today?

However, the Flood catastrophe provides the explanation. The breaking up of the fountains of the great deep, and the tectonic processes that unfolded as part of that catastrophe, account for why we see large igneous upheavals up-well from inside the earth in the past, but not in the present.

---

41. The total volume was more than 170,000 km³. Woodmorappe, J. and Oard, M.J., Field studies in the Columbia River basalt, Northwest USA, *J. Creation* **16**(1):103–110, April 2002; creation.com/field-crb.
42. Often covering an area of several million km² and having a volume of lava of the order of a million km³.

Granite

Most people are familiar with granite, with its colorful, interlocking crystals including pink, grey and white, sprinkled with black. Granite is exposed on the earth's surface in features called plutons that can be 10 to 20 km across. It has long been considered that granite plutons have taken vast periods of time to form and cool.

The idea is that enormous 'balloons' of molten rock (called magma) accumulated deep inside the crust and rose slowly to the surface over millions of years. Imagine a balloon of oil rising through a pool of water. However the analogy breaks down because the molten granite is said to have risen, as a single towering body, through *solid rock*.

Recent papers to the *Proceedings of the Geologists' Association* in the UK revealed that geologists specializing in granite abandoned the balloon idea long ago. The lead researcher, John Clemens, said, "In fact, just about everything that was taught as recently as ten years ago about granitic magmatism has been turned on its head."[43] Another author, W.J. Pitcher, who had studied granites for 60 years, said he had long considered the idea of a single towering body of magma "an offence to reason".[44]

Instead, he and the other researchers considered that the magma rose through long cracks and fissures in the crust in enormous pulses, forming dykes, which were only a meter or so wide, before pooling in saucer-shaped plutons kilometers below the surface. Some estimates for the ascent time of even some of the larger magma pools are as low as five hours.[45]

It has also been claimed that the body of magma is so large, and so-well insulated deep within the crust, that the granite would take eons of time to cool. But this assumes that the heat transferred through the granite and the surrounding sediments was by *conduction* alone—a slow cooling process. Geologists have recognized for a long time that fluids (liquids and compressed gasses) played an important role with granitic intrusions.[46] Furthermore, the plutons are now regarded as forming relatively thin horizontal sheets of rock, not towering pyramids. So, the reduced thickness of the magma body and the increased cooling via the fluids means the cooling time for granite intrusions is much less than once thought.

43. Clemens, J.D., Granites and granitic magmas: strange phenomena and new perspectives on some old problems, *Proc. Geologists' Assoc.* **116**:9–16, p. 15, 2005.
44. Pitcher, W.S., Invited comment on Clemens's 'Granites and granitic magmas', *Proc. Geologists' Assoc.* **116**:21–23, p. 21, 2005.
45. Clemens, ref. 43, p. 14.
46. Guilbert, J.M. and Park, C.F., *The Geology of Ore Deposits*, W.H. Freeman and Company, New York, pp. 26–43, 1986.

Another argument for vast ages of the granite intrusions relates to the coarse texture of its mineral grains. Large minerals take a long time to form, so the argument goes. So, if the magma had cooled quickly the texture would have been fine-grained like solidified volcanic lava or even volcanic glass.

But cooling rate is not the only thing that affects grain size. It is not uncommon to find a granitic texture in thin dykes. These thin near-vertical slabs of rock should have cooled more quickly than a granite pluton, yet they still have granite-sized mineral grains. Even larger crystals, 20 mm or more across, are found in a granite-like rock called pegmatite, which is also emplaced as dykes. In other words, a fine-grained texture is not guaranteed when the cooling rate is fast. Also, the grain size tends to be consistent *throughout* the granite body (e.g. Stone Mountain, GA), while one would expect the outer edges to cool faster and thus have smaller grain size than the central material.

In addition, measurements in the laboratory have clocked crystals of plagioclase, one of the minerals comprising granite, growing to 5 mm, a typical granite size, in as little as 1 hour.[47]

Granite researcher John Clemens suggests that belief in an old earth has long led geological thinking about granite down the wrong path. He concludes that granites belong with increasing number of geological processes that were "catastrophic in their suddenness". So much for slow-and-gradual uniformitarianism.

Boulder deposits transported vast distances

Thick deposits of rounded cobbles and boulders made of hard quartz are found across the plateaus of north-western USA and western Canada. These are a mystery for uniformitarian geologists because the nearest source of quartzite rocks is at the continental divide, 500 to 1000 km away.[48] Many of the boulders have circular indentations indicating violent collisions while being transported by deep water flows.

Photo by John Hergenrather

■ Source areas along continental divide
▨ Deposits of rounded quartzite boulders

---

47. Clemens, ref. 43, p. 15.
48. Hergenrather, J., Noah's long-distance travelers: Quartzite boulders speak powerfully of the global Flood, *Creation* **28**(3):30–32, 2006; creation.com/noahs-long-distance-travelers.

Some geologists have proposed that 'ancestral rivers' transported the boulders, but these suggestions are wholly inadequate. Dr J.E. Allen, a geologist from Portland State University suggested that the quartzite boulders up to 1 m (3 ft) in diameter that he discovered on several mountains in north-eastern Oregon were carried there by a huge ancient river. But even Allen considered that such an idea was outrageous because the river would need to be of an enormous size.

Biblical geologists Peter Klevberg and Michael Oard calculated that water currents of at least 105 km per hour would be needed in a flow 60 m deep to carry the boulders 1,000 km from their source.[49] Those sorts of water flows are three to four times greater than for flash floods today.

Deposits of rounded quartzite boulders across the countryside are another example of evidence that uniformitarianism fails to explain.

The second cord is stretched to breaking

Lyell predicted that causes now in operation would be wholly adequate to explain the yet-to-be-discovered geological evidence on Earth. Since Lyell, geologists have carefully documented the geological features of our planet and also applied themselves to explaining those features without invoking catastrophe.

Now, one hundred and fifty years down the track, with the exploration of vast areas of the earth and the publication of geological libraries of books, maps and reports, the old paradigm is stretched to breaking under the weight of contrary evidence. It has not been possible to explain things as Lyell imagined and we have only scratched the surface. The list of problems could be greatly expanded.

Warren D. Allmon, Director of the Paleontological Research Institution in Ithaca, New York, and Adjunct Associate Professor of Earth and Atmospheric Sciences at Cornell University in an article about Charles Lyell said:

> Lyell also sold geology some snake oil. He convinced geologists that ... all past processes acted at essentially their current rates (that is, those observed in historical time). This extreme gradualism has led to numerous unfortunate consequences, including the rejection of sudden or catastrophic events in the face of positive evidence for them, for no reason other than that they were not gradual.[50]

Derek Ager, whom we mentioned earlier, once professor of geology at the University College of Swansea, said much the same thing:

49. Klevberg, P. and Oard, M.J., Paleohydrology of the Cypress Hills formation and flaxville gravel. In: Walsh, R.E. (editor), *Proceedings of the Fourth International Conference on Creationism,* Creation Science Fellowship, Pittsburgh, Pennsylvania, p. 373, 1998.
50. Allmon, W.D., Post gradualism, *Science* **262**:122, 1993.

> ... we have allowed ourselves to be brain-washed into avoiding any interpretation of the past that involves extreme and what might be termed 'catastrophic' processes.[51]

It is time to stop being brain-washed. Not only do we need to reject uniformitarianism, but we also need to look at the geological evidence free of million-year-old shackles. When we do, we find the evidence is best explained by biblical history, which Lyell worked so hard to dismiss. The evidence we find is what we would expect from the Bible's account of the global catastrophic Flood of Noah's Day.

Cord #3: The Bible explains the evidence

Lyell's philosophy has three strands. We have dealt with the third and second of his claims in that order and found they do not match the geological evidence. We now come back to Lyell's starting point, the first strand in the uniformitarian rope, which was to dismiss the Bible from consideration. He could not avoid this issue because so many geological forerunners had relied on biblical ideas, and it was so much part of the culture. But in his *Principles of Geology*, Lyell was able to dismiss the Bible without addressing the evidence. He avoided any serious discussion of this issue by placing the biblical account into the same genre as ancient Egyptian and Indian cosmologies. Nowhere did he refer to any biblical text relevant to geology and discuss its implications. He simply *disregarded* the Bible as if it had no connection with the physical world.

But the Bible connects with reality because it records history, and understanding history can help us interpret the evidence we see today. Some events, such as the global Flood, are highly relevant to the geology of the globe.

Photo from wikipedia.org

There is abundant evidence that the biblical accounts are reliable, including a wealth of archaeological material at the British Museum. Its gallery on Egypt and Africa shows the biblical descriptions of life in Egypt, when the children of Israel were living there, are authentic.[52] And room 57 has a store of ancient tablets, the *Amarna Letters*, that confirm the biblical account of Joshua's conquest of southern Canaan.[53] The Bible has been described by some secular archaeologists as the best archeological book one could have. Why is this so? Because it accurately records history. So,

51. Ager, D.V., *The Nature of the Stratigraphical Record*, Macmillan, London, pp. 46–47, 1987.
52. Masters, P., *Heritage of Evidence in the British Museum*, The Wakeman Trust, London, pp. 98–103, 2004.
53. Masters, ref. 52, pp. 52–54.

why not trust its other accounts of events in the past, including its account of the globe-covering Flood?

There is additional evidence that comes from the stories preserved by cultures all around the world—the ubiquitous accounts of the world-wide Flood. Since only one family survived that catastrophe, when people multiplied and dispersed across the globe they carried their common history with them.[54]

The Geologic Column

Geologically speaking, I found that, by starting with the Bible, one can make sense of the evidence. In 1994, I presented a geological model at the 3rd International Conference on Creationism in Pittsburgh, USA.[55] It was designed as a tool to interpret geological evidence through the lens of biblical history. Over the years I and other biblical geologists have tested the model against geological features in the field and found it works amazingly well (see box on pp. 190–191 for a brief description of the model).

One controversial question among biblical geologists concerns how the uniformitarian geological column should be regarded. Some biblical geologists accept the column as an exact, linear chronology (with a reduced timescale), while others would dismiss the column entirely. The biblical geological model provides insight into this issue because it enables geological structures to be classified within biblical chronology.

When Oard compared the relationship between biblical geology and the geological column, he concluded that it provided a general order of Flood geology but with many exceptions. He uncovered several surprises.[56] First, sedimentary rocks classified on the geological column as Precambrian,[57] Paleozoic and Mesozoic are all early Flood rocks (the 'Inundatory Stage'). Second, strata labeled as Cenozoic on the column can be early Flood, late Flood or post-Flood, depending upon where they are located on Earth, and on the particular fossils used to classify them as Cenozoic. Third, Flood deposition is highly nonlinear, with a large percentage of strata deposited in the first half of the Flood during the Inundatory Stage while the waters were rising on Earth.

54. Conolly, R. and Grigg, R., Flood! *Creation* **23**(1):26–30, 2000; creation.com/many-flood-legends.
55. Walker, T., A Biblical geological model; in: Walsh, R.E. (editor), *Proceedings of the Third International Conference on Creationism (Technical Symposium Sessions)*, Creation Science Fellowship, Pittsburgh, PA., pp. 581–592, 1994.
56. Oard, M., The geological column is a general Flood order with many exceptions; in: Reed, J.K. and Oard, M.J. (eds), *The Geologic Column: Perspectives Within Diluvial Geology*, Creation Research Society, Chino Valley, AZ, ch. 7, pp. 99–119, 2006.
57. Provided the Precambrian rocks in question are Flood-deposited rocks.

Biblical geology solves uniformitarian puzzles

When we revisit the geological features described in the previous section, we find simple solutions to the problems uniformitarian geologists have not been able to solve. Most biblical geologists consider the most violent part of the Flood was at the beginning, when the land masses broke up, which was when most of the sediments on the continents were deposited, including those discussed above.

Biblical geology elegantly explains the world's coal deposits. Rather than the vegetation growing over a long period in a swamp, it represents pre-Flood environments that were uprooted and progressively buried as the floodwaters rose (although some, especially many brown-coal deposits, were buried as the floodwaters receded). It also explains the polystrate tree trunks, lacking branches, bark and roots, sitting vertically through the coal measures. These were ripped up with the rest of the vegetation, stripped and deposited, some vertically, within the sediments as they accumulated.

The Flood explains the vast sedimentary blankets covering the continents and the extensive flat gaps contained within them. The blankets were formed by rapid sedimentation from continental-scale water flows. From a Flood perspective the large cross-bedding within the thick Coconino Sandstone deposits is a water feature and to be expected—there is no need to invoke a desert environment. During the cataclysm, not only were the huge volumes of sediment deposited rapidly, but they were cemented rapidly by the minerals dissolved in the deposition water.

As for the large igneous provinces on Earth, these are not surprising within the biblical paradigm. The Flood involved an enormous tectonic upheaval of the crust and mantle.[58] That is why mantle plumes of the past were so much larger than anything we see today. Tectonic upheaval also explains the huge granite formations. The evidence that granitic magma was rapidly generated and rapidly emplaced, in enormous pulses, is a logical consequence of the tectonic upheavals during the early part of the biblical Flood.

And the boulder deposits that were obviously transported vast distances make sense within a Flood paradigm. These were carried by the water flowing from the continents during the second half of the Flood.

Biblical geology explains geomorphology

Massive continental erosion: During the Recessive Stage of the Flood, the floodwaters flowed from the continents into the deepening ocean basins, as the

---

58. Baumgardner, J.R., Runaway subduction as the driving mechanism for the Genesis Flood; in Walsh, R.E. (Ed.), *Proceedings of the Third International Conference on Creationism, Technical Symposium Sessions,* Creation Science Fellowship, Pittsburgh, pp. 63–75, 1994.

sea floor gradually sank. Retreating waters caused massive continental erosion, depositing the sediments on the continental margins. Receding floodwaters explain uniformitarian puzzles connected with geomorphology (i.e. the shape of the landscape). Initially, the floodwaters would flow across the continents, in laterally continuous sheets, to the deepening ocean basins. This would erode the landscape flat.

Biblical geologist Roy Holt called this period the *Erodozoic*, because it was characterized by great erosion on the continents. This feature is seen all over the world. One well-known landscape that displays this is in the Grand Canyon area. When we look at the surrounding countryside we see that some 3 kilometers (10,000 ft) of sedimentary material has been eroded from the Colorado Plateau in a process that evolutionary geologists call The Great Denudation.[59]

Overfit river valleys: As the receding flow of water decreased in volume, parts of the landscape would emerge above the surface and the water would flow around these areas in very wide channels. This channelized flow would dissect the flat plateaus, creating wide valleys, often with flat-topped buttes and mesas in between. During the Recessive Stage, the water flow from the continents began strong but eventually waned, and continued to wane until the land was dry.

After the Flood, the rain that fell on the land would drain from the continents in the same valleys that drained the floodwater. However, the volume of water flowing in the post-Flood rivers would be much less than the volume draining during the Flood.

According to uniformitarian philosophy, the size of valleys should match the size of the rivers in them. Within that paradigm, the present rivers carved the valley. However, virtually every valley in the world is much larger than the river flowing in it—what geomorphologists call an *overfit valley* with an *underfit stream*. The Recessive Stage of the Flood explains 'overfit' valleys but uniformitarianism does not.

Erosional remnants: This receding Flood sequence also explains the spectacular mesas scattered around the earth, such as those standing on the flat

59. Oard, M.J., The Origin of Grand Canyon Pt. IV: The Great Denudation, *CRSQ* **47**(2):146–157, 2006.

floor of Monument Valley. These mesas are isolated erosional remnants that remained after the massive water flows had departed. In fact, present processes of wind, rain, freezing and thawing, contrary to Lyell, are destroying many of these steep-sided features, creating rounded knobs and sloped walls. If "the present is the key to the past" something different *must* have occurred in the past to explain the initial formation of things not being formed today. That 'something' was the global Flood.

Receding floodwaters explain why the mesas have steep sides and only tiny aprons of rock debris at their base. The massive flow of water during the channelized phase eroded the sediment and carried it out of the area. One cannot walk downhill or downstream from most of these areas and find the eroded sands—they have been carried off the continent, and not by a mere trickling little stream! Features like this are not confined to one place on earth but are found across the planet, such as Table Mountain near Cape Town in South Africa. Without receding floodwaters, uniformitarian scenarios cannot explain what transported sediment away and left the landscape so flat and the valleys so steep.

Water and air gaps: Another surprising feature of the landscape is that many rivers flow *through* mountain ranges instead of *around* them, as uniformitarians

Photo by Michael Oard

The Shoshone water gap.

would expect. The narrow gorges the rivers flow through are called water gaps. If there is no river flowing through the gap it is called an air gap. Water gaps are common on every continent around the world. The deepest are in the Himalaya Mountains. Eleven major rivers begin on the southern Tibetan Plateau and pass *through* the mountains in deep gorges.

Water gaps are common in the USA, including many through the Appalachian Mountains. The Susquehanna River north of Harrisburg, Pennsylvania has a series of water gaps cutting through the eroded Appalachian Mountains.

Biblical geology easily explains water gaps. When the floodwaters over the continents were deep, it would flow over the mountain ranges as it flowed into the oceans. As the water level dropped, parts of the range would emerge and the water would flow over the low parts of the range, which it would continue to erode. As long as the water was flowing, it would continue to erode the water gap deeper. Once the floodwaters had completely drained, normal rainfall after the Flood would then flow in streams and rivers through the deepest of these gaps. Those gaps that are not so deep do not have rivers flowing through them now, and are called *air gaps* or *wind gaps*.

Water gaps are a mystery for uniformitarian geology but easily explained by the reducing level of the retreating floodwater.

Biblical geology explains the Ice Age

The uniformitarian paradigm fails to explain the Ice Age, but biblical history does. Today, some 10% of the earth's land surface is covered with ice sheets and glaciers, but there was much more ice cover in the past. The evidence for greater ice includes distinctive U-shaped valleys cut by glaciers, rocks that are scoured and scratched, broken rock, called tillite, pushed by glaciers into mounds called moraines, and erratic boulders dropped by floating ice into sediment.

When Louis Agassiz (1801–1873) presented evidence for the Ice Age to scientists at Neuchâtel, Switzerland, in 1837, the audience was opposed and critical. It was decades before the idea was accepted. One major problem was, and still is, what caused the Ice Age—why did it start and why did it stop.

Ideas that long-age scientists have proposed include large meteorite impacts, supervolcano eruptions, and changes in things such as atmospheric carbon dioxide, the sun's solar output and the orbit of the Moon. The most popular idea today relies on *Milankovitch cycles*, where changes in the tilt of the earth's axis and in its orbit around the Sun would make the climate cooler every 41,000 years or so.

One problem with all these ideas is that the proposed effects are too small; they do not cause a large enough change in the temperature. So, it is further proposed there must be a positive feedback mechanism that amplifies the change. The possibility of positive feedback has made today's climate scientists worried that a small change in climate may cause a large instability (hence, 'global warming' fears are partly due to a misunderstanding of earth history).

Another problem is that a cooler earth will not cause ice to build-up on the continents. It will just create a cold desert, like most of northern Siberia and Antarctica today. For ice to build up, we need increased precipitation of snow and ice.

Biblical geology provides an obvious and simple explanation for the start and end of the Ice Age.[60] The evidence for the Pleistocene Ice Age indicates it was 'very late geologically', which means it occurred *after* the global Flood. The Flood is the key. Being a catastrophic, tectonic event, much volcanism occurred and this heated the oceans warmer than they are today. Indeed, ice cores show evidence of warmer oceans in the past, which we place immediately after the Flood. This evaporated the water needed for the ice accumulation; the warm oceans increased evaporation which precipitated as snow and ice on the continents.

Also, after the Flood, there would have been fine volcanic dust high in the atmosphere, reflecting sunlight and keeping the interiors of the continents cooler in summer. The snow and ice that fell on the continents in winter was not fully melted the following summer, so the ice built up from year to year. Oard estimates that the ice accumulated for 500 years. After the oceans cooled and the volcanic dust cleared, it would have taken some 200 years for the ice to retreat to where it is today.[60] Thus, when the Flood ended, the conditions were exactly as needed to create the Ice Age.

There are many implications that flow out of this model. One is that the earth is a highly stable system. Its climate returned to equilibrium after the incredibly large deviation that occurred at the end of the Flood. This impacts thinking about climate models for the earth and about what sorts of human responses are appropriate for climate concerns.

Also, at the peak of the Ice Age, the oceans were warm, which explains mysteries about climates in such places as Siberia.[61] The warm oceans made these areas habitable, which is why significant populations of an amazing variety of animals, including tens of thousands of elephants (woolly mammoths and mastodons), lived in the area during the Ice Age, but cannot live there now.

60. Oard, M.J., *An Ice Age Caused by the Genesis Flood*, Technical Monograph, Institute for Creation Research, El Cajon, CA, pp. 135–149, 1990.
61. Oard, M.J., The extinction of the woolly mammoth: was it a quick freeze? *J. Creation* **14**(3):24–34, 2000; creation.com/snapfreeze.

Explanations based on Milankovitch cycles anticipate that conditions for an ice age should repeat on multiples of 41,000 years or so. Those who have adopted this perspective expect to find ice ages repeating through their geologic time. Such geologists are therefore quick to explain features such as scratches on rock and large boulders in sediment as forming by glaciers. However, apart from the most recent Ice Age, there are only four others in their scheme that such geologists routinely speak about: one in the Devonian, one in the Carboniferous-Permian, and two in the Precambrian. All of these are debatable. Oard[62] and Molén[63] have examined evidences for these supposed former ice ages and have concluded that the evidence had been wrongly interpreted as the result of glaciers. The geologic evidence for earlier ice ages is quite different from that for the most recent one. Most of the data are better interpreted as gigantic underwater landslides causing vast sedimentary movements during the Flood. The earth appears to have been remarkably ice free for most of its history.

On the other hand, when we work from the perspective of biblical history, only one Ice Age is expected—in the post-Flood period and stretching over several hundreds of years, not hundreds of thousands. We would not expect to find glacial conditions during the Flood, which was responsible for the earlier parts of the geologic record.

Our interpretations of the Ice Age illustrate how models based on uniformitarian and biblical assumptions lead to different predictions about what we should see and different conclusions, even though we may be looking at the same evidence. The models suggest different causes for the start and the end of the most recent Ice Age. They make different predictions about what evidence is anticipated *through* the geological record. They provide different guidance for our current understanding of the earth's climate, what is driving it, how stable it is, and how we should respond to it. When it comes to the Ice Age, the models based on biblical geology better match the evidence and provide coherent insights into what is going on.

The biblical cord undoes uniformitarianism

Before long-age thinking could be accepted, the biblical account of earth history had to be dismissed. This was done on the basis of personal preference, a 'bandwagon effect', without a proper evaluation of the relevant issues. But the failure of uniformitarianism to explain so much geology of the earth means it is time to return to square one. It is time to properly consider the geological implications of earth history recorded in the Bible.

---

62. Oard, M.J., *Ancient Ice Ages or Gigantic Submarine Landslides?* Creation Research Society Books, Chino Valley, AZ, USA, 1997.
63. Molén, M., Diamictites: ice-ages or gravity flows?; in Walsh, R.E. and Brooks, C.L. (Eds.), *Proceedings of the Second International Conference on Creationism*, Creation Science Fellowship, Pittsburgh, pp. 177–190, 1990.

Biblical geologic model

World history as recorded in the Bible allows us to understand the big geological picture of the earth, provided we are alert for geological clues. As we read about an event we simply ask, "How would this have affected the geology of the earth? What would we look for today." Most events would have had little or no effect, but others would have had a vast geological impact.

From this analysis we conclude that most rocks on Earth today formed during two very short periods of time. The first was the six-day creation week, about 6000 years ago when the entire planet and its various ecosystems were produced. The second was the one-year Flood, when the surface of the planet was destroyed and reshaped. Geologically, not much happened in the 1700-year period between creation and the Flood, or in the roughly 4500-year period since.

We see that there is an inverse relation between time and geology: the short times produced lots of rocks whereas the long times produced little. This can be illustrated on a diagram that connects the biblical time scale with its corresponding rock scale.

The Flood event logically divides into two stages. We can call the period during which the floodwaters rose and inundated the land the Inundatory Stage, and the period when the floodwaters receded from the land into the

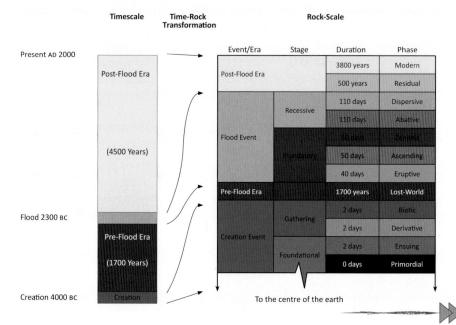

ocean the Recessive Stage. Another level of subdivision is also logically useful. The Recessive stage, for example, can be divided into two phases. The period when the floodwaters abated from the continents in geographically continuous sheets we can call the Abative Phase. After some land emerged, the waters would be dispersed into wide, flowing channels. We can call this the Dispersive Phase. Also of importance would be the Residual Phase, during which a lot of geological work can still be done as sediments de-water, as earthquakes occur, as mountains continue to uplift, and as erosion continues to occur.

Over the last fifty years, there has been a wealth of research carried out by biblical geologists who have published a growing body of literature. It is showing that models constructed from biblical history do explain the evidence. Of course there are questions that arise, and often unexpected findings, but this is par for the course for all interpretive paradigms. Such puzzles help focus research, and the problem areas often turn out to provide powerful new insights and discoveries. The literature produced by biblical geologists today, and the powerful models that are being developed, challenge the first assumption of uniformitarianism. They prove that the Bible does indeed have a powerful connection with reality.

Where does this lead?

Strategically, the strict uniformitarianism of Lyell and his contemporaries was essential to establish an old age for the earth. To allow even the tiniest grain of catastrophism into the mix would threaten it. Thus, every geological problem became a work in progress—how to explain evidence using slow-and-gradual processes when it looked like it was produced by catastrophe. The measure of scientific competence was the ability to explain catastrophic evidence in terms of uniformitarian processes. Some of the explanations were immensely creative and are still clung to, even to this day, such as the uniformitarian explanations for coal and massive water-laid sand deposits discussed earlier. Clearly, the geologic record does not support the grand-scale evolutionary timeline. It has become a significant Achilles' heel for evolutionary theory.

However, with the development of radiometric dating and the establishment of 'absolute' dates on the global stratigraphic column, the need to hold to a strict uniformitarianism diminished. Geologists felt secure enough with the geologic time scale to allow catastrophe without destroying their worldview. Yet, the situation is not as secure as is imagined because of problems being uncovered with radioactive dating, and that leads to the next Achilles' heel of evolution.

Dr Jim Mason

Ph.D. Experimental Nuclear Physics,
McMaster University, Canada

Dr Mason came to CMI after a long career in the defense industry. His background in nuclear physics and experience in electronics led to a position as Vice President of Engineering and Chief Technology Officer for one of Canada's leading defense electronics system integration companies. He was nearly 40 years old when he became a Christian, and it would be several more years before he became a biblical creationist, so most of his scientific and industry career was spent believing in evolution. He is a natural candidate to parse the difficult field of nuclear physics and show us why radiometric dating is the sixth Achilles' heel of Darwinian evolution.

See **creation.com/dr-jim-mason**

RADIOMETRIC DATING

Dr Jim Mason, Ph.D. Experimental Nuclear Physics
[McMaster University] | **6**

Why is a consideration of radiometric dating important?

As we have seen from the preceding chapters, evolution has not one but many Achilles' heels, each pierced by a deadly arrow. Biology reveals that the cell is irreducibly complex, so could not have formed gradually by chance from inanimate molecules. Genetics reveals that the alleged engines of evolution (mutation and natural selection) corrupt and destroy genetic information rather than create and enhance it. Evolutionary paleontology fails to demonstrate the many transitional forms it predicts; rather, their absence speaks as loudly as it did in Charles Darwin's day. Uniformitarian geology has given way to recognition that catastrophes have played a significant role in Earth's past, and this matches Noah's Flood. As a result, the grand tapestry of evolution is unraveling from all sides.

Evolution relies on long ages as an enabling prerequisite to allow enough time for the accumulation of the many changes needed to give rise to higher species. While the Bible clearly teaches through its chronological data that the earth is around 6,000 years old, radiometric dating is alleged to provide conclusive proof that the world is 4.54 billion years old (the currently accepted value). Even in an age when many question evolutionary theory, its corollary of millions and billions of years often remains an unchallenged icon in the debate about origins. The average layperson thinks that 'science' can prove such things as the age of a rock, a fossil, or even the earth. Consequently, radiometric dating is of paramount importance to evolutionists. As other areas of science increasingly give evidence that evolution is flawed, increasingly radiometric dating is called on to provide the long ages that seemingly discredit the Bible. Alas for evolution! Radiometric dating does not yield the support evolution needs.

What is the science behind radiometric dating?

Radiometric dating is a relatively straightforward science. Atoms of an unstable, radioactive element (called the 'Parent') transform into atoms of a stable, non-radioactive element (called the 'Daughter') (Figure 1). Sometimes this transformation is direct; sometimes it proceeds through a series of intermediate elements that are themselves radioactive. For example, radioactive carbon transforms directly into non-radioactive nitrogen and radioactive uranium transforms into non-radioactive lead through a series of 16 radioactive elements.

This transformation happens with a characteristic time interval called a half-life. This is the length of time during which exactly one-half the atoms of the Parent element that are present at the beginning transform into an equal number of atoms of the Daughter element. If we assume that we start with all Parent element and no Daughter element, then by the end of one half-life, one half of the atoms of the Parent element have changed to Daughter element (Figure 2).

During the next half-life interval, one half of the remaining atoms of the Parent element transform into atoms of the Daughter element. Consequently, at the end of the second half-life interval, we have ¼ of the original amount of Parent element left and the amount of Daughter element present has grown to ¾ of the original amount of Parent element. Now the ratio of the amount of Daughter element present to the amount of Parent element present is 3 to 1.

As the process continues, the ratio of the amount of Daughter element present to the amount of Parent element present keeps increasing, as shown in Figure 3.

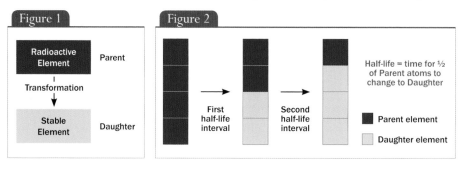

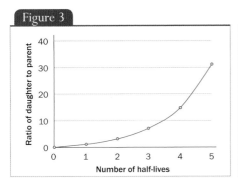

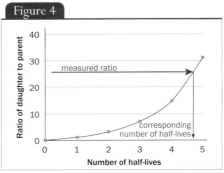

Now, if we can measure the ratio of Daughter element to Parent element present in a rock sample, then, in theory, Figure 3 can be used to determine how many half-lives have passed since the process began (Figure 4). If, in turn, we know the value of the half-life in units of time (microseconds, minutes, years, etc), then, again in theory, we can use these two numbers to calculate the length of time that has passed since the process began.

The ratio of Daughter to Parent present in a rock sample can indeed be measured, but usually requires very sophisticated instruments such as mass spectrometers.

Similarly, the current values for the half-lives can also be accurately measured. This is usually done by detecting the intensity of the radiation that is produced during the transformation, using specially-designed detectors (similar to Geiger counters) and plotting this intensity over time. As the amount of Parent element decreases, the intensity of the emitted radiation decreases at the same rate. So it would seem that in theory it should be possible to use radiometric dating to determine the age of a sample. However, as we will see later, this turns out to not be the case.

Although there are many naturally occurring radioactive transformations, there are several Parent-Daughter transformations that are commonly used for radiometric dating of rocks. These are listed in Table 1 along with the current half-lives.

Parent Element	Daughter Element	Shorthand Notation	Half-life (Billions of years)
Potassium	Argon	K – Ar	1.248
Rubidium	Strontium	Rb – Sr	48.8
Samarium	Neodymium	Sm – Nd	106
Uranium	Lead	U – Pb	4.468

Table 1: Some radioactive transformations commonly used in radiometric dating of igneous and metamorphic rock.

The ages determined in this fashion are referred to as 'model' ages, since they are determined using the model described above for the radioactive transformation involved. They can be determined either for the 'whole rock' or the individual minerals comprising the rock. For the former, the whole rock is crushed and used, whereas for the latter the rock is first separated into its constituent minerals and the measurements done for each mineral separately.

How well does it work?

Before using any measurement instrument or technique, it is good practice to calibrate it against some known quantity. This ensures it is giving accurate results. In the case of radiometric dating techniques, the obvious approach is to use the technique to determine the ages of some rocks of *known* age. So how well does this radiometric dating technique do in determining the ages of rocks of known age?

Mt. Ngauruhoe, a volcano in New Zealand, produced three separate lava flows in 1949, 1954 and 1975. In 2003, several scientists who questioned the billions-of-years interpretation and who were seeking to check the reliability of radiometric dating, collected a total of 8 samples from these three lava flows (2, 4, and 2, respectively). These were dated by an independent laboratory using the K-Ar (potassium-argon) whole-rock model technique. This technique is thought to be particularly applicable to this kind of rock since it is expected that any Ar produced in the rock prior to its cooling, being an inert gas, will be boiled off while the rock is molten. Thus, any Ar found in the rock, it is assumed, will be the result of radioactive transformation that has occurred since the rock cooled. The results are summarized in Table 2.

As can be seen, the results vary widely, from less than 270,000 years to 3.5 million

# of samples	Eruption Date	Radioage (Ma)
2	1949	<0.27
		1.0 ±0.2
4	1954	<0.27
		0.8 ±0.2
		1.3 ±0.2
		3.5 ±0.2
2	1975	<0.27
		1.0 ±0.2

Table 2: Radiometrically determined ages for lava flows from Mt. Ngauruhoe, NZ, from Snelling (1998).*The indicated uncertainties (± numbers) are often thought to be an indication of accuracy but are, in fact, indicators of precision or errors inherent in the experimental technique.

Snelling, A.A., The Cause of Anomalous Potassium-Argon "Ages" for Recent Andesite Flows at Mt. Ngauruhoe, New Zealand and the Implications for Potassium-Argon "Dating", in Walsh, R. E. (Ed), *Proceedings of the Fourth International Conference on Creationism*, Creation Science Fellowship, Pittsburgh, Pennsylvania, pp 503-525, 1998.

years. While '<270,000 years' is technically correct, since 50-year-old rocks are 'less than 270,000 years old', dates like this are not particularly helpful since quite a few other ages are also in this range. On the other hand, the other ages are clearly incorrect. Furthermore, the experimental error of ± 0.2 (200,000 years), which should encompass 95% of all repetitions of the measurements, means that these values are not simple aberrations and that the laboratory doing these analyses has confidence in the repeatability of the results. In other words, they are precise numbers, but they are precisely wrong!

To understand how this works, consider a hypothetical wristwatch that can measure time to one one-millionth of a second (one microsecond). If it is not set to the correct time, it will measure the time very precisely but always incorrectly. It, too, will be precisely wrong.

The current Mt. St. Helens (Washington State, USA) lava dome formed in 1984 and provides another opportunity for calibrating the K-Ar technique. This time, in addition to doing a whole rock analysis, measurements were made on individual minerals.[1] The results are summarized in Table 3. Once again, the measured ages are vastly different from the actual age, and the ages derived from the individual minerals are significantly different from each other, with the 'oldest' measurement being some 100,000 times the correct age!

K – Ar 'ages' (yr)		
Technique		"age" (yr)
Whole Rock		350,000
Mineral	Feldspar	340,000
	Amphibole etc.	900,000
	Pyroxene etc.	1,700,000
	Pyroxene	2,800,000

Table 3: Radiometric 'ages' for lava formed at Mt. St. Helens in 1984, after Austin (1996).[1]

Why the big discrepancies?

It appears that this calibration exercise is not working out very well. Why might that be? While the theory of radiometric dating and the associated calculations are pretty straightforward, they are based on a number of assumptions. These are:

1. The amount of daughter element present in the rock at the time it was formed is zero (but see the section on isochron dating below).

2. The rock has remained as a *closed system* since the time of its formation, which, in turn, means that:

    a. no parent element has been deposited in or removed from the rock since its formation, and

---

1. Austin, S.A., Excess Argon within mineral concentrations from the new dacite lava dome at Mount St. Helens volcano, *J. Creation* **10**(3):335–343, 1996; creation.com/lavadome.

     b. no daughter element has been deposited in or removed from the rock since its formation.

3. The rate of transformation (i.e. the half-life) has remained constant at today's rate throughout the entire period.

These all relate to things that have happened in the past, so there is no way of knowing whether they are true unless there has been a trustworthy eye-witness watching the rock throughout its history. The fact that the radiometric ages for the above rocks of known ages turn out to be so seriously inaccurate is a strong suggestion that one or more of these assumptions is incorrect.[2]

Consider, for example, the case where there is some daughter element present at the time the rock is formed, when, according to the assumptions, there should be none. Since the radiometric age is based on the ratio of daughter element to parent element, if you were to measure this age immediately after the rock was formed, you would get a non-zero number. Furthermore, since the daughter-to-parent ratio is used to determine the age in half-lives, and the age in years is determined by multiplying this by the half-life, if the half-life is very large, this could result in a very large age estimate.

This is exactly the situation we have today. Specifically for the K-Ar 'model' technique, after 6,000 years the expected amount of daughter content would be only 0.000333% of the original amount of Parent, so excess Ar corresponding to only 1% of the amount of K would result in a radiometric age of over 18 million years.

This is the general excuse used when results from the K-Ar technique do not match the expected ages. That is, the assumption that the rock contains no Ar at the time of formation is accepted as being in error and the date is disregarded. Of course, one cannot know whether this is the case in any particular situation, so it is not really justified to accept *any* K-Ar date as being valid!

Isochrons: Do they help?

Recognizing the fact that one cannot know the initial composition of a rock without an eye-witness to its formation, scientists have developed another radiometric technique, called isochron dating, to try to work around this issue.

To understand how this technique is supposed to work, we need to understand a bit more detail about atoms and, in particular, their nuclei.

---

2. One might add the assumption that there is no gravitational sorting of the parent and daughter elements in the lava prior to its ejection at the earth's surface. In that case, every fumarole that emits lava might be sourced from a different part of the lava pool and might have different elemental composition.

Atoms consist of electrons, protons and neutrons. The protons and neutrons are (relatively speaking) large and heavy. They are together in the nucleus. The electrons are, by comparison to the neutrons and protons, very light and small. They 'orbit' the nucleus at particular distances from the nucleus in what are called shells or atomic orbitals.

It is the electrons, particularly the ones in the outermost shells that determine chemical properties, or how an atom interacts with other atoms. The neutrons and protons determine the nuclear properties. In particular, the number of protons in a nucleus determines which element it is. Thus, for example, an atom with just a single proton in the nucleus is hydrogen and an atom with two protons in the nucleus is helium. Carbon has 12 protons, potassium has 19, argon has 18, uranium has 92, and lead has 82, to cite some of the other elements used in radiometric dating.

The relative number of neutrons and protons determines whether the atom (strictly speaking, the nucleus) is stable or radioactive. Generally speaking, for lighter elements (i.e. those with a smaller number of protons and neutrons), stable nuclei tend to have the same number of protons and neutrons. Thus for helium, which has two protons, the dominant form (99.999863%) also has two neutrons, although there is also a stable form that has only 1 neutron. Similarly, for carbon, which has 6 protons, the dominant form (98.9%) also has 6 neutrons although there is a stable form with 7 neutrons.

As the elements get heavier (i.e. more neutrons and protons) the stable nuclei tend to have more neutrons than protons. This is because the protons all have a positive electrical charge and repel each other. Extra neutrons, which have no electrical charge, dilute the proton concentration and allow the nuclear force to hold the nucleus together. This trend is already apparent with carbon, and by the time we get to lead, which is the heaviest stable element and has 82 protons, there are stable forms with 124, 125 and 126 neutrons.

The sum of the number of protons and neutrons is known as the 'mass number' of a nucleus and is often written with the symbol for the element. The atomic number conveys the number of protons (carbon has six), but the atomic mass conveys both the number of protons and the number of neutrons (the most abundant form of carbon has an atomic mass of 12, hence ^{12}C).

Nuclei (or atoms) which have the same number of protons but different numbers of neutrons are called *isotopes* of the element. Thus the three stable forms of lead with 124, 125, or 126 neutrons are three different isotopes of lead.

By making a chart with the number of protons along one side and the number of neutrons along the other, we can visualize what is happening during the

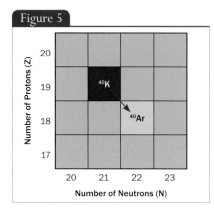

Figure 5

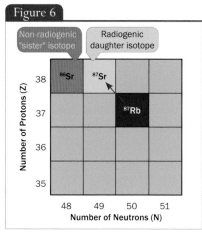

Figure 6

radioactive transformation. This is shown in Figure 5 for the Potassium-Argon transformation (written as ^{40}K–^{40}Ar using the above representation) discussed in the preceding section.

This is the background we need to understand how the isochron technique works. The isochron technique makes use of the fact that, in some cases, in addition to the daughter isotope, there is another naturally-occurring stable isotope of the same element as the daughter. The isotope formed from the radioactive transformation is called the radiogenic isotope and the other, naturally-occurring stable isotope is called the non-radiogenic isotope—or what we will call the Sister isotope.

This situation is illustrated in Figure 6 for the transformation of rubidium to strontium (^{87}Rb–^{87}Sr), yet another radioactive transformation used for radiometric dating (Table 1). The radiogenic daughter isotope of strontium has 49 neutrons to go with its 38 protons. However, there is also a naturally-occurring isotope of strontium—the Sister isotope—that is not formed by decay from rubidium. That Sister isotope is ^{86}Sr and it has 48 neutrons to go with its 38 protons.

The principles underlying the isochron dating technique are illustrated in Figure 7.

Unlike the technique described above, the isochron technique allows for the possibility that there may be some unknown amount of radiogenic daughter isotope present at the time of

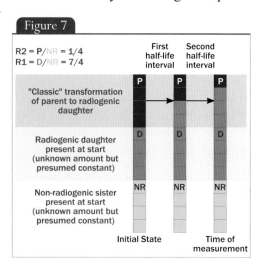

Figure 7

rock formation. In addition, it assumes an unknown amount of the sister isotope is also present. It assumes further that *additional* amounts of radiogenic daughter isotope are formed only by the transformation of the radioactive parent and that the amount of non-radiogenic sister isotope remains unchanged.

Thus, for any individual sample at the time of its formation, we have the following:

- An unknown amount of Parent element, P.

- An unknown amount of (radiogenic) Daughter isotope, D.

- An unknown amount of (non-radiogenic) Sister isotope, S.

After a period of time, a portion of the Parent, ΔP, transforms to Daughter. At this time the amount of Parent will be slightly less, the amount of Daughter will be slightly more, and the amount of increase/decrease *should* be identical. This, of course, assumes that nothing else has transpired to change the amounts of Parent, or Daughter, contained in the rock (through leeching, melting, ionic transport by water movement, etc.).

If we consider the ratios of Daughter-to-Sister and Parent-to-Sister at time T, these are respectively:

$(D + \Delta P)/S$ and $(P - \Delta P)/S$

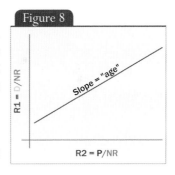
Figure 8

We can measure these ratios for many samples and create a graph of the first ratio vs the second ratio (Figure 8). With some straightforward algebra,[3] it can be shown that this relationship is in the form of a straight line, $y = mx + b$, with the

slope $= \Delta P/(P - \Delta P)$

Note that this does not involve the (unknown) starting amounts of either Daughter or Sister.

But ΔP is also the amount of Daughter that has been produced, and $P - \Delta P$ is the amount of Parent remaining after time T. The slope is thus the ratio of Daughter to Parent, i.e. D/P, which is the same ratio we saw earlier for the other technique. This ratio should increase over time[4] and could be used, as before, to determine a radiometric age.

---

3. Given $(D+\Delta P)/S$ and $(P-\Delta P)/S$, graphing ratio 1 vs ratio 2 gives us a line in the form $y = mx + b$. In this case: $(D+\Delta P)/S = (\Delta P/(P-\Delta P))*((P-\Delta P)/S) + D/S$. Note the slope of this line (m) $= \Delta P/(P-\Delta P)$, and the y-intercept (b) $= D/S$.

4. The slope depends on the length of time, measured in half-lives. After one half-life, the slope = 1 (ΔP = $1/2^1$ = 0.5, therefore $\Delta P/(P-\Delta P)$ = 0.5/0.5 = 1); after 2 half-lives, the slope = 3 (0.75/0.25); after three half-lives, the slope = 7 (0.875/0.125).

Isochron dating is used where we have a number of different samples that are considered to have formed at the same time but might have different initial compositions. These samples could be either 'whole rock' samples from the same rock formation or samples of different minerals separated from a single rock sample.

However, for the technique to work properly, the initial ratio of Daughter-to-Sister must be the same for all samples. This is because the y-intercept is, in fact, this ratio (D/S) and the straight-line relationship is not valid if it is not the same for all samples.

The ratios of Daughter-to-Sister and Parent-to-Sister are generally measured using solid-source mass spectrometers, since these devices are well suited to measuring the ratios of similar isotopes. The spectrometers can simultaneously count the number of atoms of each isotope, thereby enabling the isotopic ratio to be determined with considerable precision.

In order to illustrate the main assumptions behind isochron dating, I randomly generated a number of hypothetical rock samples with differing initial compositions. Since the technique assumes an unknown but constant initial ratio of Daughter-to-Sister for all samples, I randomly picked a value between 60% and 80% (which brackets the ^{87}Sr to ^{86}Sr ratio found in nature). I then created ten data points, with Parent and Daughter separately set to a random number between 1 and 100. The samples were then 'aged' through 3 half-lives by appropriately decreasing the amount of Parent and increasing the amount of Daughter by this same amount. The amount of Sister, of course, is assumed to remain constant over time. The result was a straight line with a slope of 7.0 (Figure 9), which is what we expected. This suggests that this technique should be insensitive to uncertainties in the initial composition of the rock when it was formed.

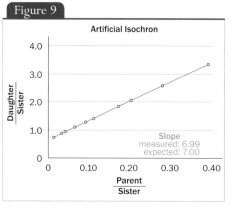

Figure 9

Artificial Isochron

How well does this technique work against real samples of rock? Figure 10 shows three isochron plots derived using three different transformation chains.[5] One is the ^{87}Rb–^{87}Sr (half-life = 48.8 billion years) chain described earlier (fig. 6). Another is

5.   Austin, S.A., and Snelling, A.A., Discordant potassium-argon model and isochron 'ages' for Cardenas Basalt (Middle Proterozoic) and associated diabase of eastern Grand Canyon, Arizona; in Walsh, R. E. (Ed.) *Proceedings of the Fourth International Conference on Creationism*, Creation Science Fellowship, Pittsburgh, PA, pp. 35–51, 1998.

Figure 10

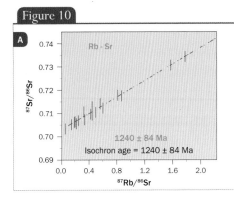

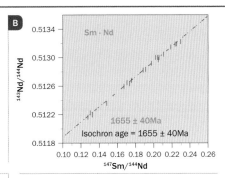

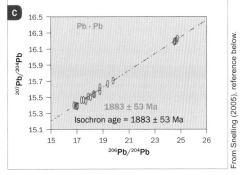

the ^{147}Sm–^{143}Nd transformation (half-life = 106 billion years). The third is a "double isochron", generated by the combination of two separate decay paths for Uranium, ^{235}U–^{207}Pb (half-life = 207 million years) and ^{238}U–^{206}Pb (half-life = 4.47 billion years) using the common stable sister isotope ^{204}Pb. These are very straight lines, suggesting a good correspondence between theory and practice. Note also that the ages calculated all appear to have very small uncertainties.

However, applying this technique to the Mount Ngauruhoe rocks yields the last three results in Table 4. As can be seen, the isochron technique that was supposed to 'fix' the problems associated with the K-Ar model technique actually gives worse results—in one case (Pb-Pb) by a factor of over 70 million! Note that

Measurement technique	Radioage (Ma)
K – Ar	<0.27
	1.0 ± 0.2
	<0.27
	0.8 ± 0.2
	1.3 ± 0.2
	3.5 ± 0.2
	<0.27
	1.0 ± 0.2
Rb – Sr	133 ± 87
Sm – Nd	197 ± 160
Pb – Pb	3,908 ± 390

Table 4: Isochron ages for the Mt. Ngauruhoe lavas (after Snelling, 2005),* together with the K-Ar model ages for the same lavas from Table 2. Note that the Pb-Pb isochron age is over 70 million times the correct age!

Snelling, A.A., Isochron Discordances, Inheritance and Mixing, in *Radioisotopes and the Age of the Earth Volume II* (Edited by Vardiman, Snelling and Chaffin), Institute of Creation Research, El Cajon, CA and Creation Research Society, Chino Valley, AZ, pp. 393–524, 2005.

the precision (i.e. the ± number) for this Pb-Pb case is only about 10%, clearly indicating the difference between accuracy and precision discussed earlier.

What about the isochron-derived ages shown in Figure 10? They are all for the same rock taken from the Grand Canyon! None of the ages agree with any other within the experimental uncertainties. How, then, do we know which one is correct? Given the results for the Mt. Ngauruhoe rocks, it is quite possible that none of them are. Despite sounding like it solves all the problems, isochron dating gives even worse results than the other technique for rocks of known ages, and widely discordant ages for the same rock when using different transform chains. This clearly indicates that the assumptions behind isochron dating are incorrect.

If it is so scientific, why doesn't it work?

Why does something that sounds so ... well ... *scientific* not work? To understand this, consider the situation depicted in Figure 11.

This shows a graduated cylinder like those used commonly in high school chemistry labs. It contains 300 ml of liquid and liquid is running in at 50 ml per hour. If asked to determine how much time has passed since this process started, most people would conclude 6 hours, calculated by dividing 300 by 50.

However, this calculation assumes that the cylinder began the process with no liquid present, that nothing has happened to the cylinder during the process to either remove or add liquid, other than that which is coming in from the tap, and that the input rate has remained the same throughout the process. If, for example, the cylinder started with 250 ml of liquid in it, the time would be much shorter. If some of the liquid had been spilled, the time would be different again. In other words, the calculation of the length of time, though apparently quite straightforward, makes a number of assumptions about the past, which, without an eye-witness present throughout the process, cannot be known to be true. Consequently, the calculated time cannot be known to be correct.

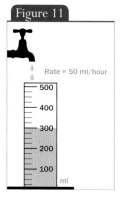

Figure 11

Rate = 50 ml/hour

500
400
300
200
100
ml

The same is true for radiometric dating. While the algebra and arithmetic are straightforward, both techniques discussed above ('model' and isochron) depend on a number of assumptions about the history of the rock, none of which can be known to be true as there was no eye-witness present throughout that history. Furthermore, when the measurement of ratios is done very near the time of formation of the rock, even a small amount of 'unexpected' radiogenic daughter makes the calculations seriously in error. As I said above, in a 6,000-year timeframe, even a small amount of 'unexpected' argon will give apparent ages in the millions of years for the K-Ar model technique. The 'excess Ar' argument is used by evolutionists to reject the results of testing rocks of *known* age, but they do not consider the idea that all these age determinations are very near the time of formation, relative to the half-life of the transformation (i.e. 6,000 years versus 1.248 billion years). Thus, any measurement that indicates a very old age may instead be indicating that a quite small amount of unexpected Daughter has been incorporated into the rock.

Additionally, all radiometric dating techniques assume that the half-lives of the transformations involved (or, equivalently, the rates of the transformations) have remained constant at today's values throughout the entire history of the rock. Although this assumption may seem much more likely that the others, recent discoveries indicate that the transformation rates of ^{60}Co to ^{60}Ni (β-decay), ^{137}Cs to ^{137}Ba (β-decay), ^{32}Si to ^{32}P (β-decay) and ^{226}Ra to ^{222}Rn (α-decay) vary in conjunction with variation in solar activity. Thus, it is clearly possible that this assumption could also be wrong.[6,7] This is supported by the findings of scientists working on the RATE project (_R_adioisotopes and the _A_ge of _t_he _E_arth), sponsored by the Institute for Creation Research, who concluded there was a pulse of accelerated radioactive decay around the time of the Flood. This was strongly indicated by helium diffusion experiments (see discussion later) and supported by other lines of evidence from the analysis of radiohalos and fission tracks. When, how much and by what mechanism this extra decay happened is still a matter of debate.[8]

Since the calculations of age are quite sensitive to these assumptions, and since it is clear that we cannot know if the assumptions are true, and since radiometric dating produces wildly incorrect results for rocks of known ages, it is quite reasonable to conclude that radiometric dates are entirely unreliable. If a 50-year-old rock can be radiometrically dated as 3.9 billion ± 10% years old, how do we know that another rock radiometrically dated as 4.54 billion years old (and alleged to represent the age of the earth) is not actually ~ 6,000 years old, even if the precision is quoted as ± 1%?

While scientists who adhere to the billions-of-years perspective can construct explanations for the discrepancies between the real, known ages and the incorrect radiometric ages, these are after-the-fact explanations, constructed when it becomes known that the measured results do not agree with reality. When no 'reality check' is possible, it cannot be known whether the measured ages are

6. Baurov, Y.A. *et al.*, Experimental investigations of changes in β-decay rate of ^{60}Co and ^{137}Cs, *Physics of Atomic Nuclei*, **70**(11):1825–1835, 2001.

7. Jenkins, J.H. *et al.*, Evidence of correlation between nuclear decay rates and Earth-Sun distance, *Astropart. Phys.*, 32:42–46, 2009.

8. *Radioisotopes and the Age of the Earth Volumes I and II* (Edited by Vardiman, Snelling and Chaffin), Institute of Creation Research, El Cajon, CA and Creation Research Society, Chino Valley, AZ, 2005.

any more correct than in the cases of the examples discussed. Consequently it seems appropriate to apply Occam's razor and conclude that the method itself is unreliable due to the unknowable assumptions about the history of the rock.

What about Carbon dating?

People often mistakenly conflate carbon dating with the types of radiometric dating just discussed. While carbon dating is a radiometric dating technique, it is applicable only to non-living, organic (plant or animal) samples, or sources of carbon once derived from life processes (e.g. coal or limestone). In addition, carbon dating involves a transformation with a relatively short half-life. This, combined with the capabilities of the modern equipment used in this technique, means that there is a very short upper limit to the ages that can be measured using the technique.

Carbon dating is based on carbon-14 (^{14}C) also referred to as radiocarbon, a radioactive isotope of carbon. This isotope is formed by the interactions of cosmic rays with molecules in the atmosphere, eventually resulting in the transformation of ^{14}N to ^{14}C. Because it is chemically identical to normal carbon (^{12}C), this radioactive form of carbon combines with oxygen to form carbon dioxide. This is taken up by plants during photosynthesis and is then ingested by animals when they eat the plants, where it spreads throughout the animals' bodies, becoming part of the blood, bone, muscle, nerves, and hair. Radioactive carbon is incorporated into the human body as a result of the normal process of eating veggies and/or meat products.

As long as the plant or animal is living, the radioactive carbon in its body is roughly in equilibrium with the radioactive carbon in the atmosphere. Some ^{14}C in its body is always transforming back to nitrogen, but new ^{14}C is constantly being incorporated into its body. However, when the plant/animal dies, it stops eating and breathing, so it stops exchanging carbon with the environment and stops incorporating new radioactive carbon into its body, while the radioactive carbon already there continues to transform back to nitrogen. As a result, the amount of ^{14}C in the dead plant/animal decreases over time, with a half-life of about 5,730 years.

Since the stable Daughter element resulting from this transformation is nitrogen (a gas), it is not possible to measure the ratio of stable daughter element to radioactive parent element in the sample as is done in the 'model' technique described previously because the nitrogen escapes into the atmosphere as the plant/animal decomposes.

However, the amount of normal carbon in the dead plant/animal does not change since ^{12}C is stable. This is illustrated in Figure 12. Consequently, if we can measure the ratio of radioactive carbon to normal carbon, *assuming that the ratio in the atmosphere at the time of death was the same as it is today,* and *assuming no change in the half life over time,* we can calculate the length of time since the death of the plant/animal.

Carbon dating was developed by Dr William Libby in 1949, when he was a professor at the University of Chicago, and for which he was awarded the 1960 Nobel Prize in Chemistry.

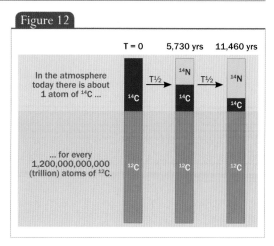

Figure 12

He and his graduate team of post-doctoral fellow James Arnold and graduate student Ernie Anderson demonstrated its utility by dating some wood from an ancient Egyptian royal barge, and comparing it with the age published in historical sources.

Originally, determining the amount of radioactive carbon in the sample was done using scintillation counters (similar to the more familiar Geiger counter) to count the number of ^{14}C to ^{14}N transformations in a number of consecutive time intervals by detecting the radiation emitted during the transformation. This, however, requires a large amount of sample material and/or a very long measurement period because of the small fraction of ^{14}C (there is only about 1 atom of ^{14}C for every 1.2 trillion atoms of ^{12}C in the atmosphere today) and its half-life of 5,730 years. Today, measurements are done using the more sensitive Accelerator Mass Spectrometers (AMS) which count all the ^{14}C atoms, not just those that transform. These machines have made it possible to detect much smaller amounts of ^{14}C, but eventually there is so little ^{14}C left in the sample that it becomes undetectable even by these sophisticated machines. It would take about 15.6 half-lives of ^{14}C (about 90,000 years) for the ^{14}C in a sample to decay to the point where these modern machines could no longer detect it. Thus, ^{14}C dating cannot determine ages of things that are theoretically older than about 90,000 years.

Typically coal is mostly carbon (with minor amounts of hydrogen, nitrogen, oxygen and other elements). It is found in nearly all strata of the geological column. In 2003, scientists obtained 10 coal samples that had been collected by the US Department of Energy and carefully stored in its Coal Sample Bank, maintained at Pennsylvania State University. These coal samples were from a number of different strata in a number of different states in the US. According to uniformitarian geology, these coals ranged in age from 37 million years to

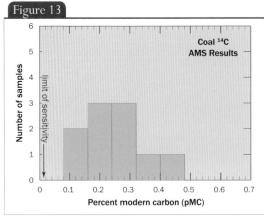

Figure 13

The measured ages ranged from 44,500 to 59,000 years old, with a mean of 0.247 (+/- 0.109 SD) percent modern carbon. These are for coals allegedly ranging from 37 to 318 million years old! Note also that the mean was 123x the sensitivity of the instrument. After Baumgardner (2005).[9]

318 million years, so any ^{14}C present at formation should have long since decreased to well below the detection sensitivity of the AMS machines. However, the scientists sent these samples to an AMS laboratory for carbon dating. The results are shown in Figure 13 along with an indication of the typical sensitivity limit of the AMS.[9]

As can be seen in Figure 13, the coal samples all contained between 0.1 and 0.5% ^{14}C, and even the smallest amount of ^{14}C was well above the sensitivity of the AMS, clearly indicating that these measurements were not some anomalous blip. Doing the calculations results in a radiocarbon 'age' for these coal samples of about 45,000 to 60,000 years. This is a far cry from the 37 to 318 million years assigned to these coals by uniformitarian geologists.

People intent on preserving the evolutionary timescale have suggested a number of reasons for the presence of this high level of ^{14}C. Things such as contamination with modern carbon during the testing process, contamination in situ by migration of ^{14}C from the atmosphere to the coal seam, double capture of thermal neutrons produced by fission of uranium in the surrounding rock, etc. None of these suggestions survive careful scientific analysis.[10] For example, the laboratories that do these measurements have developed sophisticated procedures to ensure that results are not affected by contamination from modern carbon.

Furthermore, radiocarbon measurements have also been made on diamonds. Diamonds are also primarily carbon and the atoms are in a tightly packed crystal lattice that is the hardest known naturally occurring mineral. Therefore, diamonds are quite impervious to infiltration. Contamination of diamond samples during measurement is definitely not an issue. The results of testing 7 diamond samples are shown in Figure 14. Once again, all measurements are

9.   Baumgardner, J.R., ^{14}C Evidence for a Recent Global Flood and a Young Earth, in *Radioisotopes and the Age of the Earth Volume II* (Edited by Vardiman, Snelling and Chaffin), Institute of Creation Research, El Cajon, CA and Creation Research Society, Chiro Valley, AZ, pp 587–630, 2005.

10. Sarfati, J., Diamonds: a creationist's best friend, *Creation* **28**(4):26–27, 2006; creation.com/diamonds.

many times the minimum sensitivity limit of the AMS. Although the average level of ^{14}C is different from that of the coal samples, the radiocarbon age for the diamonds, at ~50,000 years is essentially the same as that of the coal. However, uniformitarian geology puts the age of the diamonds as ranging from 1 to 3 *billion* years.

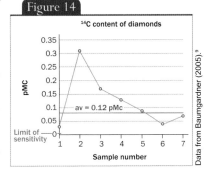

Radiocarbon dating clearly shows that the coal and the diamonds are not as old as uniformitarian geology would have us believe and, indeed, may well have been formed at about the same time. However, the calculated ages are also quite different from what would be determined from the Bible. Why is this?

Accepting that coal is formed from buried vegetation, the burial would have happened during the Genesis Flood, which, according to the Bible, occurred about 4,500 years ago (about 1,500 years after the creation of the universe). That being the case, one would expect to measure 'percent modern carbon' (pMC) of about 58% rather than the 0.024% that is actually measured *if the ratio of ^{14}C to ^{12}C in the atmosphere at the time of burial was the same as it is today.* However, this was almost certainly not the case.

On the one hand, it is quite possible that the original creation had no ^{14}C in the atmosphere and that the level of ^{14}C had to build up over time. The rate of formation would have depended on the cosmic ray flux which, in turn, would have depended on the strength of the earth's magnetic field, which is known to have been steadily decreasing for at least the last century.[11,12] A stronger magnetic field in the past would have meant fewer cosmic rays and, hence, slower ^{14}C production.

Furthermore, since the Flood buried a huge amount of ^{12}C that was previously active in the biosphere, it is probable that the level of carbon dioxide in the pre-flood atmosphere was also much higher than it is today. This would account for the bountiful, lush vegetation required to produce the vast amounts of coal.

These factors would act to make the ratio of ^{14}C to ^{12}C in the pre-Flood world much smaller than it is today (less ^{14}C, more ^{12}C). Also, the intense volcanism associated with the Flood (there is a huge amount of volcanic material in the rocks that would have been formed during the Flood) would have dumped

11. MacDonald, K.L., and Gunt, R.H., An analysis of the earth's magnetic field from 1835 to 1965, *ESSA Technical Report, IER 46-IES1,* US Government Printing Office, Washington, 1967; referenced in Sarfati, J., The earth's magnetic field: evidence that the earth is young; creation.com/magfield.
12. Merrill, R.T., McElhinney, M.W., and McFadden, P.L., The magnetic field of the earth: paleomagnetism, the core and the deep mantle, Academic Press, 1996.

billions of tons of non-radioactive carbon into the atmosphere, further diluting any ^{14}C that may have been present. Thus, after the Flood, the ratio of ^{14}C to ^{12}C would have to increase to reach today's levels, meaning anything alive in the years immediately after the Flood would have a radiocarbon age much older than reality. Accounting for this could easily put the calculated time since burial at 4,500 years for even the 'oldest' samples.

Radiometric dating using helium

The radiometric dating techniques discussed so far use the radioactive parent and the stable daughter as the measurement items of interest and ignore the other particles resulting from the radioactivity. Some recent research, however, has used the alpha particles produced during the transformation of uranium to lead as a way of estimating age, with some surprising, but very interesting, results.

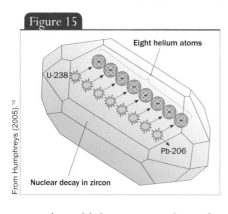

Figure 15

Eight helium atoms

U-238

Pb-206

Nuclear decay in zircon

From Humphreys (2005).[13]

Alpha particles consist of two neutrons and two protons. They are, in fact, helium nuclei, that is, helium atoms stripped of their electrons.

The alpha particles used in this study were those formed by the transformation of uranium in tiny zircon crystals that were extracted from rocks in the earth's crust from a hole bored by Los Alamos National Laboratory at Fenton Hill, New Mexico, USA.[13] Zircon crystals often contain a high concentration of uranium. Uranium-238 transforms to lead through a number of intermediate (radioactive) stages. In so doing, a total of 8 alpha particles are emitted. As noted earlier, alpha particles are actually positively charged helium nuclei. As such, they strongly attract electrons to become neutral helium atoms. For each uranium-238 atom that transforms to lead, 8 helium atoms are produced in the zircon crystal. This is illustrated in Figure 15.

Helium is a 'noble' gas, which means it does not form compounds with other elements. It is also the lightest, and extremely small, with a Van der Waals radius of only 140 picometers (10^{-12} meters). Together, these characteristics mean that helium diffuses through materials, even rocks, very readily, as anyone who has purchased a helium-filled balloon too far in advance of a party knows only too well! As the uranium atoms transform to lead in the zircon crystals, the

13. Humphreys, D.R., Young Helium Diffusion Age of Zircons Supports Accelerated Nuclear Decay, in *Radioisotopes and the Age of the Earth Volume II* (Edited by Vardiman, Snelling and Chaffin), Institute of Creation Research, El Cajon, CA and Creation Research Society, Chiro Valley, AZ, pp 25–100, 2005.

concentration of helium builds up, which causes the helium to diffuse out of the zircon crystals into regions where the concentration of helium is lower.

Based on the amount of uranium, thorium and lead isotopes found in the zircon crystals, the radiometric age of these crystals was calculated using the techniques previously described to be 1.50 ± 0.02 billion years.[14] Because of the ease with which helium diffuses through things, it would be expected that, in 1.5 billion years, essentially all the helium that would have been produced by the transformation of uranium to lead would have diffused out of the zircon crystals. Surprisingly, this was not the case. Up to 58% of the helium was still in the crystals!

Using the measured amount of helium found in the zircon crystals, the rate at which helium would diffuse through zircon (the *diffusivity*) was calculated based on the alleged age of the crystals of 1.5 billion years. The diffusivity depends on the temperature of the material. Since the zircon crystals came from different depths (ranging from 960 m to 3.9 km) and, therefore, different temperatures (ranging from 105°C to 277°C [=388K to 550K]), it was necessary to do this calculation for the different temperatures involved. This is shown in Figure 16. A similar calculation was done using the measured amounts of helium and an assumed age for the zircon crystals of 6,000 years in accordance with the Bible. The results of these calculations are also shown in Figure 16. Because of the logarithmic nature of the vertical axis, these two models differ by a factor of 100,000.

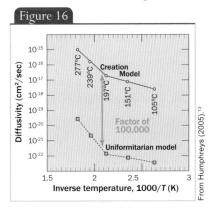

The predictive calculations were done in the year 2000. In 2003 some additional zircon crystals were obtained from the same bore hole and sent to an independent laboratory to have the actual helium diffusivity measured. This was done through an independent third party to remove the potential for observer bias in the measurements. The results are shown in Figure 17. As can be clearly seen, the measured diffusivities correspond very well with the predictions based on the biblical, 6,000-year-old age for the zircons.

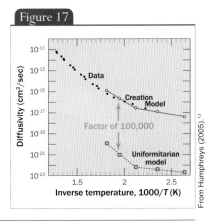

---

14. Humphreys (2005), ref. 13.

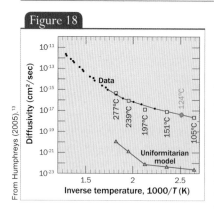

Figure 18

Diffusivity (cm²/sec) vs Inverse temperature, 1000/T (K)

Data

277°C 239°C 197°C 151°C 124°C 105°C

Uniformitarian model

From Humphreys (2005).[13]

Redoing the model calculations to provide a "best fit" with the measured data (Figure 18), resulted in an age for the zircon crystals of 5681 ± 2000 years, which can be rounded to 6,000 ± 2,000 years without misstating the result.

What can we conclude?

Evolution needs millions/billions of years. Radiometric dating is alleged to provide unequivocal proof that the earth is 4.54 billion years old. However, as has been shown, radiometric ages are unreliable and this is irrespective of whether these are whole rock, mineral "model" ages, or isochron ages.

- Whole rock model measurements of the Mt. St. Helen's lava dome formed in 1984 give an age of 350,000 years, while mineral model ages range from 340,000 years to 2.5 million years, depending on which mineral within the rock is used.

- Whole rock ages for lava flows from Mt. Ngaurahoe in NZ formed from 1945 to 1975 range up to 2.5 million years and isochron ages for these same rocks range from 133 million to 3.9 billion years.

In all cases, the claimed experimental error is just a few percent. Therefore, while these ages may be precise, they are all wrong, in some cases by a factor of about 80 million.

Radiocarbon (^{14}C), which should be undetectable after about 90,000 years, is found in abundance in coal allegedly ranging in age from 35 million to 315 million years and in diamonds allegedly 1–3 billion years old. Moreover, the amount of radiocarbon in both the coal and the diamonds is approximately the same, indicating that they were all formed at about the same time. Taking into account the amount of normal carbon (^{12}C) buried during the global flood to form the coal, the amount of low-radiocarbon CO_2 released through volcanism during the Flood year, the massive reabsorption of carbon during the formation of rocks (e.g. limestone),we expect a dramatic change in the ratio of radio-carbon to normal carbon. Thus, the measured levels of ^{14}C are compatible with a true age for the coal of only about 4,500 years: the approximate length of time from the global flood to the present, as derived from the biblical text.

Furthermore, the amount of radiogenic helium found in zircons formed at depth, combined with the measured value of the rate of diffusion of helium through zircon, indicates that these crystals are just 6,000 ± 2,000 years old.

In summary, radiometric dating does not provide the unequivocal support for the millions and billions of years required by evolution. In fact, radiometric dating provides evidence for a much younger earth, in line with the history recorded in the Bible.

Where does this lead?

If radiometric dating exposes yet another Achilles' heel of evolution, what is left? The last remaining hope for evolution's millions/billions of years is a universe that is billions of light-years in size and, allegedly, also billions of years old. However, in the next chapter, it is explained how the universe can be billions of light years in size and yet we can see starlight from these distant galaxies on an earth that is only about 6,000 years old, just as the Bible says.

Dr John Hartnett

Ph.D. Physics, University of Western Australia

Dr Hartnett is an experimental physicist with numerous publications and several significant awards under his belt. He works with the Frequency Standards and Metrology research group at his university, holding the rank of tenured Research Professor (the equivalent of Reader in the UK or Full Professor in the USA). John's research interests include the development of ultra-stable cryogenically cooled microwave oscillators based on a sapphire crystal, ultra low-noise radar, tests of fundamental theories of physics such as Special and General Relativity and measurement of drift in fundamental constants and their cosmological implications. The author of multiple creationist articles on cosmology and several books, including the best-selling *Starlight and Time and the New Physics*, his background makes him the perfect choice to discuss the seventh in our list of *Evolution's Achilles' Heels*, big bang cosmology.

See **creation.com/dr-john-hartnett-cv**

COSMOLOGY:
EXPOSING THE BIG BANG'S FATAL FLAWS

Dr John Hartnett
Ph.D. Physics [University of Western Australia]

7

A Brief History

Over eighty years ago (1929) the astronomer Edwin Hubble discovered what has now become known as the Hubble Law. That was the discovery that redshifts[1] of the spectral lines seen in the light of nearby galaxies have a simple relationship to the distances to those galaxies. The further away the object, the greater the redshift. This result was interpreted to mean that *the universe is expanding*. Interestingly, Hubble himself did not strongly believe in

Idealized galaxy spectra showing typical 'absorption' lines (black against a rainbow-coloured background) produced by hydrogen atoms absorbing light (log scale). The faster an object is receding, the greater the redshift (shift to the right on this diagram), and Hubble's Law states that redshift is proportional to distance (for small redshifts).

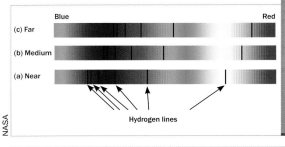

Blue | Red
(c) Far
(b) Medium
(a) Near

Hydrogen lines

NASA

---

1. This means that the wavelength of the light received has been shifted toward the red end of the spectrum.

the expanding universe idea and at times wrote that redshifts result from some hitherto-undiscovered mechanism.[2] Hubble's discovery answered one of the big science questions of the day, by showing that galaxies were rushing away from our own galaxy in all directions. Some of the 'nebulae' seen in telescopes were actually separate galaxies, and these galaxies were rushing away from our own galaxy in all directions.

Several years before, in 1917, Albert Einstein had developed his own cosmology from his general theory of relativity. But Einstein's universe was static. When Einstein heard about Hubble's discovery, he scrapped his static (stationary) universe and proclaimed it as his 'biggest blunder'. Einstein's cosmology had included a 'cosmological constant' (Λ), a fudge factor added to his equations to counteract the attractive effect of gravity. We'll soon see that Einstein's blunder has come back again to haunt us.

In the decade after the publication of Einstein's 1917 paper, two cosmologists, Alexander Friedmann and Abbé Georges Lemaître, working independently, found the same solution to Einstein's field equations in 1922 and 1927, respectively.[3] This provided the mathematical model—now called the Friedmann-Lemaître model—to describe the expanding universe discovered by Hubble. Lemaître himself described his theory as 'the cosmic egg exploding at the moment of the creation'. It became better known as the 'big bang theory,' a term coined as a derisive comment by Sir Fred Hoyle while being interviewed on BBC radio around 1950.

George Gamow, a former student of Friedmann, predicted in 1948 that leftover radiation from the big bang fireball should be observed today, with a temperature variously between 5 K and 50 K[4] (he revised his prediction over time, eventually arriving at the higher temperature). By 1965 Arno Penzais and Robert Wilson, two Bell Laboratories radio astronomers, discovered, somewhat serendipitously, the Cosmic Microwave Background (CMB) radiation, coming from all directions on the sky and with a temperature near 3 K (-270° C). For this they were awarded the Nobel Prize in 1978.[5] This discovery gave big bang cosmology an enormous boost. Coupled with the redshift evidence for an expanding universe, it seemed that the big bang was all but proven.

2. Hubble, E.P., The 200-Inch telescope and some problems it may solve, *Proc. Astron. Soc. Pacific* **59**:153–167, 1947.
3. Friedmann died in 1925 and never met Lemaître. Lemaître met Einstein at the famous Solvay Conference in 1927 where Einstein was reputed to have said to him "Your math is correct, but your physics is abominable." Einstein obviously did not like his model. But Lemaître went on to popularize it; Einstein even co-lectured with him. It is worth noting that in 1933, Lemaître found an important inhomogeneous solution of Einstein's field equations, the Lemaître–Tolman metric, describing the universe as an expanding, spherically symmetric ball of dust.
4. K is the unit of the Kelvin absolute temperature scale where 0°C = 273.15 K.
5. Press release: the 1978 Nobel Prize in Physics, 17 October 1978; www.nobelprize.org.

Cosmology the philosophy

Even though he derided the idea of a big bang, Hoyle was an atheist and believed in an eternal universe without beginning or end. The model that now bears his label, the 'big bang', has an origin in time and has become the dominant worldview of the majority of the scientific community. Here is a very important and crucial point: the big bang theory is accepted *a priori* as the correct description for the origin and structure of the universe. The mathematical model that describes the expansion from a singularity at the big bang to the present is believed to be the correct history of the universe.

The irony is that an absolute beginning *ex nihilo* points to a transcendent cause of the universe beyond space and time. Yet, most proponents of this worldview today are on the atheist side of the debate. Thus, many big bang believers have sought to find a naturalistic cause to the universe. Once one understands the philosophical nature of the issue, however, all objections raised to date against the cosmogony described in the first chapters of Genesis cannot be sustained, as explained below.

Over the last decade, the claim has been made that the big bang theory has been further strengthened by precise observations of the CMB radiation from several space-borne telescopes—COBE, WMAP and PLANCK. From this have come claims of 'precision cosmology'[6] and more Nobel prizes.[7] The astrophysicist George Smoot, who led the team that launched the COBE space telescope, described the detected anisotropies (microscopic ripples) in the 3 K temperature of the CMB radiation as 'the handwriting of God.' Terminology like this, that interprets the ripples in the cosmic background radiation as though one were reading God's journal of the first days of creation, gives clues to the real nature of the belief system.

But one should not be deceived by idle comments like these. At most, this is a reference to a deist's god, who fired up the initial explosion and since then has had little else to do. This is not a reference to the Creator of the Bible, but to some impersonal 'force' at most, or even to the universe itself.[8] Physicists often make such references when they refer to the requirement that the laws

6. Ellis, R., New age of precision cosmology, *physicsworld.com*, 1 July 1999; Primack, J.R., Precision cosmology, *New Astron. Rev.* **49**:25–34, 2005; Tegmark, M., Precision cosmology, *MIT World*, 7 June 2008; mitworld.mit.edu.

7. The Nobel Prize in Physics 2006 was awarded jointly to John C. Mather and George F. Smoot "for their discovery of the blackbody form and anisotropy [or ripples] of the cosmic microwave background radiation"; nobelprize.org.

8. Professor Stephen Hawking, of Cambridge University, co-authored a book *The Grand Design* wherein he says that God was not necessary because the universe created itself. See, for example, Agomuoh, F., Stephen Hawking: Universe created itself, law of science is God, *Christian Today Australia*, 5 August 2011; au.christiantoday.com; and Thomas, B., Hawking says universe created itself, 13 September 2010; icr.org.

of physics be finely tuned in order for life to exist. They even call this the 'Goldilocks universe'; not too hot, not too cold, but just right. In such a place, the laws and constants of nature are so finely tuned that life just had to evolve, to their mind.

Methods have been devised to test this theory. But this is not the same as the repeatable experimental or operational science performed daily in laboratories worldwide. In cosmology, one can only make observations. Models are constructed for some feature being tested and statistics are taken. Generally this means large numerical simulations—calculations that simulate mock galaxies in a mock universe, for example. Certainly any models that fail to reproduce observations can be excluded, but one cannot interact with the universe; one cannot even make a direct measurement of the size of a galaxy! The universe is too vast and the astronomer is limited to what he receives with his telescopes. Interpreting any measurement involves the use of a set of assumptions. Hence there are many possible models, including those the researcher has not yet imagined. As a result, this branch of science is very weak, when compared to the work of the experimentalist in a lab.

Image NASA, wikipedia.org

We might ask, with all the modern technology—including space-borne telescopes like the Hubble Space Telescope and numerous others, and large, earth-based telescopes with adaptive optics and advanced supercomputers for image processing and simulations—hasn't the evidence now been firmly found to establish the big bang as correct? The following citation (emphases added) from a 2007 article in the prestigious journal *Science* includes quotes from three well known cosmologists. The author states:

Researchers have measured the temperature variations in the CMB so precisely that the biggest uncertainty now stems from the fact that we see the microwave sky for only one Hubble volume [i.e. only one possible observable universe—JH], an uncertainty called cosmic variance. 'We've done the measurement,' [Charles] Bennett says. 'It's not going to get any better.'

That barrier to knowledge, some argue, is cosmology's Achilles' heel. 'Cosmology may look like a science, but it isn't a science,' says James Gunn of Princeton University, co-founder of the Sloan survey [currently the biggest large-scale survey of millions of galaxies—JH]. 'A basic tenet of science is that you can do repeatable experiments, and you can't do that in cosmology.'

'The goal of physics is to understand the basic dynamics of the universe,' [Michael] Turner says. 'Cosmology is a little different. The goal is to reconstruct the history of the universe.' Cosmology is more akin to evolutionary biology or geology, he says, in which researchers must simply accept some facts as given.[9]

This is the state of cosmology today. Now let's unpack this a little. What are they really talking about? Since we have only one universe, they cannot test their theories on another; they cannot compare and make deductions based on the different outcomes of an experiment. This is what we do in the lab. Bennett admits this and that it is the best we have.

But this lack of ability to experimentally test the model is, by the big bang cosmologists' own admission, *the Achilles' heel of cosmology*. In reality, cosmology is what we call historical science, because it tries to reconstruct the past history of the universe from observations we make today. It is no stronger than constructing the unknown-yet-assumed geological history of our planet (Chapter 5) or the putative sequences of biological organisms that produced a microbiologist from a microbe (Chapters 3 and 4) over several billion years. It was the presupposition of denial of biblical authority, particularly regarding the Creation and Flood accounts, which led to long-age beliefs about the earth. It then followed that geological evolution led to biological evolution.[10] 'Cosmic evolution' is the application of the same sorts of naturalistic (no Creator) assumptions to the origin of the earth and all heavenly bodies, the universe itself. Despite heroic efforts to portray it as 'God's way of creating', the big bang in fact epitomizes the currently fashionable model: a fully materialistic system of cosmic evolution.

So, you see, cosmology is not so much about empirical science but about a philosophy—a worldview. What are you prepared to accept as a fact? No evidence stands on its own. It is all interpreted in light of the worldview of the researcher, the cosmologist in this case. He is not trying to disprove or falsify his model; it is accepted as the 'truth' and then evidence is accumulated to establish that truth, especially in the minds of the wider lay audience. Often the evidence is chosen based on the model, then cycled back to 'establish' it even further. This is what is now referred to as 'precision cosmology'. Examples of this will be discussed below.

Cosmologist George F. R. Ellis candidly explained,

People need to be aware that there is a range of models that could explain the observations. For instance, I can construct you a spherically symmetrical universe with Earth at its center, and you cannot disprove

---

9. Cho, A., A singular conundrum: How odd is our universe? *Science* **317**:1848–1850, 2007.
10. Mortenson, T., *The Great Turning Point*, Master Books, Green Forest, AR, USA, 2004.

it based on observations … you can only exclude it on philosophical grounds. In my view there is absolutely nothing wrong in that. What I want to bring into the open is the fact that we are using philosophical criteria in choosing our models. A lot of cosmology tries to hide that.[11]

The cosmological principle

The standard big bang FLRW model[12] (the modern version of the Friedmann–Lemaître model), relies on the 'cosmological principle', which states that the distribution of matter throughout the universe is homogeneous (or uniform) and isotropic (the same in all directions). That is, regardless of when or where an observation is made from, on the large scale, you see the same thing. Without this assumption there is no model, and the principle is believed today more by blind faith than by observation. I will say it again: the cosmological principle is not the consequence of observational evidence, it is the *starting assumption* used in interpreting all such evidence.

> The FLRW metric can be expressed in this form:
> $$-c^2 d\tau^2 = -c^2 dt^2 + a(t)^2 d\Sigma^2$$

The cosmological principle is, historically, an extension of the Copernican principle, which states that the earth does not occupy a special place in the universe and that observations made from Earth can be taken to be broadly characteristic of what would be seen from any other point in the universe at the same epoch. That principle broke with the Ptolemaic geocentric system which had the earth at the centre of the universe. Ptolemy's system was not the biblical view. Certainly, the Bible promotes the idea that we are at the centre of His attention and purpose, but there is no biblical prerequisite for a geocentric universe. In the 16th and 17th centuries, it was the scientific scholars of the day, not the Bible, that were in opposition to the discoveries of Copernicus and Galileo.[13] Some in the Church were persuaded by the geocentric believers, just as many in the church today have been persuaded by secular scholars to accept the big bang story for the history of the universe, in contradiction to the account in Genesis.

> The *Copernican Principle* states that the earth is not in any special place in the universe

> The *Cosmological Principle* states that, on a sufficiently large scale, no matter where an observer is located in the universe he would observe the same uniform distribution of matter at the same epoch of time.

However, there are those who now challenge the veracity of the cosmological principle. The CMB itself has produced results that are inconsistent with a

---

11. Gibbs, W.W., Profile: George F. R. Ellis, *Scientific American* **273**(4):55, October 1995.
12. FLRW = Friedmann-Lemaître-Robertson-Walker metric is used today.
13. Grigg, R., The Galileo 'twist', *Creation* **19**(4):30–32, 1997; creation.com/the-galileo-twist.

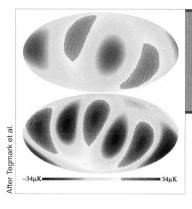

Calculated CMB quadrupole (above) and octopole (below) modes appear to be very closely aligned to the same spatial axis.*

Tegmark, M., de Oliveira-Costa, A. and Hamilton A., A high resolution foreground cleaned CMB map from WMAP, astroph/0302496, *Phys. Rev. D.* **68**:123523, 2003.

−34μK ■■■■■■■■ ■■■■■■■■ 34μK

After Tegmark et al.

homogeneous and isotropic universe. The famous 'Axis of Evil'[14] is a preferred direction in the sky—making the universe analogous to a birefringent crystal[15] with a preferred axis—and comes from measurements of those ripples in the CMB radiation. This preferred direction means that some features of the CMB ripples (anisotropies) are aligned around that direction in space, which, if confirmed, would strongly contradict the cosmological principle. And as some observers have pointed out, the ripples in the CMB data (especially those from the WMAP space telescope) do not appear to be consistent with the big bang picture. Amazingly, the 'Axis of Evil' even seems to be aligned with the plane of the solar system and the path of the Sun in the sky (the ecliptic). But how could that be if it is relic radiation left over from the big bang itself?

NASA/WMAP Science Team

WMAP cosmic microwave anisotropy map. Colors represent +/- 200 millionths of a degree (K) temperature differences.

Nevertheless, the presuppositional underpinnings of the big bang are quite obvious. The now famous Friedmann–Lemaître equation is a result of that cosmological assumption. But is that assumption valid? Physicist Richard Feynman succinctly describes the problem:

> ... I suspect that the assumption of uniformity of the universe reflects a prejudice born of a sequence of overthrows of geocentric ideas. ... It would be embarrassing to find, after stating that we live in an ordinary planet about an ordinary star in an ordinary galaxy, that our place in the universe is extraordinary ... To avoid embarrassment we cling to the hypothesis of uniformity.[16]

14. Hartnett, J., CMB conundrums, *J. Creation* **20**(2):10–11, 2006; creation.com/cmb-conundrums.
15. Calcite is a good example. It is anisotropic in the propagation of light rays through the crystal. There is a preferred axis around which that propagation is uniaxial.
16. Feynman, R.P., Morinigo, F.B. and Wagner, W.G., *Feynman Lectures on Gravitation*, Penguin Books, London, p. 166, 1999.

The challenge

There are not many cosmologists and astrophysicists that are so frank in their descriptions of the state of cosmology today. Why is that? Is it because the unverifiable starting assumptions are inherently wrong? But some brave physicists have the temerity to challenge the ruling paradigm—the standard big bang ΛCDM inflation cosmology.[17] One of those is astrophysicist Richard Lieu of the University of Alabama, Huntsville. Lieu wrote:

> Cosmology is not even astrophysics: all the principal assumptions in this field are unverified (or unverifiable) in the laboratory ... because the Universe offers no control experiment, i.e. with no independent checks, it is bound to be highly ambiguous and degenerate.[18,19]

This seems a fair analysis, because cosmologists today have invented all sorts of stuff that has just the right properties to make their theories work, but stuff that has never been observed in the lab. Things like the mysterious 'dark matter' and 'dark energy'. Lieu says they have become 'comfortable with inventing unknowns to explain the unknown.'

But does a universe teeming with unobservable exotica really reflect reality? Or does the Emperor need new clothes? Lieu wrote:

> ... astronomical observations can never by themselves be used to prove 'beyond reasonable doubt' a physical theory. This is because we live in only one Universe—the indispensible 'control experiment' is not available. There is no way to interact and get a response from the Universe to test the theory under question, like an experimentalist might do in a laboratory experiment. At most the cosmologist collects as much data as he can and uses statistical arguments to try to show that his conclusion is likely. .... Hence the promise of using the Universe as a laboratory from which new incorruptible physical laws may be established without the support of laboratory experiments is preposterous ...[18]

Five 'unknowns'

Lieu lists five evidences where cosmologists use 'unknowns' to explain 'unknowns', and hence he says they are not really astrophysicists. Yet these evidences are claimed to be all explained (and in the case of the CMB even predicted[20]) by the big bang ΛCDM inflation model. None of them are based on laboratory experiments and they are unlikely ever to be explained this way.

---

17. ΛCDM = cold dark matter cosmology with a non-zero cosmological constant (Λ).
18. Lieu, R., ΛCDM cosmology: how much suppression of credible evidence, and does the model really lead its competitors, using all evidence?, 17 May 2007; preprint available at arxiv.org.
19. Hartnett, J., Cosmology is not even astrophysics, 3 December 2008; creation.com/not-astrophysics.
20. But for the logical and scientific fallacies of this claim, see Sarfati, J., Nobel Prize for alleged big bang proof, 7–8 October 2006; creation.com/bigbangnobel.

They are:

1. Galaxy redshifts, explained by **expansion of space**,

2. CMB radiation, explained as the **afterglow of the big bang**,

3. Rotation curves of spiral galaxies,[21] explained by **dark matter**,

4. Distant supernovae dimmer than expected, hence an *accelerating* universe, explained by **dark energy**,

5. Flatness and isotropy, explained by **inflation**.

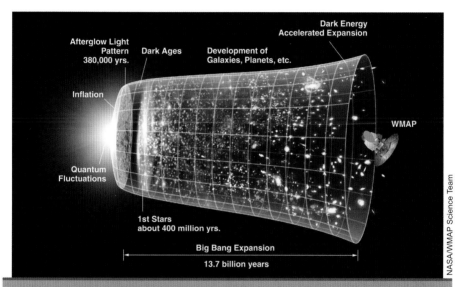

The big bang theory in a nutshell. From left to right, a "quantum fluctuation" produces the matter and energy of the future universe, which then goes through a brief period of "inflation". This inflation creates "flatness" in the energy distribution and prevents the universe from collapsing in on itself. After stars form, "dark matter" is required to explain the shape of galaxies and "dark energy" is required to explain the apparently accelerating expansion of the universe. The cosmic microwave background radiation is the afterglow of the post-inflation fireball, but the light is extremely red-shifted due to the stretching of space.

Emphasized in bold are the five 'unknowns' that the big bang community want you to *just accept by faith*. As an experimentalist, I know the standards used in so-called 'cosmology experiments' would never pass muster in my lab, where I have built the world's most stable cryogenic 'clocks' that we use to

---

21. The speeds of gases (and stars) in the outer regions of the disks in spiral galaxies are inferred from observed Doppler line redshifts or blueshifts. They don't obey Keplerian motion as predicted by Newton's law of gravitation.

test Einstein's theories.[22] Yet it has been said we are now living in the era of 'precision cosmology.[10] Cosmologist Max Tegmark said:

> 30 years ago, cosmology was largely viewed as somewhere out there between philosophy and metaphysics. You could speculate over a bunch of beers about what happened, and then you could go home, because there wasn't a whole lot else to do … . [But now they are closing in on a] consistent picture of how the universe evolved from the earliest moment to the present.[11]

How can that be true if none of Lieu's five evidences can be explained by 'knowns'? They are explained by resorting to 'unknowns', with a sleight of hand that allows the writer to say, 'We are closing in on the truth.' I recall Nobel Laureate Steven Chu speaking to a large gathering of high school children on the occasion of the Australian Institute of Physics National Congress at the Australian National University in 2005. He said that we now understand nearly all there is to know about the universe, except for a few small details, like what are dark energy and dark matter. The irony that, by his own statements, about 95% of the stuff in the universe is allegedly made of these was seemingly lost on him.

We are told that we live in a universe filled with this invisible, unobserved extraordinary stuff—25% dark (unobserved) matter and 70% dark energy. But

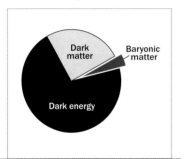

The big bang model suggests the universe is composed of about 70% dark energy, about 25% dark matter, and about 4% baryonic matter, most of which is intergalactic dust. Stars compose only about 0.4% of the matter-energy in the big bang universe.

what *is* this stuff that we cannot detect, yet is supposedly all around us? For 40 years, one form or another of dark matter has been sought in the lab—the axion, for example. This is a hypothetical particle which, if it existed, would have 'cleaned up' some problems in physics of the 1980s. Hence, it was named after a brand of laundry detergent. Today again it is of interest to astronomers and particle physicists because if it exists and has certain properties, it can be invoked as a component of some cold versions of the hypothesized exotic dark matter that supposedly makes up 85% of the matter in most galaxies, which in theory includes our own. This conjecture has arisen, in part, because of the anomalous dynamics observed in the motions of particles in the arms of most spiral galaxies. And though enormous

---

22. These 'clocks' are cryogenically cooled microwave sapphire oscillators which have a precision of a part in 10^{16}, or, you could say, would gain or lose a second in several hundred million years.

effort has gone into trying to detect the elusive particles from our own Galactic halo, all endeavours have so far failed.[23]

Long before these efforts, scientists invoked dark matter to explain puzzling dynamics in the solar system, such as an imaginary planet, named Vulcan, hiding behind the Sun, to account for the discrepancy with the orbit of the planet Mercury. But Einstein solved that problem with his general theory of relativity. Back then what was needed was new physics, not some unseen dark matter. Is this the same situation today?[24]

And today we also have dark energy that is supposedly driving the universe apart at an even faster pace than in the past.

> New evidence has confirmed that the expansion of the universe is accelerating under the influence of a gravitationally repulsive form of energy that makes up two-thirds of the cosmos.

> It is an irony of nature that the most abundant form of energy in the universe is also the most mysterious. Since the breakthrough discovery that the cosmic expansion is accelerating, a consistent picture has emerged indicating that two-thirds of the cosmos is made of 'dark energy'—some sort of gravitationally repulsive material.[25]

Even the expansion of space, also called cosmological expansion, has not been experimentally verified in any earth-based or solar-system-based experiment. It totally relies on the fact that the Hubble Law can be derived from Einstein's general theory. Theory says it results from the finite speed of light and an increase in the size of the universe during the time the light was travelling to Earth from a distant galaxy. The nature of Einstein's tensor theory permits different mathematical solutions; but there is no guarantee that they describe the physical reality. The indeterminacy results from not knowing the correct boundary (or initial) conditions. And all evidence for cosmological expansion comes from the cosmos itself.

Supernovae (exploding stars) are among the brightest light sources in the sky. Astrophysicists believe they have successfully understood the origin of a certain class of these explosions using general relativity theory, where a white dwarf star, after accumulating sufficient mass from a companion star to reach a critical limit, catastrophically collapses in on itself under its own gravity. It then explodes in a blinding flash of light. The luminosity of the explosion rapidly increases, peaks, and then slowly decreases over days and months. By modeling this it is believed that one can understand what the intrinsic brightness at the

23. Aprile, E. *et al.*, (XENON100 Collaboration) *Phys. Rev. Lett.* **105**:131302, 2010.
24. Hartnett, J., *Starlight, Time and the New Physics*, 2ⁿᵈ Ed., Creation Book Publishers, Powder Springs, GA, USA, 2010; available through creation.com.
25. Caldwell, R.R., Dark energy, 30 May 2004; physicsworld.com.

peak of the explosion was and hence one can establish, for a certain class of these supernovae, a 'standard candle'. The theory says that the intrinsic brightness at the peak of the explosion is the same for all supernovae in this class, the type Ia, which are identified from their spectra. If you know their intrinsic brightness, you can theoretically determine their distance in the cosmos. Then, using the redshifts of their host galaxies and the Hubble redshift-distance relation, as derived from the standard cosmology, the theory can be tested with the matter density (mostly dark matter), the dark energy density and the Hubble constant as the only unknown parameters which need to be determined.

From this, astronomers have inferred not only that the universe is expanding, but also that the expansion is accelerating. These type Ia supernovae are the very best evidence for expansion of the cosmos.[26] But, in order to make their observations fit the standard cosmology, they have had to add a significant amount of dark energy with a non-zero value for the cosmological constant (L) and also a significant amount of dark matter.[27] Without them, the ΛCDM big bang model seriously fails to describe the observed luminosities.

Some critics even claim selection bias. Since one cannot determine the absolute luminosities of the candidate supernova without assuming a cosmology, the values of the above-mentioned parameters in the standard concordance model (30% matter, which includes about 25% dark matter, 70% dark energy, and a Hubble constant of 70 km/s/Mpc) are used to choose the candidates, whose intrinsic luminosities must lie in a narrow range. The acceptable ones are then used to test the same model, and therefore determine values for the dark matter and dark energy densities. This is circular reasoning; select only the candidates that fit the desired luminosity-distance criteria and use them to determine the luminosity distance.[28]

One of the consequences of cosmological expansion is *time dilation*. When the light curves, which show the rise and fall in luminosity of the supernova explosion, are compared at increasing redshifts, their time axes with respect to the observer at the earth should be stretched due to time dilation. In other words, processes that follow a flow of time in the distant cosmos are slowed relative to Earth time, i.e. when observed from Earth. It is claimed that time dilation has been clearly observed in the light curves of these supernovae and is provided as definitive evidence for expansion.[29] Yet, no time dilation has been observed

26. Reiss, A. *et al.*, Observational evidence from supernovae for an accelerating universe and a cosmological constant, *Astron. J.* **116**:1009–1038, 1998.

27 Perlmutter, S. *et al.*, Measurements of Omega and Lambda from 42 high-redshift supernovae, *Astrophys. J.* **517**:565–586, 1999.

28. Luminosity distance is a model dependent distance determined using the input parameters to the model.

29. Goldhaber, G. *et al.*, Timescale stretch parameterization of type Ia supernova B-band light curves, *Astrophys . J.* **558**:359–368, 2001.

in the luminosity variations of quasars,[30] which are thought to be at very great distances, as interpreted from their large redshifts and the Hubble Law. The data have been collected over 28 years and the evidence against time dilation associated with quasars is robust. No time dilation means no expansion over cosmological time. How can these contradictory claims be reconciled? There is a mounting body of evidence along additional lines that suggests the universe is not expanding, evidence that can be better interpreted within a static universe.[31]

In the post-WWII era, after US declassification of nuclear reaction rates, George Gamow and his student Ralph Alpher performed calculations using the hot big bang scenario. These produced the relative abundance of helium in the universe. They claimed this as a successful prediction of the big bang theory. But critics have said that they knew the answer from astronomical measurements before they began and accused them of fiddling the result—certainly it was not a prediction. However, it has been claimed by others that the remnant 'afterglow of the big bang' could not be classified as an *ad hoc* postdiction. Is that really true? The CMB radiation could only be claimed as a successful prediction of the big bang theory if it could be proven that there is no other possible cause, otherwise it commits the logical fallacy of *affirming the consequent*.[32] Also, other mechanisms had been suggested for a uniform background radiation filling the universe, even before its 1965 discovery.[33]

If the CMB radiation is from the big bang, it would be from the most distant background source in the sky. That means all closer objects, like galaxy clusters, should cast a shadow in their foregrounds.[34] Lieu, Mittaz and Zhang[35] (2006) showed that when 31 relatively nearby clusters of galaxies were studied for any decrement in temperature, a shadowing of the CMB radiation by the clusters, it was only detected in 25% of the clusters—statistically insignificant. They looked for the expected temperature decrement of the X-ray-emitting intergalactic medium via the Sunyaev-Zel'dovich effect (SZE) and found sometimes even a

30. Hawkins, M.R.S., Time dilation and quasar variability, *Astrophys. J.*, **553**:L97–L100, 2001; Hawkins, M.R.S., On time dilation in quasar light curves, *MNRAS* **405**:1940–1946, 2010.
31. Hartnett, J.G., Is the Universe really expanding? 2011, preprint available at arxiv.org.
32. Affirming the consequent is a logical fallacy that appears in this form: If P is true then Q is true. Q is true. Therefore, P is true.
33. Ironically, it is commonly held that the discovery of the CMB radiation delivered a fatal blow to the Steady-State cosmology, promoted by Hoyle, Bondi and Gold through the 1950's and 60's. Using their model they had predicted the presence of 'far-infrared' radiation through a mechanism of thermalization of starlight. See Bondi, H., Gold, T., and Hoyle., F., *Observatory* **75**:80–81, 1955, and Ibison, M., Thermalization of Starlight in the Steady-State Cosmology, 1st Crisis in Cosmology Conference: CCC-I, AIP, p.171–180, 2006; www.earthtech.org.
34. Hartnett, J., The Big Bang fails another test, 15 September 2006; creation.com/cmb.
35. Lieu, R., Mittaz, J.P.D., and Zhang, S-N, The Sunyaev-Zel'dovich Effect in a sample of 31 clusters: a comparison between the X-ray predicted and WMAP observed cosmic microwave background temperature decrement, *Astrophys. J.* **648**:176–199, 2006.

heating effect. Bielby and Shanks[36] (2007) extended that work in 38 clusters to show that not only was the SZE less than what was expected but that it tended to progressively disappear for redshifts from 0.1 to 0.3. Their result is statistically equivalent to a null result (no shadowing) at about the 2σ level.

This result then brings into doubt the fact that the CMB radiation is from the background, i.e. from the big bang, and therefore whether cosmic expansion is even a valid hypothesis.

According to the standard big bang model, over 95% of the mass/energy content of the universe is extraordinary. Its very existence is inferred from the failure of the Standard Model of particle physics and Einstein's general relativity to describe the behavior of astrophysical systems larger than a stellar cluster (clusters of stars much smaller than the average galaxy). We are also told that the very homogeneity and isotropy of the universe is due to the influence of an inflation field whose particle-physics identity is completely *mysterious* even after a three-decade-long theoretical effort. This is Lieu's last unknown—inflation—the theorized extremely rapid exponential expansion of the early universe by a factor of at least 10^{78} in volume, lasting from 10^{-36} seconds after the big bang to sometime between 10^{-33} and 10^{-32} seconds.[37] It was invoked to solve a number of serious problems yet it still beggars belief. It invokes an unknown exotic entity totally ad hoc, without any physical justification.

The identity of dark energy is a serious problem in cosmology and is linked with the famous *cosmological constant problem*. Astronomically the cosmological constant is determined from the dark energy density required to make the ΛCDM big bang model fit observations as described above. However, using various approaches theoretical particle physicists have tried to calculate its value assuming it results from vacuum energy. If the universe is described by an effective local quantum field theory down to the Planck scale (near 10^{-33} cm), theorists get a very big number. This stems from the fact that most quantum field theories predict a huge value for the quantum vacuum (i.e. that there is a lot of energy in "empty" space). But the cosmological constant determined from astronomical observations is smaller than their best theoretical estimates by a factor of 10^{-120}. This discrepancy has been called "the worst theoretical prediction in the history of physics!"[38] It is a massive fine-tuning problem.

In addition to the CMB radiation and the 'Axis of Evil' mentioned above, several other anomalous observations suggest our observable universe is quite remarkable indeed. For example, from observations of very distant quasars

36. Bielby, R.M. and Shanks, T., Anomalous SZ contribution to three-year WMAP data, *MNRAS* **382**:1196–1202, 2007.
37. Additional details can easily be found online.
38. Rugh, S., The quantum vacuum and the cosmological constant problem, *Studies in History and Philosophy of Modern Physics* **33**(4):663–705, 2001.

some have found evidence[39] for a statistically significant correlation in the linear polarisation angles of photons in the optical spectrum over huge distances of the order of 1 Gpc.[40] They have found a preferred axis in the sky which aligns with the cosmological dipole found from the preferred frame in the CMB radiation. The preferred axis breaks the needed uniformity and isotropy inherent in the ΛCDM big bang model.

One suggested solution,[41] which is really to preserve the homogeneity and isotropy of the cosmological principle, is the proposal that dark energy is a Hubble-length-scale[42] light-pseudo-scalar field; not a particle, because the scale size is that of the observable universe.[43] The existence of this pseudo-scalar field violates isotropy on the local scale, meaning our whole observable universe. The suggestion is that, if you could see much farther than we do, one would see many bubbles that have random photon polarizations from one bubble to another.

The idea proposed is the bubble universe where we live near the centre of a bubble which then makes it unremarkable.[44]

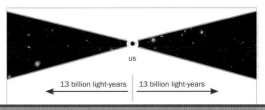

Flatness describes the fact that, from all indications, the universe is Euclidean.[45] To the cosmologist, this is one of the big questions of the century. It is yet another cosmological fine-tuning problem. From the standard model, it has been determined that the universe has evolved away from the needed critical density[46] over cosmic time. Therefore, it must have been closer to *perfect flatness* soon after the big bang. But there is no inherent reason for this.

Today, light coming to us from distant parts of the universe has the same temperature. There is no reason to think distant points started out with the same temperature, and even though we can see each point (because, in big bang cosmology, they are less than 13 billion light years away from us), they are supposedly so far apart (much greater than 13 billion light years) that light could not have gotten from one place to the other since the beginning of the universe. Thus, there has not been enough time to even out the temperature differences. This is known as the "Horizon Problem" and is one of the many Achilles' heels of big bang cosmology.

39. Hutsemekers, D., Cabanac, R., Lamy, H., and Sluse, D., *Astron. Astrophys.* **441**:915–930, 2005.
40. 1 Gpc = 3.26 billion light-years.
41. Urban, F.R. and Zhitnitsky, A.R., P-odd universe, dark energy, and QCD, *Phys. Rev. D* **83**:123532, 2011.
42. Hubble length = size of the visible universe.
43. Quantum mechanics describes a duality between particle and wave nature. On scale sizes equal or less than the Hubble length we could only detect the wave nature of the putative entity.
44. It amazes me at times to what lengths some will go to deny the possibility of Design and a Creator.
45. This means that space is not curved; triangles comprise 180 degrees and parallel lines are always equidistant.
46. The critical density is the mass/energy density that makes the universe exactly Euclidean.

Another intractable issue is the *horizon problem*, which has to do with the fact that light has not had enough time since the big bang to travel between what should be causally coherent regions of the visible universe. This means separate regions of the universe are not causally connected—a light-travel-time problem.[47] We observe light reaching us for the first time from diametrically opposite sides of the universe. In it we observe the very same properties, yet according to the believed chaotic nature of the early universe, temperature and density should have varied from place to place. Why, then, is the universe *isotropic,* the same in every direction we look?[48] This is particularly true for the CMB radiation where the same temperature of 2.7 K is measured in all

directions to within 1 part in 100,000. It is an incredible fine-tuning problem.

For more information and the latest articles on cosmology, go to: creation.com/astronomy.

Inflation is the answer most often given to the horizon problem. According to theory, soon after the initial big bang, the different regions of space started off with widely different temperatures because of the violent fluctuations. But, after a rapid "inflation" stage, the clumpiness of the early density variations was smoothed out. Inflation smoothed out all the other problems too. However, the proponents have no explanation for why inflation started or even for how it stopped, or the reason why the laws of physics were so different for this brief but incredibly important early stage of the big bang. No evidence, only special pleading. Again, this is circular reasoning based on an *a priori assumption* that there was no Creator. The universe just happened.

One of the primary attacks on creationist cosmology is the starlight-travel-time problem. How does light reach Earth from the most distant galaxies in the six thousand years since the Creation? As already stated, such a problem is not the exclusive domain of the creationist—the big bang model also has a light-travel-time problem. Creationist cosmology is also presuppositional and limited by the same constraints discussed above, except that it takes biblical history as the starting point. The cosmogony of the earth, the solar system and the whole universe must conform to that narrative. Coupled with our earlier understanding of the ephemeral, model-dependent and philosophically underpinned nature of all cosmological statements, it should be plain that to disbelieve a straightforward reading of Genesis because of allegedly 'unanswerable' light-travel issues is untenable.

Though new discoveries may come in the future, which may involve new hitherto unknown particles, unknown unverifiable entities are not the way to advance

---

47. Lisle, J., Light-travel time: a problem for the big bang, *Creation* **25**(4):48–49, 2003; creation.com/lighttravel.
48. This is not contradictory with the claim of broken isotropy above. The CMB radiation is very nearly isotropic. When we say isotropy is broken we mean the small anisotropies need explaining.

our knowledge. The naturalistic speculations of many scientists attempting to explain the properties of this universe without a Creator seem to increasingly border on the bizarre. For example, the invoking of the so-called multiverse, where the universe we live in is only one of many "bubbles" that evolved out of the primeval quantum foam. This is not far removed from believing in fairies in the bottom of the garden.[49]

Summary and conclusion

The fatal flaw of the big bang model of cosmic evolution is that it is based on unverifiable assumptions, primarily the cosmological principle. After that, key evidences are explained by 'unknowns' that cannot be experimentally verified. The big bang must be believed by faith because it falls outside our normal concepts of experimental science. We have only one universe and so we cannot test models for the universe by comparing it against other universes. This is cosmology's Achilles' heel. The fact is that one cannot determine the history of the universe from a model which cannot be independently tested. The big bang cosmology is only verified in the minds of those who already hold to that belief that billions of years ago the universe created itself *ex nihilo*.

Where does this lead?

Thus far, we have examined seven major Achilles' heels of naturalistic evolutionary theory. We began with Darwin's main thesis, that natural selection can explain the common ancestry of all species. We then looked at the mechanisms behind natural selection, genetics. From there, we began to dissect the main idea behind biological evolution—deep time—including the fossil record, the rock record, radiometric dating and, now, cosmology. In all of these areas we found major problems with both the theory and its fit to the evidence. And, occasionally, we have given counter examples to show how biblical history fits the evidence better. What follows next is the final Achilles' heel of them all: human nature. In order to truly understand these issues, we have to look at the universe through the lens of both naturalistic philosophy and its alternatives. We need to look into the scientific process itself. For that, we turn to two Ph.D. scientists who have thought long and deep on these issues.

---

49. Not to be confused with the (similarly bizarre and equally non-testable) notion of parallel universes put forward to explain observations in the field of quantum mechanics. The proposal is that when one throws a die to get the number '3', at that moment all the other possible outcomes of that throw take place in these 'parallel worlds'. Though string theorist Michio Kaku now equates this notion also to the multiverse.

Drs Catchpoole and Harwood were asked to co-write the most important chapter in this book, an analysis of the final Achilles' heel of evolutionary theory, morality and ethics. We need to see where evolution *leads* in order to know how to handle its effects on world society.

Dr David Catchpoole
Ph.D. Plant Physiology, University of New England
(New South Wales), Australia

Dr Catchpoole was an ardent, atheistic, evolutionist Ph.D. scientist before being challenged to look critically at the problems of evolution and the scientific evidence for creation and the Bible. He now works full-time for CMI and is the co-author of *The Creation Answers Book*, co-editor and writer for *Creation* magazine, and has contributed numerous articles for CMI's popular website, creation.com.

See **creation.com/dr-david-catchpoole**

Dr Mark Harwood
Ph.D. University of Sydney

Dr Harwood is a telecommunications specialist, playing a key role in the development of Australia's national satellite system, from its inception in 1980. He specializes in antennae design (a matter of no small importance for a satellite!) and recently retired from his role as General Manager for Strategy and Planning for a leading satellite business centered in Australia.

See **creation.com/dr-mark-harwood**

ETHICS AND MORALITY

Dr David Catchpoole Ph.D. Agronomy
[University of New England, New South Wales]
Dr Mark Harwood Ph.D. Engineering
[University of Sydney]

8

Of all the 'Achilles' Heels' presented in this book, the important matter of ethics and morality is probably the one guaranteed to most potently raise the emotive ire of evolutionists. That's because this is where the rubber hits the road for every man, woman and child living on the earth today. More than likely, evolutionists are going to disagree with our conclusions about the social ramifications of their theory. Nevertheless, acceptance of evolutionary theory has strong societal implications.

While some people actively dodge, or are blithely ignorant of, the issues addressed by the first seven chapters of this book (covering biology, chemistry, geology, and astronomy), a person's ethics is an undeniable reflection of their belief system and is pivotal to how they live (or try to live) their daily lives. And how a person lives their daily life is profoundly influenced by their belief about where they think they came from. Either we are the result of a giant cosmic accident, and therefore there is no ultimate meaning or purpose to life and no objective basis to morality, or we are created by a transcendent God, for a purpose, and will ultimately be held to account for how we have lived our lives. Such beliefs can have a huge impact on the lives of those around us—*even potentially life-terminating impacts*. No wonder the topic of this chapter stirs up such passions and heated anger, even among those who might claim to be neutral in the creation-evolution controversy.

Ethics and morality—beliefs in action

Every person has a fundamental belief system that determines how they see the world and how they respond to it. Such a belief system is usually based on assumptions, or axioms, which are not directly testable. Yet a framework of conclusions and consequences is in turn built upon *them*. This presumably logical framework forms what is called a *worldview*. A worldview is generally not taught explicitly, but is unconsciously caught from the prevailing culture. Each one of us processes and filters the various inputs our senses receive to determine if what we are seeing and hearing is consistent with our worldview. Those things that are consistent serve to confirm our beliefs. Those that aren't consistent are generally rejected, denied or, at best, shelved pending further investigation. In other words, our worldview colours our perceptions and determines our biases. Even as you read this book you are testing its claims against your worldview and deciding how you might respond.

Worldviews are not easily changed. If it were not so, we would become relationally dysfunctional by frequently changing our perception of the world and other people. But how do we determine if a worldview is reasonable, and, therefore, if the axioms on which it is based are correct? Everyone experiences the physical world—gravity, pain, hot, cold, etc—so testing the reasonableness of a worldview against the realities of the observable physical universe is an effective method of evaluation. In the previous chapters, we have examined the correlation of the materialistic evolutionary worldview with the observable realities of the physical world and found it to be profoundly wanting. However, there is another arena in which worldviews can be evaluated for their reasonableness and that is in regards to morality and ethics.

Analogy of two trees representing the atheistic and theistic worldviews.

A worldview can be likened to a tree which has its roots in a chosen belief system. The tree produces fruit which is a reflection or an outworking of that belief. For instance, if one believes there is a God and, in particular, that the Bible is God's Word, then the existence of the universe is understood to be the result of creative fiat by a supernatural Being, in accordance with the historical record of Genesis. The roots of this tree are firmly embedded in the special revelation of God, the collection of 66 books we call the Bible. All the evidence in the physical world is then interpreted in the light of this biblical worldview. How a Christian behaves (their moral conduct) is the fruit of this tree, and will directly reflect the godly nature of its roots. Among other things, this will include the recognition of moral absolutes as having originated from the Creator of the universe and that there will be an ultimate calling to account.

On the other hand, if one rejects the supernatural and believes there is no God, then man alone decides truth and the only possible explanation for the existence of the universe is that it occurred by naturalistic processes without any form of divine intervention. The roots of this tree are firmly embedded in the rejection of God, with its associated evolutionary account of origins. All the evidence in the physical world is then interpreted in the light of this evolutionary or materialistic worldview. How one behaves (one's moral conduct) is the fruit of this tree which will directly reflect the atheistic nature of its roots. Importantly, since there is no God, there can be no moral absolutes and there will be no ultimate calling to account.

We are not trying to set up a false dichotomy here and are well aware that many Christians also believe in evolution (a position called 'theistic evolution') despite there being no biblical support for such a view[1]. Indeed, both the authors of this chapter are Christians who once believed in evolution until confronted over the issue of the authority of the Bible and, in particular, of the creation account in Genesis. The theistic evolutionist defers to the authority of ever-changing secular science rather than to the authority of the Word of God. One of the authors (MH), although having been a Christian since age 11, became a 'closet' Christian during his university years because he was unable to defend his faith, having no answers to his own questions let alone the questions of others—questions like 'If God is a God of love, why do bad things happen?' Belief in the secular millions of years of death, struggle and suffering before Adam renders the theistic evolutionist helpless to defend the faith in the face of atheistic attack on the question of origins. After all, if death prevailed before Adam's sin, it cannot be the consequence of that sin, and there can be no logical meaning to Christ's redemptive sacrifice for mankind. It is little wonder the secularists attack the biblical account of origins! Indeed, the dangers of such a compromise position are revealed by William B. Provine, Professor of Biological Sciences, Cornell University, a high profile atheist who said:

---

1. Duboisée de Ricquebourg, M., The theological case against evolution, 3 May 2012; creation.com/theological-case-against-evolution.

> ... belief in modern evolution makes atheists of people. One can have a religious view that is compatible with evolution only if the religious view is indistinguishable from atheism.[2]

It is beyond the scope of this chapter to explore the inconsistencies of theistic evolution further but the reader is encouraged to consider the readily available material on the topic.[3]

That the evolutionary worldview is belief based, and is therefore religious in nature, is underscored by the atheist Professor of Zoology of Harvard University, Richard Lewontin, who admitted:

> Our willingness to accept scientific claims that are against common sense is the key to an understanding of the real struggle between science and the supernatural. We take the side of science *in spite* of the patent absurdity of some of its constructs, *in spite* of its failure to fulfill many of its extravagant promises of health and life, *in spite* of the tolerance of the scientific community for unsubstantiated just-so stories, because we have a prior commitment, a commitment to materialism. It is not that the methods and institutions of science somehow compel us to accept a material explanation of the phenomenal world, but, on the contrary, that we are forced by our *a priori* adherence to material causes to create an apparatus of investigation and a set of concepts that produce material explanations, no matter how counter-intuitive, no matter how mystifying to the uninitiated. Moreover, that materialism is absolute, for we cannot allow a Divine Foot in the door.[4] (emphasis in original)

In essence, the materialist is obliged to reject the supernatural because of their *a priori* assumption that there is no God. Atheistic materialism is therefore an active religious belief system[5] although this is vehemently denied by its adherents who seek to maintain the myth that it is a neutral position.

Morality and evolution

If random molecular rearrangements led to the first cellular life, which, purely by time and chance, eventually became people, then there is no basis for determining value for anything aside from the shifting sands of human opinion. There are many different ways to illustrate this. For example, one may believe that sending aeroplanes into skyscrapers is evil and therefore wrong, and another may believe that it is pleasing to God and therefore right. Without an

2. Provine, W.B., No free will, in Rossiter, M.W. (ed.), *Catching up with the Vision,* Chicago University Press, p. S123, 1999.
3. See for instance Creation compromises, creation.com/creation-compromises; Sarfati, J., *Refuting Compromise* (2nd ed.), Creation Book Publishers, Powder Springs, GA, USA, 2011; available through creation.com.
4. Lewontin, R., Billions and billions of demons, *The New York Review,* p. 31, Jan. 9, 1997.
5. Smartt, D., Atheism: a religion, 4 May 2010; creation.com/atheism-a-religion.

external higher moral code, how could anyone know whether such actions were right or wrong? There can be no such universal principles as 'right' or 'wrong' in an evolutionary system as there is no higher authority for such principles than man himself.

One may attempt to counter this by saying that, even though moral decisions are made on the individual level, the community decides what is acceptable and, over time, the evolutionary process has led to the development of a general code of conduct across society. Yet, societies have justified all sorts of horrendous behaviours throughout history (from genocide to racism to slavery to abortion). There are examples of theistic societies, even 'Christian' societies, who have run roughshod over biblical morality, but these were operating *inconsistently* with their espoused beliefs. The opposite is true of atheistic or evolution-based societies, which have no ultimate guiding principles and, operating consistently with their beliefs, some have perpetrated gross atrocities. We will consider this point in more detail later in the chapter.

With an evolutionary worldview, there can be no such thing as absolute morality, objective good or evil, or free will. That is the clear conclusion from evolutionary teaching, as William B. Provine, points out:

Photo wikipedia.org

William B. Provine

> Let me summarize my views on what modern evolutionary biology tells us loud and clear ... There are no gods, no purposes, no goal-directed forces of any kind. There is no life after death. When I die, I am absolutely certain that I am going to be dead. That's the end for me. There is no ultimate foundation for ethics, no ultimate meaning to life, and no free will for humans, either.[6]

Provine would be correct in saying "there is no ultimate foundation for ethics" if our origins were indeed naturalistic. However, that leaves unanswered the question, why do ethics and moral standards exist? Attempts by the atheistic community to identify a coherent explanation for the existence of morality are sorely inadequate. Such attempts include observations on the behavior of apes, which suggest a correlation with human behaviors. With the assumption of common ancestry, this is claimed to be an evolutionary explanation for morality. In fact, Darwin made long argument for this very idea in two of his books, *The Descent of Man* and *Emotions in Man and Animals*. Another approach is to reason that everything that has survived has done so because it is the most fit,

---

6. Provine, W.B., *Origins Research* **16**(1):9, 1994.

which must, therefore, be the result of natural selection. Moral standards exist, so they must be the result of natural selection. Both of these attempts assume the conclusion being sought and so beg the question. Yet another approach is to define moral actions as those that don't cause harm to another. This shifts the definition of ethical or unethical to the consequence of the action so nothing can be *inherently* wrong but is so only if harm is caused to another.

But some actions *are* inherently wrong and even non-theistic societies have recognized this throughout recorded history. Why is there a sense of what *ought* to be done, or not done, embedded in mankind? The 'ought' is a non-material principle which can hardly have been present in the cosmos waiting for mankind to evolve to the point where he could comprehend it! Materialistic evolution attempts to explain the origin of man but cannot explain how he *ought* to behave. A far more logical explanation is that man was made in the image of God (Genesis 1:26) so, as God's image bearer, it makes sense that each person has a conscience that provides an innate sense of right and wrong. Murder is wrong, adultery is wrong, stealing is wrong, but only because there is a reference point external to mankind that permits us to discern right from wrong. So the very existence of moral laws implies a moral law Giver. As the apologist Mariano explains:

> An ethical code based on God is determined by God's communication to man of what is ethical and unethical. … Under such an ethical code, and in contrast to any Godless moral code, a given action such as adultery is still wrong even in absence of adverse consequences to another party. Thus, under a God-authored ethical code some actions are inherently wrong.[7]

At the Nuremberg trials, in which former Nazi leaders were tried for war crimes, a dispute arose as to which laws should be used to try the accused. The Nazi laws had redefined personhood to exclude Jews and other undesirables so the leaders argued they had not committed mass murder but were acting within the law of their land. They protested that the court had no jurisdiction over them. However, Robert H. Jackson, chief counsel for the United States, argued that "there was a law above the law" that stood in judgment of all men in all countries and societies.[8] As Erwin Lutzer observes:

> … if God does not exist, no such transcendent laws exist. If all laws are relative, and each country has its own ideas of what laws it should enact, there is no universal standard by which laws can be judged. Only an appeal to God and revelation can give us laws by which individuals and countries can be uniformly judged. Even those who would argue that there are certain universal laws based on nature and conscience assume (perhaps

---

7. Mariano, Atheism, 11 June 2009; creation.com/atheism.
8. Quoted in Montgomery, J. W., *The Law Above the Law*, Bethany, Minneapolis, pp. 25–26, 1975.

without knowing it) the existence of God from whom those universal laws are derived. *Without a belief in God, nothing is unconditionally wrong.* [9] (emphasis in original)

It is interesting to note that some atheists recognize the undesirable moral consequences of their worldview and so attempt to adopt a moral code disconnected from its roots. Richard Dawkins, today's most vociferous advocate for evolution, admits to divided thinking when he claims:

I'm a passionate Darwinian when it comes to science, when it comes to explaining the world, but I'm a passionate anti-Darwinian when it comes to morality and politics.[10]

But such a position reveals the atheist is without an objective basis for his morality. And that leaves him subject to arbitrary changes in moral code in response to changing external pressures such as drifting societal values. It is surely disingenuous to borrow the moral code of Christianity while rejecting its roots. Furthermore, it is naïve to expect people who believe in evolution not to apply it in everyday life.

Is the God of the Old Testament a Moral Monster?

One common reason, or rather excuse, for rejecting the God of the Bible is the claim that the God of the Old Testament is some kind of moral monster who commanded the genocide and ethnic cleansing of the inhabitants of the land promised to the Israelites. Such a moral standard is completely antithetical to anything the Western mind would consider to be acceptable. Who would want to rely on the God of the Bible for a moral code when that is what he commanded? Furthermore, how is it consistent with Jesus' teaching of forgiveness and turning the other cheek? "I want nothing to do with such a God!" cries the atheist. But is the God of the Old Testament a malevolent moral monster?

This highly emotion-charged challenge to Christianity deserves an answer and has been effectively addressed by numerous authors throughout history, including Paul Copan in a recent book which thoroughly examines this and related issues. The following is a brief summary of some of the observations[11] Copan makes in addressing this oft-asked question.

- God waited over four centuries before the sin of the people inhabiting the land promised to Israel was complete (Genesis 15:16). The practices of the Canaanites included child sacrifices, adultery, bestiality and homosexual acts (Leviticus 18:20–30). Only God can decide when enough is enough, when a

9. Lutzer, E., *When a nation forgets God*, Moody Publishers, Chicago, p. 61, 2010.
10. Dawkins, R, *The Science Show,* ABC Radio, 22 January 2000.
11. Copan, P., *Is God a Moral Monster?*, Baker Books, Grand Rapids, MI, USA, Part 3, pp. 158–197, 2011.

culture is irredeemable. He gave Israel clear divine guidance, without which they would not have been justified in taking the land, nor would they have succeeded.

- God is clearly not a genocidal maniac since he promised to bless all people through Israel, which must have included the inhabitants of the Promised Land. Anyone who left the land or repented could have been redeemed. Indeed, we read in Joshua 2 how Rahab, a Canaanite prostitute, had faith and her whole household was saved. She became the ancestor of King David, King Solomon, and Jesus Christ!

- It was not as though the Israelites arrived unannounced and demanded the people leave their homes and land. There had been 40 years of warning as Israel had been miraculously provided for in the wilderness, news of which would doubtless have been spread by traders plying the routes between Egypt and Assyria and about which Rahab was already well informed (Joshua 2:8–11).

- God's focus was on destroying the Canaanite religion rather than destroying the people. Keeping Israel morally and theologically separate from the practices of the Canaanites was His objective. It is interesting to note that the language used is more about dispossessing the people than about destroying them.

- God's instructions to Israel were limited to a particular time, place and people and for a particular religious purpose and were not to be generalized for all time and all situations (unlike the holy wars of other religions).

- God's character of pure love is unmistakably revealed in Christ—in particular, in his sacrificial death for mankind. While we may not fully grasp all the reasons behind the Canaanite conflicts, God's love and faithfulness stand supreme and unassailable to all who would consider the evidence.

However, in spite of God's forbearance and patient warnings to the occupiers of the Promised Land, there were those who refused to believe and obey. Israel, under God's directive, destroyed those remaining inhabitants thus executing a Divine judgment.

While God is a God of love, He is also a God of perfect justice and righteousness. When the first man, Adam, rebelled against God the penalty was death, just as God had lovingly warned him, and that act of rebellion brought death and suffering into the world (1 Corinthians 15:21). It also imposed on all Adam's descendants the curse of that original sin so that all mankind has been subject to death ever since. As the Creator of all things, including the inhabitants of the lands promised to Israel, God has the right to do with his creation as He sees fit.

The biblical analogy is the relationship between a potter and the clay vessels he makes (Romans 9:20–24). The potter is entitled to fashion the clay as he sees fit and to destroy what he knows to be irredeemable. So it is with God and man.

But there has been a pivotal event in history that divides time and defines radically different eras in God's dealings with mankind—the cross of Christ. By that one supreme act of loving sacrifice by the perfect Son of God, the penalty for man's sin was paid and God's wrath against sin was poured out on Jesus. It was the great exchange, the just for the unjust, the righteous for the unrighteous. As Paul says in Romans 5:8; "But God demonstrates his own love for us in this: While we were still sinners, Christ died for us." Any answer to the challenge that the God of the Old Testament is not the same as the God of the New must take this radical transition into account. It is not that God's nature has changed—He still demands the same justice—but that now those who believe by faith in the atoning sacrifice of Jesus, and who thereby become children of God, will not face the judgment reserved for those who reject Christ (1 Thessalonians 5:9). The God of the Old Testament is the God of the New.

Apart from the issue of the occupation of the Promised Land, there have been accusations that the God of the Old Testament endorsed human sacrifice, rape, misogyny, murder and slavery. All of these have been resoundingly refuted[12,13] as they generally demonstrate a lack of knowledge of the Scriptures, of cultural understanding and of hermeneutics.

God reveals himself consistently throughout the Bible as a God who is righteous, just, loving, merciful, compassionate and faithful and not one who is malevolent or capricious. His purposes are always to redeem fallen man and we can have total trust in his goodness towards us. The claim of the atheist that God is a moral monster is utterly bereft of scholarship and hollow and disingenuous in the extreme!

But are the claims of the 'enlightened' atheist defensible if the very existence of reason and logic is entirely inconsistent with origins through random unguided evolutionary processes? Let's examine this question in the next section.

Reasoning and evolution

There is no doubt that most people believe they are capable of logical reasoning. But, if evolution were true, reasoning (indeed, *any* thought) is just an epiphenomenon of the brain and the results of the laws of chemistry and random processes. But that raises some very awkward, indeed self-contradictory, thoughts.

12. Cosner, L, Is the Bible 'evil'? 21 September 2010; creation.com/evil-bible-fallacies.

13. Sarfati, J., Anti-slavery activist William Wilberforce: Christian hero, 20 February 2007; creation.com/wilberforce.

For example, given evolutionists' own presuppositions, they have not freely arrived at the conclusion that evolution is true, because their conclusion was *predetermined by brain chemistry*. At the very least, the conclusion was heavily influenced by the perception filters and survival mechanisms handed down to us from our supposed fish and monkey ancestors (no wonder William Provine, in his quote cited earlier, concludes that there is no free will!). Therefore, having a human brain does not guarantee that we see everything clearly. In fact, since reproduction is the *only* thing important in evolutionary history, one can argue that the brain we have today is there only because it helped our ancestors have children. They did not need to understand reality. They only needed to figure out how to stay alive long enough to sire children. In debating with people who disagree with them about evolution, why should evolutionists trust their own brain chemistry over that of their opponents, since both obey the same infallible laws of chemistry? In reality, if evolutionists were right about evolution, they can't help what they believe (including their belief in evolution!). Yet they often call themselves "freethinkers", overlooking the glaring irony.

Photo wikipedia.org

C. S. Lewis

Genuine initiation of thought is an insuperable problem for someone who believes in evolutionary origins. So is consciousness itself. The famous author and Christian philosopher, C. S. Lewis, observed:

If the solar system was brought about by an accidental collision, then the appearance of organic life on this planet was also an accident, and the whole evolution of Man was an accident too. If so, then all our thought processes are mere accidents—the accidental by-product of the movement of atoms. And this holds for the materialists' and astronomers' as well as for anyone else's. But if their thoughts—i.e., of Materialism and Astronomy—are merely accidental by-products, why should we believe them to be true? I see no reason for believing that one accident should be able to give a correct account of all the other accidents.[14]

Ultimately, if evolution is true, there is no reason to trust our own thoughts as rational. We can only respond to stimuli according to the chemical reactions in our brain that are, in turn, controlled by the genes we inherited from our early ancestors. What's more, we have no way of even knowing what we are missing! It basically comes down to the stiflingly inescapable thought that our existence is predicated upon the survival of our DNA—no more, no less.

But such mind-numbing, purpose-crushing hopelessness is alien to our actual history, and to our very evident present reality. Man *can initiate* thoughts and

---

14. C. S. Lewis, *God in the Dock,* Eerdmans, Grand Rapids, MI, USA, pp. 52–53, 1970.

actions; they are not merely the results of deterministic laws of brain chemistry. This is a deduction from the biblical teaching that man has both a material and immaterial aspect (e.g. 1 Kings 17:21–22, Matthew 10:28, 1 Thessalonians 5:23). This immaterial aspect of man means that he is more than matter, so his thoughts are likewise not bound by the makeup of his brain.

The logical outcome of this, of course, is that readers do indeed have a free will, with a capacity for independent and rational thought, giving them the ability to ponder carefully the information presented in this book and come to a reasoned conclusion as to what is right to believe about origins.

Nihilism and evolution

Evolutionary ideas about origins, that we're just here to propagate our DNA, lead unswervingly to an utterly depressing nihilism. As Richard Dawkins said:

> The universe we observe has ... no design, no purpose, no evil and no good, nothing but blind, pitiless indifference. ... DNA neither knows nor cares. DNA just is. And we dance to its music.[15]

And evolutionary psychologist Dr Susan Blackmore affirmed:

> In the end nothing matters ... If you really think about evolution and why we human beings are here, you have to come to the conclusion that we are here for absolutely no reason at all.[16]

But evolutionists are not acting consistently with their nihilistic belief system. If evolution really were true, there is absolutely no reason to care about it— yet leading evolutionists such as Dawkins and Blackmore are passionate in their enthusiasm for evolution. What gives? The same can be said about other contemporary issues. For instance, what about the current strident voices of many evolutionists concerning 'climate change'? If evolution really were true, why get upset? So what! If man is the result of evolution, savaging nature has no inherent meaning!

'Ah, well, there's the possibility of extinction', they say. But so what! If evolution were true, the extinction of humans and other species is simply a case of 'stuff happens'.

And why all the concern about science education? So what! The only 'rule' is to have more babies than the person next to you. If you can do that, you win! And if there are winners, then, in an evolutionary context, there must also be losers. No wonder then, evolution's nihilistic teaching has resulted in the suicide rate among young people being the leading cause of death in some Western countries.

---

15. Dawkins, R., *River out of Eden*, Weidenfeld & Nicholson, London, p. 133, 1995.
16. Blackmore, S., The world according to ... Dr Susan Blackmore, *The Independent* (UK), 21 January 2004.

If you're just rearranged pond scum and the going gets tough, ending your life perhaps seems a rational decision to take, as a young man called Gerard reasoned on Australian radio:

> I think that some people may have an inability to cope, and maybe this might sound a bit extreme, but that might be Darwinian theory, the Darwin theory of survival of the fittest. Maybe some of us aren't meant to survive, maybe some of us are meant to kill ourselves … There's too many people in the world as it is. Maybe it is survival of the fittest, maybe some of us are meant to just give up, and maybe that would help the species.[17]

At the other end of the scale, serial killer Jeffrey Dahmer explains the roots of his mindset at the time he killed his victims:

> If a person doesn't think there is a God to be accountable to, then— then what's the point of trying to modify your behavior to keep it within acceptable ranges? That's how I thought anyway. I always believed the theory of evolution as truth, that we all just came from the slime. When we, when we died, you know, that was it, there is nothing …[18]

Confronted with the fruit of evolution's nihilism, many people understandably recoil, as evolutionist Jaron Lanier, in conversation with Richard Dawkins at the time, observed:

> 'There's a large group of people who simply are uncomfortable with accepting evolution because it leads to what they perceive as a moral vacuum, in which their best impulses have no basis in nature.' But Dawkins' reply to Lanier was immediate: 'All I can say is, That's just tough. We have to face up to the truth.'[19]

The 'truth' that Dawkins is so passionate about is an atheistic, religious *belief* that rejects out of hand any notions of the supernatural—matter and energy is all there is. It also emphatically denies the Truth of God in Scripture, shoehorning its adherents into searching for some kind of meaning and purpose in the blind, wasteful, cruel forces of nature. It's a grievous thing indeed that so many young students read Dawkins' books as though they are the words of a twenty-first century sage.

The public arena and evolution

The debate between creation and evolution is acted out in the public arena of science. Interestingly, modern science was born in Western civilizations based on the assumption that there is a God who has created an ordered universe based

---

17. Black dog days—The experience and treatment of depression, *Life Matters* with Norman Swan, ABC (Australia) radio, 4 May 2000; www.abc.net.au.
18. Jeffrey Dahmer, in an interview with Stone Phillips, *Dateline* NBC, 29 Nov 1994.
19. Evolution: The dissent of Darwin, *Psychology Today* **30**(1):62, Jan–Feb 1997.

on predictable laws and principles which, in turn, have engendered investigation to understand how the universe operates. It was by reading the biblical text as an understandable historical account of Divine Providence that philosophers and theologians laid down the framework and logical structure of modern science. It was within this philosophical framework that modern science flourished in Western cultures, whereas it was still-born in others.[20] How ironic that 'science' is now used as a weapon against the very Christianity which gave it birth. Of course, *operational* science based on observable, repeatable experiments—which accounts for today's amazing technological developments—does not, and will never, conflict with the true, eyewitness account of the history of the universe as recorded in Scripture. It is only *historical* science that seeks to reconstruct the past based on modern secular man's creation myth (evolution) that produces conflict with the Bible's account of history found in Genesis.

When a society embraces the evolutionary paradigm and rejects the Creator God of the universe, plunging its roots deep into atheistic soil, the fruit is tragically predictable. "Righteousness exalts a nation" declares the Scriptures in Proverbs 14:34, "but sin is a reproach to any people." In the public arena, a nation's character is undeniably reflected in its laws. But on what are the laws of a nation based? Either God is the lawgiver or man is. And if there is no God, then man is the ultimate authority.

The legal systems of Western nations were founded on the Judeo-Christian principles embodied in the Law (the first five books of the Bible), which was given by God to Israel to set them apart from other nations to be a kingdom of priests and a blessing to all nations. Germane to the Law is the acknowledgement of God, the sanctity of life and consideration of others. These principles were summarized by Jesus in the commands to love God and love your neighbor as yourself (Matthew 22:37–40). However, the rejection of God is increasingly reflected in the liberalization of the laws of Western nations. The evolutionary paradigm erodes the essential value of human life, since we are all merely the result of a cosmic accident, so the ever burgeoning laws legalizing abortion, euthanasia, prostitution, etc. all progressively devalue humanity. However, Christianity declares the sanctity of life grounded on the revelation that God made man in His image (Genesis 1:26–27). Tragically, that sanctity is violated on a massive scale through the hideous practice of abortion—the killing of unborn babies.

Evolutionary theory was for many years taught hand-in-hand with the idea that the human embryo goes through (or recapitulates) various evolutionary stages, such as having gills like a fish, a tail like a monkey, etc., during the first few months that it develops in the womb. This idea has not only been presented

---

20. Sarfati, J., The biblical roots of modern science, 29 September 2009; creation.com/roots.

to generations of biology/medical students as fact, but has also been used for many years to persuasively justify abortion. Abortionists often claim the unborn child being killed was still in the fish stage or the monkey stage, and had not yet become a human being.

Called *embryonic recapitulation*, this idea was vigorously expounded by Ernst Haeckel from the late 1860s to promote Darwin's theory of evolution in Germany, even though Haeckel did not have legitimate evidence to support his views. What's more, Haeckel's drawings were fraudulent.[21] Most informed evolutionists in the past 70 years have realized that the recapitulation theory is false. Nevertheless, the recapitulation idea is still advanced as evidence for the theory of evolution in many books—contributing to the ongoing tragic killing of many babies. The authors of this chapter recently met a young man who testified that while at secondary school his biology text book taught that *ontogeny recapitulates phylogeny*, based on Haeckel's fraudulent drawings. A friend of the young man, on observing the drawings, remarked, "So abortion *is* OK!" The association between Haeckel's evolutionary lie and the moral acceptability of killing unborn babies was made instantly. Judge Harry Blackmun accepted Haeckel's embryos in *Roe v Wade* and so declared the fetus a non-citizen and unleashed a wave of abortions throughout the Western world.

At the other end of the age scale is the question of euthanasia (the intentional killing of a human being, often, but not always, for 'mercy's sake'). This is not to be confused with other difficult ethical decisions like the question of whether or not to turn off life support equipment in a brain-dead patient. One involves the intentional cessation of life earlier than would otherwise occur. The other involves allowing things to follow their natural course. As Matthew Piercy observes:

> Evolution has played a major role in paving the way for the acceptance of euthanasia. Evolution reduces humans to the level of animals, making it just as acceptable to put down a human as put down a dog.[22]

Whenever a life is considered not worth living, either because of disability or age or inconvenience (as is often the case in abortions), the door is open to violating the sanctity of the life that was given by God. No person has the right to terminate the life of another human being or, for that matter, even their own.

However, in the evolutionary scenario, we are purposeless beings who will simply cease to exist when this life ends, which ultimately it surely must. So why not end it all if the going gets tough? Thoughts like this have wreaked havoc in the minds of many people, but especially the young. Lack of self esteem

21. Grigg, R., Fraud rediscovered, *Creation* **20**(2):49–51, March 1998; creation.com/fraud-rediscovered.
22. Piercy, M., Euthanasia: hospital humanism, *Creation* **19**(3): 21–22, June 1997; creation.com/euthanasia.

is a direct and logical consequence of belief in the evolutionary story of origins.

But why fight against creationists? Evolution will march on regardless! However, theists tend to have more children on average than atheists/evolutionists.[23] And their children are often high achievers, being raised under the loving protection of parents with stable marriages, with a high value placed on the importance of truth, truthfulness and education. If theists have more children than atheists, as a philosophy, evolution lets down its own adherents—it is not an 'evolutionarily stable strategy'! According to the evolutionists' own survival-of-the-fittest framework, it's the theists who are the winners. Creationists win according to the evolutionists' own rules! But we digress …

If, as Richard Dawkins has advocated, religion in general is an evolutionary *meme* (an idea or concept that permeates a society), it is a very successful one, and how else is evolution to be judged except by its own definitions of evolutionary success? And, since there is no value judgment that can be applied (because there is no ultimate Source of values), there is, as earlier noted, no rational reason for them to care about the issue. Nor is there any rational reason to try and thwart Christians or creationists (or any other theist) in the public sphere.

But it is inevitable that a society's fruit will be the product of the root beliefs, as the tragic examples in the next section demonstrate.

Consequences of evolutionary belief in recent history

The 20th century heralded a tragic litany of the fruits of evolutionary teaching. Millions died; their deaths sometimes rationalized away in the context of 'improvement' of the surviving gene pool and sometimes as a moral justification for the elimination of competition. In fact, about 130 million people (not including the hundreds of millions killed by abortion) were killed in the 20th century in the name of atheism, whereas all those killed in 'the name of Christ'

---

23. Rees, T., Why do atheists have fewer kids? 21 September 2009; epiphenom.fieldofscience.com.

in all of recorded history was *at most* around 17 million.[24] The most infamous slaughter was the Holocaust in the 1940s, but social Darwinism's bitter fruit was in evidence by the late 1800s and was a major influence in the events leading up to World War I, and the ideology that drove earlier shameful events, for example, in Australia and Namibia. In every case, the perpetrators of these heinous crimes were acting in a way that was consistent with their beliefs.

Treatment of Indigenous Australians

Within just a few decades of the publication of Darwin's *On the Origin of Species*, Australia's indigenous people were bearing the brunt of the surge of evolutionary belief. A dark period in Australia's history ensued where Aboriginal people were murdered and their body parts sent to European museums for display purporting to provide evidence of an evolutionary dead-end in the descent of man—a living 'missing link'.[25] Many have tried to distance Darwin from the human consequences of his ideas but Darwin himself made his own beliefs clear concerning the status of Aboriginal people when he wrote:

> At some future period, not very distant as measured by centuries, the civilized races of man will almost certainly exterminate, and replace, the savage races throughout the world. … The break between man and his nearest allies will then be wider, … instead of as now between the negro or Australian [Aboriginal] and the gorilla.[26]

In recent times, Aboriginal communities have been lobbying the Australian and British governments for the repatriation of their ancestors' remains so they can receive a traditional burial. Interestingly, media reports of these negotiations have been silent, presumably for political correctness reasons, on *why* these body parts ended up in European museums in the first place.

In February 2008, the then Australian Prime Minister, Kevin Rudd, issued an apology to the Aboriginal people for the 'Stolen Generation'. These were half-caste children, usually with European fathers and Aboriginal mothers, who were deemed to be more human than full-blood Aboriginals and who could therefore be educated and civilized whereas the full-bloods presumably could not. One inspector from the Department of Aborigines in Western Australia wrote in 1908, "I would not hesitate for one moment to separate a half-caste from an Aboriginal mother, no matter how frantic her momentary grief."[27] The use of the qualifier 'momentary' was doubtless a reflection of the view that the mother was somehow less than fully human and so could not experience real grief.

24. Kennedy, J. and Newcombe, J., *What if Jesus had never been born?* Thomas Nelson, Nashville, TN, USA, 1994.
25. Wieland, C., *One Human Family,* Creation Book Publishers, Powder Springs, GA, USA, pp. 51–61, 2011.
26. Darwin, C., *The Descent of Man*, 2nd ed., John Murray, London, p. 156, 1887.
27. Monaghan, D., The body-snatchers, *The Bulletin*, 12 November 1991, p.38.

And yet the Scriptures are clear—we are all of 'one blood' and descendants of the first man and woman, Adam and Eve.

Herero Genocide

During the late 1880s, African countries were being colonized by European nations. Germany annexed Namibia, then called South-West Africa. German settlers began to occupy the land, riding roughshod over its inhabitants, the Herero people. The German settlers had imbued the idea of belonging to a superior race and the Herero were regularly referred to as 'baboons'; the men were commonly beaten to death for minor infringements, and the women were made sex slaves by the soldiers and settlers. Racism was rife. Not surprisingly, there was an uprising, in early 1904. The German government dispatched 14,000 troops under the command of Lieutenant-General Lothar von Trotha, a ruthless man, to suppress the rebellion. In the massacre that followed, the Herero population was reduced from a tribe of 80,000 to a mere 15,000 starving refugees.[28]

Darwin's *On the Origin of Species* had been translated into German in 1875 and his ideas had been earnestly promoted by Ernst Haeckel (1834–1919), the most famous German Darwinist of the time, and notorious forger of the embryo diagrams discussed earlier. Haeckel believed that evolution would "… bring forth a complete revolution in the entire world view of humanity."[29] He argued that Darwinism required the abandonment of Christian morals, so the stage had been set to justify the 20th century's first genocide by regarding the Herero people as sub-human.

Eugenics

In the decades post-Darwin and leading up to the Great War (1914–1918, also known as World War 1), intellectuals embraced Darwinism and its ethical implications as a welcome alternative to the prevailing Christian belief and ethics. Until the advent of Darwinism, the sanctity of human life was taken for granted in European law and thought. On the Continent, many German intellectuals began to argue that some had a greater right to life than others, namely, those who were deemed more valuable to society. This inequality was mainly based on race (firmly based on Darwinian ideas), but the Darwinists argued that there

Photo wikipedia.org

Francis Galton

28. Ambler, M., Herero genocide, *Creation* **27**(3):52–55, June 2005; creation.com/herero-genocide.
29. Weikart, R., Darwinism and death: devaluing human life in Germany 1859–1920, *J. History of Ideas* **63**(2):323–344, 2002.

were inferior individuals within a race as well. It should thus not be surprising that the world's first eugenics society was founded in Germany, promoting the genetic purification concepts espoused by Darwin's cousin, Francis Galton (1822–1911).

However, it was the enthusiastic adoption of eugenics by the Americans that imparted much of the momentum to the German movement. For example, by 1913, one-third (and from the 1920s on, more than half) of the US States had laws allowing for the compulsory sterilization of those held in custody who were deemed to be 'unfit'. This resulted in the forced sterilization of some 70,000 victims, including criminals, the mentally retarded, drug addicts, paupers, the blind, the deaf, and people with epilepsy, TB or syphilis. Over 8,000 procedures were done at the one city of Lynchburg, Virginia, and isolated instances continued into the 1970s.[30]

While the term 'eugenics' is not politically acceptable today, the same concepts live on under different guises, like 'social biology', 'human genetics' and 'population science'. The practice of purifying the race is continued today through the abortion of less-than-perfect babies and euthanasia of the terminally ill. Undergirding it all is the evolutionary belief that we are just cosmic accidents and not created in the image of a purposeful loving God.

World War I

While the belief in German superiority led the Nazis to exterminate 'undesirable' individuals, during WWI German Darwinists used the same idea to justify war on states which they deemed inferior. German social Darwinists were enamoured with the vision of the 'master race', which in their mind was the Nordic or Germanic race. They believed that the destiny of the master race was to dominate or eliminate 'inferior' races, and the most obvious way to accomplish this was through war. In their view, all races and states were in competition for survival, and those who would not wage war would perish. In other words 'war is inevitable and peace is merely an armistice in the continuous battle between races and groups for survival.'[31] War was also looked on as a way to purge a society of the weaker elements, as the strong would tend to survive conflict more than the weak. This did not mesh well with modern, mechanized forms of warfare, especially after the invention of the machine gun, but that thought had not yet dawned on most. Because of the view of war as an evolutionary instrument, the German leaders regarded war as a desirable option, even though they could not be sure of victory.

30. Grigg, R., Eugenics … death of the defenceless, *Creation* **28**(1):18–22, December 2005; creation.com/eugenics.
31. Weikart, R., The origins of social Darwinism in Germany: 1859–1895, *J. History of Ideas* **54**(3):469–489, 1993.

Some argue that because Darwin did not directly apply the principles of social Darwinism, the term, and its connection to evolutionary thought, is invalid. But Darwin himself said that killing in the animal kingdom was a way for evolution to progress:

> It may be difficult, but we ought to admire the savage instinctive hatred of the queen-bee, which urges her to instantly destroy the young queens her daughters as soon as born, or to perish herself in the combat; for undoubtedly this is for the good of the community; and maternal love and maternal hatred, though the latter fortunately is most rare, is all the same to the inexorable principle of natural selection.[32]

Darwin appeared reluctant to apply this principle to humans, whether for expediency or lack of conviction we cannot know, but the German social Darwinists did not share his disinclination. While there were other factors that caused World War 1, the German leadership's universal belief in social Darwinism and its anti-Christian ethical system justified their militarism and construed it as a moral good.[33]

World War II: Hitler and The Holocaust

In the lead-up to WWII, the German social Darwinists' ideas became much more widespread (not only in elite academic circles, but they had also filtered down into the popular Viennese press during Hitler's pre-WWI days). After Hitler's rise, Nazi propaganda spread these ideas still further. One propaganda film in 1937 showed a disfigured handicapped person and declared:

> All weak living things will inevitably perish in nature. In the last few decades, mankind has sinned frightfully against the law of natural selection. We haven't just maintained life unworthy of life, we have even allowed it to multiply! The descendants of these sick people look … like this person here![34]

Adolf Hitler's reign resulted in the murder of six million Jews as well as many Christians, blacks,

Adolf Hitler

Hitler photo: NARA, Darwin photo: TFE Graphics

32. Weikart, R., Darwinism and death: devaluing human life in Germany 1859–1920, *J. History of Ideas* **63**(2):323–344, 2002. See also Muehlenberg, B., Darwin and eugenics: Darwin was indeed a 'Social Darwinist', 18 March 2009; creation.com/darwin-and-eugenics.
33. Cosner, L., Darwinism and World War I, *Creation* **32**(2):15–17, 2010; creation.com/darwinism-and-world-war-one.
34. *Opfer der Vergangenheit*, 1937; creation.com/weikart.

gypsies, the retarded, and other groups deemed unfit to live. The evolutionary 'science' of eugenics provided him with justification for his decrees. Some have attempted to claim that Hitler was a Christian, but Churchill's assessment was that Nazi Germany was a "power which spurns Christian ethics, [and] which cheers its onward course by a barbarous paganism."[35] That the Nazi regime was firmly grounded in evolutionary dogma is confirmed by evolutionist Sir Arthur Keith, who wrote:

> The German Führer, as I have consistently maintained, is an evolutionist; he has consciously sought to make the practice of Germany conform to the theory of evolution.[36]

In examining the findings of the Nazi war trials, Leo Alexander concluded:

> Whatever proportions these crimes finally assumed, it became evident to all who investigated them that they had started from small beginnings. The beginnings at first were merely a subtle shift in emphasis in the basic attitude of the physicians. It started with the acceptance of the attitude, basic in the euthanasia movement, that there is such a thing as life not worthy to be lived. This attitude in its early stages concerned itself merely with the severely and chronically sick. Gradually, the sphere of those to be included in this category was enlarged to encompass the socially unproductive, the ideologically unwanted, the racially unwanted and finally all non-Germans.[37]

How could civilized men commit such fearful acts as gassing pregnant women and shooting children and then burning their bodies and bulldozing them *en masse* into pits? Such things can only occur when an absolute rejection of God and His Word, the Bible, allows an ideology of death to prevail which convinces its adherents that the cause is just. The concept of a 'life not worthy to be lived' is completely incompatible with the Biblical revelation of man made in the image of God. When a nation rejects the God of the Bible, the fruit is bitter indeed.

Image wikipedia.org

Joseph Vissarionovich Stalin

Stalin

The murderous Russian dictator Joseph Stalin acquired a copy of Darwin's *Origin of Species* when he was about 13. One day, he and some friends were talking about the injustice of there being rich and poor. Stalin amazed them all by saying, "God's not unjust, he doesn't actually

35. Wieland, C., Clearing the name of Christ, 22 March 2008; creation.com/clearing-the-name-of-christ.
36. Keith, Sir A., *Evolution and Ethics*, Putnam, New York, p. 230, 1947.
37. Alexander, L., Medical science under dictatorship, *New England J. Med.* **241**(2):39–47, 1949.

exist. We've been deceived. If God existed, he'd have made the world more just. I'll lend you a book and you'll see." He produced a copy of Darwin's book.[38]

As Soviet leader in the late 1930s, Stalin consolidated absolute power for himself through several campaigns, known as the Great Purge or the Great Terror, to dispose of all political opponents and anyone he suspected might threaten his position. Around one and a half million people were shot. Many more died in penal labour camps and Siberian exile.

How and why did Stalin become one of the greatest mass murderers in history, one for whom killing a million people seemed to be no different to mowing a lawn.[39] Undoubtedly a huge part of the answer goes back to his reading Darwin at the tender age of 13. It paved the way for him to remove any restraint he might have had to killing off his opponents. Human life having no inherent value easily leads to the ruthless elimination of the 'unfit', even when people are designated 'unfit' for political reasons. Such attitudes are not inconsistent with belief in evolution.

Mao Zedong

Becoming Chairman of the Communist Party of China in 1945, Mao Zedong ruled the Party until his death in 1976. His rule was typified by brutal suppression of his political opponents, both within the Party and those perceived to be rightists. The misguided economic policies of the Great Leap Forward and the purges of the Cultural Revolution lead to the deaths of 40 to 70 million people, making Mao the greatest perpetrator of genocide in all history. Chairman Mao's two favorite books were by the evolutionists Darwin and Huxley. With tens of millions dying from his forced famine, his physician records that Mao said, "We have so many people we can afford to lose a few."[40]

Image wikipedia.org

Mao Zedong

Cambodia and Pol Pot

The death in 1998 of Cambodia's Pol Pot marked the end of one of the world's worst mass murderers. From 1975 to 1979, he led the Khmer Rouge in genocide against his own people during a bloodthirsty reign inspired by the communism of Russia's Stalin and China's notorious Mao Zedong. Between two and four

38. Montefiore, S., *Young Stalin*, Weidenfeld & Nicolson, London, p. 40, 2007.
39. Wieland, C., Evolution and social evil, *Creation* **27**(2):48, 2005; creation.com/evolution-and-social-evil.
40. The great dying, *The Sunday Mail*, Brisbane, pp. 59–60, 2 February 1997.

million people in that tiny country (perhaps more than 20% of the population) died during those terrible years, based on their version of communism, and all justified by evolutionary theory. "To keep you is no benefit, to destroy you is no loss," was a popular Khmer Rouge slogan, consistent with a strict application of evolutionary atheism.

The Columbine Tragedy

In 1999, 15 people died in a killing spree at Columbine High School in Colorado, USA. Many wondered afterwards what the two teenage murderers, Eric Harris and Dylan Klebold, had been thinking. It was soon revealed that one of the killers was wearing a white T-shirt with the inscription 'Natural Selection' on the front and that the killers were fascinated by Nazi beliefs, the idea of a 'master race', and the Darwinian struggle for life.

Most public schools in Western nations now teach that violence and death are 'natural' evolutionary mechanisms that have operated with chance processes to produce man over millions of years. What possible answer to this horrible killing spree can be found in such teaching?

Tragic lessons from Finland

In 2007, a young man named Pekka-Eric Auvinen went on a shooting spree at a school in Finland, killing seven students and a head teacher before killing himself. Because of home-made video clips he'd posted on the YouTube website and elsewhere, detectives soon had an insight into the mind of the killer. Overwhelmingly, Auvinen's statements[41] revealed his belief in evolution and that there is no ultimate purpose to our existence:

- "Life is just a coincidence … result of long process of evolution and many [*sic*] several factors, causes and effects."

- "Religious people, your gods are nothing and exists [*sic*] only in your heads. Your slave morals means [*sic*] nothing to me."

- "HUMANITY IS OVERRATED!"

- "Human life is not sacred. Humans are just a species among other animals and [the] world does not exist only for humans. Death is not a tragedy, it happens in nature all the time between all species. Not all human lives are important or worth saving. Sometimes I feel like no one is really worth [*sic*] of life at all."

- "It's time to put NATURAL SELECTION & SURVIVAL OF THE FITTEST back on track!"

---

41. Torma, S., *Nine die in Finland after YouTube post*, 7 November 2007; uk.reuters.com.

- "I cannot say that I am of the same race as this miserable, arrogant and selfish human race. No! I have evolved a step higher."

- "I am prepared to fight and die for my cause. I, as a natural selector, will eliminate all who I see unfit, disgraces of the human race and failures of natural selection."

All of Auvinen's statements above derive from the idea that everything just came into existence by itself—in other words, there is no God—*the evolutionary doctrine taught in our schools and universities throughout the world*. And as the shootings in Finland and Columbine show, the world is reaping the consequences. Yet, if evolution is true one could argue there was no problem with their actions, other than the fact that they selected themselves out of existence in the process of murdering others.

From childhood, Harris, Klebold and Auvinen had been taught that man is just an animal and that death and violence are a natural part of life. In fact, from an evolutionary perspective, death is a good thing, for without the selection pressure of death removing the weak, man would not have evolved. So death and violence become, in the eyes of those willing to logically apply Darwinian principles to the real world, natural evolutionary mechanisms that have operated with chance processes over millions of years to produce today's life-forms—including man. Of course, this does not mean that everyone who adopts an evolutionary worldview will become a mass murderer, but, with a worldview that does not include an ultimate authority, such consequences are logically consistent. Thus, by teaching evolutionary theory at schools and universities, society is basically giving a student all the 'programming' he needs to justify, in his own mind, 'helping evolution along', i.e. removing certain individuals from the gene pool.

Clearly, the creation/evolution controversy is not merely 'of academic interest'. As the wars of the 20th century, the recent spate of school shootings, and the murderous reign of the abortion doctors demonstrate, what a person believes about origins can be devastatingly destructive—not just to their own life, but to the lives of people around them. In short, the major influencing factor in determining a person's worldview, and therefore their conduct, is their belief about where they came from—human origins.

Of course, holding an evolutionary worldview does not necessarily lead to such extreme actions as mass murders. In a myriad of minor ways our daily lives reflect our worldview. For example, it is interesting to notice how motorists will slow down when approaching a location known to have a speed camera but then exceed the speed limit immediately they are out of camera range where there is no risk of being photographed. In a similar way, even 'good' people often see no problem with bending the truth if it is convenient, cheating on a test or sharing destructive gossip if there is no perceived consequence or chance of being caught. If one imbues the societal belief in no moral absolutes and no calling to account then there is no real reason to constrain one's behavior, even in minor everyday matters.

It is interesting to note the recent increasing trend in fraud in scientific reporting.[42] There have been some very well documented past frauds and blunders in the field of evolution, such as Haeckel's embryos, Piltdown Man and Nebraska Man but the trend is markedly upward and is posing a significant challenge for the scientific community. A recent case of fraud is *Archaeoraptor*, heralded by The National Geographic Society as the evolutionary find of the century that proved birds evolved from dinosaurs, but which was found to be fraudulent.[43] The pressure to publish, competition for grant renewals, the lure of money, prestige and career ambitions etc. can be strong temptations to fabricate results, plagiarize and report dishonestly. Once Christianity and moral absolutes are rejected, there is little to constrain people from deception if they are reasonably confident they can get away with it. According to Bergman, 'Fraud is especially a problem in the fields attempting to support Darwinism, and in this field it tends to take a long time to root out.'[44]

In summary, the fruit that emanates from people whose roots are embedded deeply into atheistic evolution are all too easily seen in Western society today. On the other hand, the fruit that emanates from those whose roots are embedded deeply into biblical Christianity are a great blessing to their nation and to others. As Margaret Thatcher, former Prime Minister of the United Kingdom, said:

> I think back to many discussions in my early life when we all agreed that if you try to take the fruits of Christianity without its roots, the fruits will wither. And they will not come again unless you nurture the roots. But we must not profess the Christian faith and go to Church simply because we want social reforms and benefits or a better standard of behaviour; but because we accept the sanctity of life, the responsibility that comes with freedom and the supreme sacrifice of Christ expressed so well in the hymn:
>
> > When I survey the wondrous Cross,
> > On which the Prince of glory died,
> > My richest gain I count but loss,
> > And pour contempt on all my pride.[45]

---

42. Bergman, J., Why the epidemic of fraud exists in science today, *J. Creation* **18**(3):104–109, 2004; creation.com/science-fraud-epidemic.
43. Simons, L.M., Archaeoraptor fossil trail, *National Geographic* **198**(4):128–132, 2000.
44. ref. 42, p. 108.
45. Thatcher, M., *Christianity and Wealth*, Speech to the Church of Scotland General Assembly, 21 May 1988.

A Consistent application of evolution

What would a purely evolutionary world be like? 'Nature red in tooth and claw'? Survival of the most aggressive? Genghis Khan is a brilliant evolutionary success story, since he is the ancestor to so many people alive today (1 out of every 200!).[46] And, as we have seen, no evolutionist has an objective basis to say that raping and pillaging across a continent is 'immoral', 'wrong', or 'contrary to evolutionary strategies'. Good and evil cannot logically exist within a worldview that defines everything by chance. In the evolutionary belief system, only (fallible) human preference can determine ideals of right and wrong, and such preferences can and will shift from society to society.

In stark contrast, biblical Christians have a much more satisfying and rational point of view. In the beginning, a holy and immutable (unchanging) God created human beings with a sense of right and wrong built into their very being. This sense of right and wrong is known as God's *moral law*. God, the moral lawgiver, also revealed His moral standards more perfectly and directly following Creation by way of the Old Testament Law, including the Ten Commandments, as revealed to the children of Israel, and subsequently in the New Testament through the teachings of Jesus Christ and His disciples.

Although man's moral intuition has been severely damaged through the effects of sin (from the *Fall*, see Genesis 3), each human being has an innate sense of right and wrong; we are all without excuse before God and man for our evil actions. Moral absolutes do exist because they emanate from the fact that there is an unchanging, omniscient (all-knowing), and holy God. These are not subjective opinions invented and written down by man. Rather, 'good' expresses the innate characteristics of God Himself and He has built into every human being an awareness of such through the agency of the conscience. Every human being is responsible to live up to those standards. But herein lies the human dilemma—it is impossible to fulfill the righteous requirements of God's law through human endeavour! Without a rescuer, mankind is hopelessly lost and doomed to eternal death.

Is Christianity just another code of ethics?

There is a danger in discussing the topic of ethics and morality that the reader is left with the mistaken impression that Christianity is just another code of ethics, albeit a very high one. The Bible clearly teaches that this is not so.[47] No amount of keeping the rules will ever reform the heart of man so that he can once again be in relationship with his Creator. The rebellion of Adam brought death and

---

46. Zerjal, T. *et al.*, The genetic legacy of the Mongols, *Am. J. Hum. Gen.* **72**:717–721, 2003.
47. Supporting Bible references: Romans 3:20, Galatians 2:21, Romans 5:8, Ephesians 2:8, Romans 4:13, 23–24, Hebrews 10:16, Ephesians 1:13–14, John 3:16.

suffering into the world and man's heart has ever since been at enmity towards God. But, through the most incredible expression of love the universe has ever witnessed, God Himself laid on His only Son, Jesus, the consequences of man's rebellion against Him. Christ died for us and so paid the price that we could not pay. It is therefore through faith in Christ alone and not by trying to live a moral life that mankind can be rescued from his desperate dilemma and experience a living relationship with his Creator, the God of the Bible.

Herein lies a great irony. Atheists often reject God because they do not wish to face the reality and consequences of absolute moral law. There is a desire to justify themselves and be free of guilt so they try to reason God out of existence. The preceding chapters in this book show the futility of the many efforts to do so. However, God Himself offers the only way to be truly guilt free—through faith in Jesus Christ, the perfect Son of God. As Romans 8:1 says; "Therefore, there is no condemnation for those who are in Christ Jesus".

Therefore, it is *belief* in Christ that brings us into relationship with him, not the keeping of religious rules and regulations. That relationship is forged as God gives to every believer his own Holy Spirit and forgives all their sin in what the Bible calls the new birth. It is the indwelling presence of the Holy Spirit, rather than his own personal efforts, that empowers the Christian to fulfill God's moral code.

So the message the church is called to proclaim is one of God's loving redemption of mankind, bringing him to a place of intimate relationship with his Creator where he finds peace, joy and forgiveness and his eternal destiny is secured. Why is such an attractive and compelling proposition rejected by so many? Because man's arrogance and pride baulk at humbly accepting the hopelessness of his situation without God and then repenting of his rebellion against God's righteous moral law and accepting His free gift of eternal life. We want to fix our own problems through our own efforts and thereby exalt ourselves to be like God—the sin of Adam!

Dear reader, it is our earnest prayer, if you have not done so already, that you consider the claim that Jesus Christ has on your life and respond in faith and humility to His call for repentance. As someone once said, 'He is no fool who gives up what he cannot keep to gain what he cannot lose'.

Where does this lead?

The first seven chapters in this book have provided the foundation for understanding that the basis for evolutionary 'ethics' is false. Germane to Darwin's theory of biological evolution is the idea of an 'old earth', which gave Darwin the millions of years that his theory needed. Ultimately, belief in a vast antiquity of the earth and in random processes of biological evolution served to do away with God as the creator. This has had a significant effect on his, and now our society's, perception of morality.

One particular geologist helped to sow the idea of 'long eras of time' in Darwin's mind, Adam Sedgwick. Darwin worked as an assistant to Sedgwick prior to his famous around-the-world voyage on the *Beagle*. Although Sedgwick did not support Lyell's uniformitarianism, he was also no biblical creationist, being instrumental in the development of the idea of long geological eras (e.g. the *Devonian* and *Cambrian* eras). Indeed, Darwin pays tribute to Sedgwick, writing of Sedgwick's lectures, "What a capital hand is Sedgewick [sic] for drawing large cheques upon the Bank of Time!" And time, of course, is what Darwin needed. But Sedgwick was horrified to read *Origin*, telling his former apprentice:

> If I did not think you a good tempered & truth loving man I should not tell you that … I have read your book with more pain than pleasure. Parts of it I admired greatly; parts I laughed at till my sides were almost sore; other parts I read with absolute sorrow; because I think them utterly false & grievously mischievous—You have *deserted*—after a start in that tram-road of all solid physical truth—the true method of induction …

> There is a moral or metaphysical part of nature as well as a physical. A man who denies this is deep in the mire of folly. Tis the crown & glory of organic science that it *does* thro' final cause, link material to moral … You have ignored this link; &, if I do not mistake your meaning, you have done your best in one or two pregnant cases to break it. Were it possible (which thank God it is not) to break it, humanity in my mind, would suffer a damage that might brutalize it—& sink the human race into a lower grade of degradation than any into which it has fallen since its written records tell us of its history.[48]

Sedgwick did nothing less than predict the history of the 20th century, where millions of people were killed under regimes guided by an evolutionary worldview. If only Sedgwick had realized that, like Lyell, it was his own long-age teaching that opened the way for humanity to be thus brutalized, perhaps Sedgwick would have had cause to ponder his own distorting of the Bible's account of origins. Sadly, many in the church today still compromise the Word of God with the pronouncements of historical science—pronouncements based on an atheistic ideology about the unobserved untestable events of our origins.

That's why this topic of ethics is really the linchpin to bringing people to a point of engagement in the debate. That's why the previous seven chapters have led naturally to this final one.

---

48. Adam Sedgwick to Darwin, 24 November 1859; darwinproject.ac.uk/entry-2548.

And now, we draw this book to a close. We hope that you have been open to testing the claims of evolution and deciding how you might respond. The eight pillars of evolutionary theory have been analyzed and found wanting. Our conclusion is that evolution is a house of cards built upon the faulty assumption of naturalism. When one learns to question the evolutionary assumptions, the house comes tumbling down.

In contrast, the biblical account of creation is logical, consistent, workable, and, we believe, correct, especially since it derives directly from the infallible Word of God. And so it's now up to you, dear reader, to pass on the crucial information in this book to those who don't yet realize that evolution has many Achilles' Heels, weaknesses that not only render it lame, but *dead in the water*. For those who challenge you, or who want to dig deeper, direct them to **creation.com**— an ever-growing resource of information affirming the truth of the Bible.

INDEX